QUICK
CROSSWORDS

ARCTURUS

ARCTURUS

This edition published in 2014 by Arcturus Publishing Limited
26/27 Bickels Yard, 151–153 Bermondsey Street,
London SE1 3HA

ISBN: 978-1-78404-001-7
AD003992UK

Printed in China

61

Across

1 Embarrassing mistake (6)
4 Mud or small rocks deposited in an estuary (4)
6 Compass point at 135 degrees (5-4)
8 Former US airline (1930–2001) (inits) (3)
10 Brine-cured (6)
13 Novice (4)
14 Come up (5)
16 Daze (4)
17 Open space at the top of a house (6)
20 Anger (3)
21 Choice (9)
22 Treaty (4)
23 Period of instruction (6)

Down

1 Screws, rivets (5)
2 Belonging to the organ of smell (5)
3 With greater volume (6)
4 Protection (7)
5 Small insectivorous bird (3)
7 One who rides breaking waves (6)
9 Building material, ___ and daub (6)
11 Line touching a curve (7)
12 Archaeological site (3)
15 Ironic parody (6)
18 Bands of metal worn on the fingers (5)
19 Native of Dallas, for example (5)
21 Small drink (3)

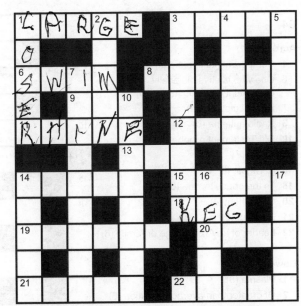

62

Across

1 Above average in size (5)
3 Appetising (5)
6 Travelled through water (4)
8 Sealed in a tin (6)
9 Offer (3)
11 European river that rises in the Swiss Alps (5)
12 Will (5)
13 Force by impact (3)
14 Lightweight cord (5)
15 Fool (5)
18 Large cask for beer or wine (3)
19 Middle-Eastern (6)
20 Crime syndicates (4)
21 Act of stealing (5)
22 Money or property brought by a bride (5)

Down

1 Unsuccessful person (5)
2 Abandoned child who roams the streets (5)
3 Send from one place to another (8)
4 Oldest independent country in Europe (3,6)
5 Alpine vocal call (5)
7 Find repugnant (9)
10 Abandoned, falling in ruins (8)
14 Crisp bread (5)
16 Walt Disney film of 1941 (5)
17 Easily irritated (5)

63

Across
1 Fruit with yellow flesh (6)
6 Astonished (6)
7 Item of dried fruit (6)
9 Goddess of retribution (7)
13 Giants who like to eat human beings (5)
14 Give a speech (5)
15 Gusset (5)
18 Finnish steam bath (5)
19 Dress (7)
21 Compound capable of turning litmus blue (6)
22 Brigand (6)
23 Protein which acts as a catalyst (6)

Down
1 Occasional (8)
2 Serving woman (8)
3 Become smaller (4)
4 Heavy wooden pole tossed as a test of strength (5)
5 Accounting entry recording a sum owed (5)
8 Being in the original position (2,4)

10 Bit of food (6)
11 Beneficial (8)
12 Calming or sleep-inducing drug (8)
16 Person with no fixed residence (5)
17 Short composition for a solo instrument (5)
20 Pal, chum (4)

64

Across
1 Compartments in a stable (6)
6 One who is physiologically dependent on a substance (6)
7 Horse colouring (4)
8 Radio antenna (6)
10 Old Testament prophet (5)
13 Cadet (7)
16 Abrogate (5)
18 To the opposite side (6)
20 Competent (4)
21 Kept out (6)
22 Leader of an Arab village or family (6)

Down
1 Plasma (5)
2 Of greater than average duration (6)
3 Epic tale (4)
4 Inhabitant of a town or community (7)
5 Coral reef (5)
9 Highest volcano in Europe (4)
11 Cook rapidly over a high heat while mixing briskly (4,3)
12 Droops (4)
14 Enclose in (6)
15 Possibly (5)
17 Bloodsucking parasite (5)
19 Soap froth (4)

65

Across
1 Embrace (5)
4 Beautiful young woman (5)
8 Examine (6)
9 Chemically inactive (5)
10 Save up for future use (5)
12 Short musket of wide bore with a flared muzzle (11)
15 Easily impressed emotionally (11)
17 Acquiesce (5)
20 Push roughly (5)
21 A bet on four or more horses in different races (6)
22 Pass (time) (5)
23 Dexterous (5)

Down
1 Ascend (5)
2 Thoroughly tidy and remove dirt from the entire house (6-5)
3 Caress gently (3)
4 Form of transport, double-decker (3)
5 Set up (11)
6 Field covered with grass (3)
7 Distinctive spirit of a culture (5)
11 Musical pace (5)
13 Mr Reed who took a *Walk on the Wild Side* (3)
14 ___ volatile, smelling salts (3)
15 Crustlike surfaces of healing wounds (5)
16 Discharge (5)
18 Cereal crop (3)
19 Bring to a close (3)
20 Body of salt water (3)

66

Across
1 Applauds (5)
3 Commence (5)
6 Clock that wakes a sleeper at a preset time (5)
8 Large artery (5)
9 Cleansing agent (4)
11 Make quiet (7)
13 Cut part of a tree trunk (3)
15 Waterproof filler and sealant (5)
17 Collection (3)
19 Church tower (7)
21 Examination (4)
22 *A Town like* ___, Nevil Shute novel later made into a film (5)
23 Dais (5)
24 Young female horse (5)
25 Divisions of a dollar (5)

Down
1 Uncouth (5)
2 Astronomical unit of distance (6)
3 Having no definite form (9)
4 Pertaining to hearing (5)
5 Exaggerated nasality in speech (5)
7 Residence of a religious community (9)
10 Severe (5)
12 Coat a cake with sugar (3)
14 Liquid mineral (3)
16 Water boiler (6)
17 Employees (5)
18 Musical warble (5)
20 Level betting (5)

35

67

Across

1 Sprang (5)
3 Sorcery (5)
6 Provide food for an event (5)
7 Dance involving a long line of people (5)
10 Harmful to living things (11)
13 Machine with a revolving drum used in making concrete (6,5)
15 Slacken off (5)
18 Breakfast rasher (5)
19 Full amount (5)
20 Of great weight (5)

Down

1 Coherent (5)
2 Example used to justify similar occurrences at a later time (9)
3 Waterproof raincoat (abbr) (3)
4 Firearm (3)
5 Caste (5)

8 Bring into being (9)
9 Bunk in a ship, train, etc (5)
11 Before, poetically (3)
12 Consumption (3)
13 Intonate (5)
14 Capable of flowing (5)
16 Pertinent (3)
17 Snake-like fish (3)

68

Across

1 Woollen item worn about the neck (5)
4 Earnings (5)
7 Repeat (7)
8 Select as an alternative (3)
9 Go away from a place (5)
12 Sauce typically served with pasta (5)
15 Motorised bicycle (5)
18 Currently in progress (5)
20 Duvet warmth rating (3)
21 Kitchen utensil used for spreading (7)
23 Ballroom dance of Latin American origin (5)
24 Rub out (5)

Down

1 Cause to flow out or over (5)
2 Shortened forename of US president Lincoln (3)
3 Crystal of snow (5)
4 Give birth to puppies (5)
5 Give a shine to (5)
6 Fight (3-2)
10 Consciousness of one's own identity (3)

11 Compete (3)
13 Mischievous gnome (3)
14 Ultimate principle of the universe (3)
15 Anthem (5)
16 Heathen (5)
17 Public dance hall (5)
18 Plant also known as the century plant (5)
19 Tantalise (5)
22 Large nation (inits) (3)

69

Across

1 Creeping low plant (4)
3 Wearisome (6)
5 Took in solid food (3)
6 Go by boat (4)
7 Refusal to admit something (6)
9 Not capable of being done (10)
14 Chinese communist leader (1893–1976) (3)
15 A person in general (3)
17 Depository for goods (10)
20 Pale (of colour) (6)
22 Cab (4)
23 Hatchet (3)
24 Fast gait of a horse (6)
25 Risqué (4)

Down

1 Follower of the Islamic religion (6)
2 Volley (5)
3 Plot of ground in which plants grow (3)
4 Puts things in order (7)
8 Seize suddenly (3)
10 Make-up used on the eyelashes (7)
11 Cooking vessel (3)
12 H Rider Haggard novel (3)
13 ___ Ferrigno, actor who played *The Incredible Hulk* (3)
16 In a spooky manner (6)
18 Frequently, poetically (3)
19 Further from the centre (5)
21 Circuit of a racecourse (3)

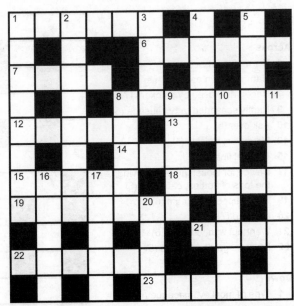

70

Across

1 Several parallel layers of material (6)
6 Necktie (6)
7 Continent (4)
8 Acute and highly contagious viral disease (7)
12 Strong string (5)
13 Lift (5)
14 Falsehood (3)
15 Rascal (5)
18 Group of elite soldiers (1-4)
19 Hang freely (7)
21 Live-action film about a piglet (4)
22 Area set back or indented (6)
23 Arouse or elicit a feeling (6)

Down

1 First courses (8)
2 Barrier consisting of horizontal bars and supports (8)
3 Pinnacle (4)
4 Lariat (5)
5 Projecting edge of a roof (5)
8 Confused scuffle (5)
9 In advance (5)
10 Learned people (8)
11 Wild headlong rush of frightened animals (8)
16 Located externally (5)
17 Increased, raised (5)
20 Olfactory organ (4)

71

Across

1 Taxi-driver, colloquially (5)
4 Collect or gather, hoard (5)
8 Army division (4)
9 Hold in high regard (6)
10 Owned (3)
11 Married woman (4)
13 Prescribed selection of foods (4)
14 Ferrous mineral (4,3)
15 Lower limbs (4)
16 Cuckoo pint, for example (4)
17 The alphabet (inits) (3)
18 Advanced medical student gaining supervised experience (6)
19 Expression of dislike (4)
21 Lasses (5)
22 Arctic canoe (5)

Down

2 Beard found on a bract of grass (3)
3 Swimmers (7)
5 Artist's workroom (7)
6 Occasionally (9)
7 No longer needed or useful (9)
8 Disinclined (9)
12 Pugilist (7)
13 Formerly the basic unit of money in Greece (7)
20 Health resort (3)

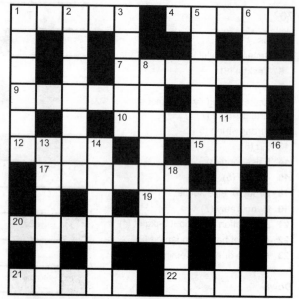

72

Across

1 Garments (5)
4 Natural brown earth pigment (5)
7 Receptacle used by smokers (7)
9 Highly seasoned fatty sausage (6)
10 Ask over (6)
12 Move very quickly (4)
15 Musical finale (4)
17 Device for loosening or removing the tops of bottles, cans, etc (6)
19 Roof-supporting beam (6)
20 Loomed (7)
21 Went out with, courted (5)
22 Fragrant garden flowers (5)

Down

1 Type of monkey, macaque (6)
2 Result of the process of accumulation (5-2)
3 Hindu religious teacher (5)
5 Decimal measurement system (6)
6 Circumvented, dodged (6)
8 Genuine (7)
11 Walks unsteadily (7)
13 Outermost region of the Sun's atmosphere (6)
14 Cut or eliminate (6)
16 To the opposite side (6)
18 Measuring instrument that uses echoes (5)

73

Across

2 Nut with an edible green kernel (9)
6 Expression of greeting (5)
7 Group containing one or more species (5)
9 Food in a pastry shell (3)
10 Got up (5)
12 Sticky plant extract (5)
14 Puts a name to (5)
17 Gorse (5)
19 Nothing (3)
20 African country, capital Tripoli (5)
21 Reproductive structure (5)
22 Uninhabited wilderness that is worthless for cultivation (9)

Down

1 Practice session (9)
2 Acute viral disease (5)
3 Ambit (5)
4 Hand tool for boring holes (5)
5 Rotating pointers on the face of a timepiece (5)
8 Not marked by the use of reason (9)
11 Transgression (3)
13 Bird similar to an ostrich (3)
15 Changes course by swinging the sail of a boat across a following wind (5)
16 Limbless reptile (5)
17 Plant life (5)
18 Ball-shaped (5)

74

Across

1 Marriage partner (6)
4 Hint (4)
6 Deepest (9)
8 Inflated feeling of personal worth (3)
10 One-hundredths of a pound (5)
11 Beauty parlour (5)
12 Strong-scented perennial herb (3)
13 Pale brown colour (5)
15 Adjust again after an initial failure (5)
18 Strong washing solution (3)
19 Russian musical instrument (9)
20 Gait (4)
21 Gender that refers to inanimate objects (6)

Down

1 Woolly mammals (5)
2 Aromatic, edible bulb (5)
3 Heartfelt (7)
4 Punctuation mark (5)
5 Consume food (3)
7 Single floor of a building (6)
9 Groups containing one or more species (6)
11 Fawning in attitude or behaviour (7)
14 Serious (5)
16 Tip at an angle (5)
17 Adult male singing voice (5)
19 Early form of modern jazz (3)

75

Across
1 Trademark of an elastic fabric (5)
4 Distress (5)
7 Grandmother (3)
8 Uncouth (5)
10 The two in a pack of playing cards (5)
11 Peculiar (3)
12 Female ruler of many countries (7)
13 Once common insecticide, now banned (inits) (3)
15 Shoddy or tasteless articles (3)
17 Muscular weakness caused by nerve damage (7)
20 Drenched with water (3)
21 US state in the Rocky Mountains (5)
22 Lacking enthusiasm or concern (5)
23 Nothing (3)
24 Supple (5)
25 Large northern sea duck (5)

Down
1 Informal term for money (5)
2 Muscular spasm (5)
3 Device that records incoming calls and messages (11)
4 Not worthy of being chosen (11)
5 Small army unit (5)
6 Post a short message on the internet site Twitter (5)
9 Ballroom dance (5)
14 Loses moisture (5)
15 Experiment (5)
16 Grilled bread (5)
18 Stretch of grassy turf (5)
19 Castrated bull (5)

76

Across
1 Smile contemptuously (5)
3 Bear, convey (5)
7 Go back on one's promise (6)
9 By an unknown author, in short (4)
10 Negative word (3)
12 Zealous (4)
13 Machine used for printing (5)
15 Central part of a car wheel (3)
17 Notions (5)
19 Manage, make do (4)
21 Unspecified member of a large series (3)
22 Burden of responsibility (4)
23 Starter course of a meal (6)
25 Nominal (5)
26 Fake, false (5)

Down
1 Native of Damascus, for example (6)
2 Calm central region of a cyclone (3)
4 Become less intense (5)
5 Pull with a sudden movement (4)
6 Clerk who does boring, repetitive paperwork (3-6)
8 Fountain nymph (5)
11 Spherical object (3)
14 Clean with hard rubbing (5)
15 Item worn on the head (3)
16 Niche or alcove (6)
18 End in a particular way (5)
20 Measure of twelve inches (4)
24 As well (3)

77

Across

1 Small box for holding valuables (6)
6 Person who serves at table (6)
7 Thinly distributed (6)
9 Attentive (7)
10 Famous American battle, Davy Crockett's last (5)
12 Combustible substance derived from organic matter (7)
17 Paces (5)
18 Act as a go-between (7)
20 Take for granted (6)
21 Hairy facial growths (6)
22 Rests on bended legs (6)

Down

1 One of two actors who are given the same status in a film (2-4)
2 Sacred beetle (6)
3 Affectedly dainty or refined (4)
4 Characteristic mental attitude (7)
5 Variety show with topical sketches and songs (5)
8 Expression used to frighten away animals (4)
11 Imitative behaviour (7)
13 Puts into service (4)
14 Bean or pea plant (6)
15 Things of material value or usefulness (6)
16 Number indicated by the Roman VII (5)
19 Duty (4)

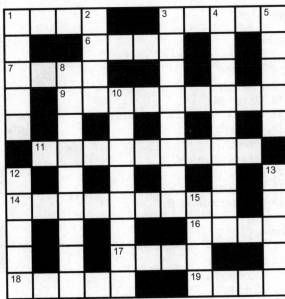

78

Across

1 Diagrammatic representations of roads (4)
3 Outer covering of some fruits or seeds (5)
6 Collection of miscellaneous things (4)
7 Land force (4)
9 One from the Orient (9)
11 Arm of the Mediterranean between Greece and Italy (6,3)
14 Overbearing pride (9)
16 River of Russia and Kazakhstan (4)
17 Affirm (4)
18 Daily written record of events (5)
19 Bathroom fixtures (4)

Down

1 ___ Vice, TV series (5)
2 Asian plant widely cultivated for its oily beans (4)
3 Direct onto a target, especially by automatic navigational aids (4,2,2)
4 Person who verbally attacks the reputation of another (9)
5 Carnivorous marine fish (5)
8 Extravagant theatrical piece (9)
10 Bottom-dwelling fish with a venomous spine on a whiplike tail (8)
12 Stunned (5)
13 Mild viral infections (5)
15 Short, abrupt (4)

79

Across
1 Club that is used as a weapon (6)
6 Calculating machine (6)
7 Fat used in cooking (4)
8 Moving to music (7)
12 Quench (5)
13 And not (3)
14 Allow (3)
15 Application (3)
17 Class of people enjoying superior status (5)
18 Hang freely (7)
21 International alliance begun in 1949 (inits) (4)
22 Pickled flower buds used in various sauces (6)
23 The act of coming out (6)

Down
1 Person of exceptional importance and reputation (8)
2 Period of history between classical antiquity and the Italian Renaissance (4,4)
3 Tibetan or Mongolian priest (4)
4 Bath powder (4)
5 Product of seabirds, used as a fertiliser (5)
8 Dig deeply into (5)
9 Made a written record of (5)
10 Close, familiar (8)
11 Very severe or serious (8)
16 Sweetening agent (5)
19 Having patches coloured differently (4)
20 Olfactory organ (4)

80

Across
1 Thin sliver of wood (6)
4 Bucket (4)
8 Figure (5)
10 Change (5)
11 Feed as in a meadow or pasture (5)
12 Owned (9)
18 Expect (5)
19 Bohemian dance (5)
21 Au revoir (5)
22 Back garden (4)
23 Shouts of approval (6)

Down
1 Echo sounder (acronym) (5)
2 Inventory (4)
3 Approach (4)
5 Alight (6)
6 Identification tab (5)
7 Kindly endorsement and guidance (5)
9 Belonging to that woman (4)
13 Public speaker (6)
14 Grilled food on a skewer, served with peanut sauce (5)
15 Foot-covering (4)
16 Lawn flower (5)
17 Underground tunnels (5)
19 Essence (4)
20 Racing sled for one or two people (4)

81

Across

1 Strong wooden or metal post with a point at one end (5)
4 Fortuitous (5)
7 Shakespeare play (7)
8 Hawaiian greeting (5)
9 Posture (6)
12 One dozen dozen (5)
15 Has in mind (5)
17 Towards the tail of a ship (6)
18 Surplus to need (5)
19 Plans for attaining a particular goal (7)
20 Mechanical bar (5)
21 Once more (5)

Down

1 Leapt (6)
2 Of an appropriate or pertinent nature (7)
3 All together, as a group (2,5)
5 Sophisticated, refined (6)
6 Baby cat (6)
10 Loss of memory (7)
11 Musical setting for a religious text (7)
13 Lay waste to (6)
14 Figurine (6)
16 Sailor (6)

82

Across

1 Member of a Germanic race that conquered England (5)
3 Distinguishing features (5)
7 Christian celebration of the Resurrection of Christ (6)
9 Compound capable of turning litmus red (4)
10 To a severe or serious degree (10)
13 Spectator who can describe what happened (10)
16 Strong restless desire (4)
17 Open to public view by the ceremonial removal of a covering (6)
19 Sir Walter ___, British author (1771–1832) (5)
20 Assumed name (5)

Down

1 Preliminary drawing (6)
2 Abbreviation for the tenth month (3)
4 Be of service (5)
5 Face (4)
6 Divisive (9)
8 Covered with a thick and slippery liquid substance (5)
11 Belgian city (5)
12 Sacred songs (6)
14 Construct (a building) (5)
15 Uses a knife (4)
18 Mr Doonican, Irish singer (3)

83

Across

2 Offensive to the mind (9)
6 Wrath (5)
7 Gyrates (5)
9 Acquired (3)
10 Curt, brusque (5)
12 Corpulent (5)
14 Hurls, lobs (5)
17 Loom (5)
19 Make a knot (3)
20 Sweat room (5)
21 Bicker (5)
22 Lacking flavour (9)

Down

1 Roman slave who led an uprising against Roman legions (9)
2 Jolly ___, pirates' flag (5)
3 Rid of impurities (5)
4 Vigorous and enthusiastic enjoyment (5)
5 Liquorice-flavoured seeds (5)
8 Be the leader of (9)
11 Fixed (3)
13 Hoot with derision (3)
15 Moves along quickly (5)
16 Look at intently (5)
17 Tantalise (5)
18 Earnings (5)

84

Across

4 Footwear items (5)
7 Graceful woodland animal (3,4)
8 Adam's wife (3)
10 Composed (5)
12 Move to music (5)
13 Waste product useful as a fertiliser (4)
15 Officially forbid something (9)
19 Alleviate (4)
21 Norwegian composer (1843–1907) (5)
24 Pasta in short tubes with diagonally cut ends (5)
25 ___ Baba, fictional character (3)
26 Thick heavy material with a raised pattern (7)
27 Item of dining room furniture (5)

Down

1 Makes tea (5)
2 Diversion (6)
3 Native American tents, usually of conical shape (6)
4 Caused to procreate (animals) (4)
5 Overt (4)
6 Snooze (5)
9 Overnight case (6)
11 Gardening tool (6)
14 Playing card (3)
16 Bird of prey, such as the eagle (6)
17 Geographic region between Bangladesh and India (6)
18 Arab republic (5)
20 High temperature (5)
22 Metrical unit with unstressed-stressed syllables (4)
23 Taunt (4)

85

Across
1 Feeling of distress and disbelief (5)
3 Second planet from the sun (5)
7 A long way off (4)
9 Make possible (6)
10 Dandy (4)
11 Extended journey (4)
12 Turn away from by persuasion (5)
15 Great danger (5)
17 Loose flowing garment (4)
19 Mountain goat (4)
20 Physical science relating to light (6)
21 Religious song (4)
22 In an early period of life (5)
23 Deep chasm (5)

Down
1 Sailors' rhythmical work song (6)
2 One who looks after a sick relative (5)
4 Perform as if in a play (5)
5 Garden toolhouse (4)
6 Social system that developed in Europe in the eighth century (9)
8 Evil or corrupt practice (5)
13 Resin used chiefly in strong adhesives (5)
14 Game associated with Wimbledon (6)
16 Have sovereign power (5)
17 Course of therapy following addiction or illness (abbr) (5)
18 Small gentle horse (4)

86

Across
1 Greek author of fables (5)
4 Adult male elephants (5)
7 Sicken (3)
8 Contented (5)
10 Definite article (3)
11 Sneering look (4)
12 Brief fling of unrestrained spending (5)
14 Herb (5)
17 Rush (5)
20 Units of distance (5)
22 Succulent plant (4)
23 Drinking vessel (3)
24 Excellent (5)
26 Be in a horizontal position (3)
27 Digging implement (5)
28 Assemble (3,2)

Down
1 Throbs dully (5)
2 Plant fluid (3)
3 Recipient of money (5)
4 Promotional statement (as found on the dust jackets of books) (5)
5 Water lily (5)
6 Take without permission (5)
9 Gather into a ruffle (5)
13 Leguminous plant (3)
15 Au revoir (5)
16 Nickname of US president Eisenhower (3)
17 Component of soil (5)
18 18th Greek letter (5)
19 Bird of prey (5)
20 Old Testament prophet (5)
21 Morsel (5)
25 Tap lightly (3)

87

Across

2 Proclaimer of public announcements (4,5)
6 Port in north-western Israel on the Bay of Acre (5)
8 Slang of thieves (5)
11 Actual (7)
12 Crevice (5)
13 Smudge, daub (5)
14 Light-beam amplifier (5)
17 Small pieces of stiff paper on which greetings are printed (5)
19 Nobility (7)
20 Fine cords of twisted fibres (5)
21 Great feast (5)
22 Most strong (9)

Down

1 In a morally correct way (9)
2 Thin cotton or linen dress material (5)
3 Sir Thomas ___, English poet (1503–42) (5)
4 Burns superficially (5)
5 Fireplace (5)
7 Number represented by the Roman XV (7)
9 Storm around (7)
10 Sill of a house door (9)
15 Branchlet (5)
16 Take (an examination) again (5)
17 Overseas telegram (5)
18 Respond (5)

88

Across

1 Cut off (5)
3 Comedy characterised by improbable situations (5)
6 Formerly (4)
8 Part of a dress above the waist (6)
10 Kingdom in the South Pacific (5)
12 Lock of hair (5)
14 Type of hunting dog (7)
15 Flatfish (5)
16 Accurate (5)
18 Rivulet (6)
19 Most fitting (4)
20 Wears out (5)
21 Fish with a hook (5)

Down

1 Grunt (5)
2 Female sheep (3)
3 Wilderness at the edge of a settled area (8)
4 Say again (9)
5 Level betting (5)
7 Holder (9)
9 Marked by lack of attention (8)
11 Acquire (3)
13 King (3)
15 Very small fish (5)
17 Identifying appellation (5)
19 Wastepaper basket (3)

89

Across

1 Angel of the highest order (6)
6 Plant similar to the rhododendron (6)
7 Rouse from slumber (6)
10 Utter obscenities or profanities (9)
12 Gas formerly used as an anaesthetic (5)
13 Complex system of interconnected elements (3)
15 Noisy altercation (5)
18 Erratic (9)
20 Cause to be (6)
21 Raymond Briggs's Bogeyman (6)
22 List of items for discussion (6)

Down

1 Left over, superfluous (5)
2 Joint just above the foot (5)
3 ___ Christian Andersen, storyteller (4)
4 Fictional character notorious for murdering his wives (9)
5 Tall tower referred to in the Bible (5)
8 Detestable (9)
9 Common garden insect (6)
11 Small smooth rounded rock (6)
14 Very short time (coll) (5)
16 Kitchen appliance used for cooking food (5)
17 Immature insect (5)
19 ___ Major, the Great Bear constellation (4)

90

Across

1 Biographical movie (6)
6 Have a lofty goal (6)
7 Milk pudding ingredient (4)
8 Act of washing and dressing oneself (8)
11 Overturn (a boat) accidentally (7)
14 State of relatedness by blood or marriage (7)
18 Dark oily liquid used as a wood preservative (8)
19 Brief written record (4)
20 Breakfast food (6)
21 Unpleasantly cool and humid (6)

Down

1 Fundamental (5)
2 Plans secretly (5)
3 Ancient port city in south-west Spain (5)
4 Pair of pictures, especially with a religious theme, painted on hinged wooden panels (7)
5 At no time (5)
9 Squeals like a pig (5)
10 Bent from a vertical position (5)
12 Very drunk (slang) (3-4)
13 Scallywag (5)
15 Order of Greek architecture (5)
16 Plant that produces pods used as a laxative (5)
17 Religious righteousness (5)

91

Across

1 Palaeontological relic (6)
6 Blood vessel leading from the heart (6)
7 Sultanate in north-western Borneo (6)
8 Appealing to refined taste (6)
10 Adjusts a text ready for publication (5)
13 Contrition (7)
16 Civil or military authority in Turkey (5)
18 Relatives by marriage (2-4)
20 State of commotion, noise and confusion (6)
21 Treeless Arctic plain (6)
22 Money dealer (6)

Down

1 Ancient tale (5)
2 Assembly possessing high legislative powers (6)
3 Secular (4)
4 In any case (7)
5 Keyed into a machine (5)
9 Musical instrument associated with Wales (4)
11 Country known to the Romans as Hibernia (7)
12 Fish-eating diving duck (4)
14 Fish that travels up a river to spawn (6)
15 Great merriment (5)
17 On the move (5)
19 Poke or thrust abruptly (4)

92

Across

1 Cleaning implement (5)
4 Hidden storage space (5)
7 Variety of mandarin orange (7)
8 Bustle (3)
9 Dukedom (5)
11 Trap for birds or small mammals (5)
12 Undersides of shoes (5)
14 Board game (5)
16 Gone by (3)
17 Father of a parent (7)
19 Hearty (5)
20 Off-colour (5)

Down

1 Founded (5)
2 Abbreviation for the tenth month (3)
3 Quiet, timid and ineffectual (5)
4 Caste (5)
5 Absurd pretence (7)
6 Give expression to (5)
10 Insensitive or heartless (7)
12 Gastropod with a spiral shell (5)
13 Dripping wet (5)
14 Santa ____, Father Christmas (5)
15 Unstable (5)
18 Directly or exactly, straight (3)

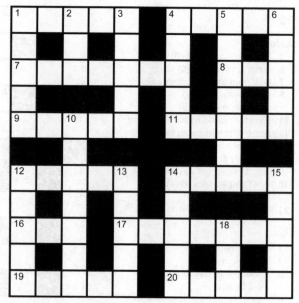

93

Across

1 Loose-fitting garment (5)
4 Plants often found in arid regions of the world (5)
7 Ancient jar used to hold oil or wine (7)
8 Train driver's compartment (3)
9 Special way of doing something (5)
11 Silky net fabric (5)
12 French river (5)
14 Modified leaf of a plant (5)
16 The night before (3)
17 Unexceptional (7)
19 Name of a book (5)
20 Grasslike marsh plant (5)

Down

1 Show appreciation (5)
2 Small sharp bite (3)
3 Utter a hoarse sound, like a frog (5)
4 Map (5)
5 Tube-shaped structure of the inner ear (7)
6 Suffuse with colour (5)
10 Sustenance (7)
12 Inhaled the odour of (5)
13 Circumvent (5)
14 Consecrate (5)
15 In that place (5)
18 Also (3)

94

Across

1 Aggressive remark directed at a person like a missile (5)
4 Piece of cloth used to mend a hole (5)
7 Method of delivery of a cricket ball (7)
9 Chair of state of a monarch (6)
10 Animal fat used in cooking (6)
12 Added to (4)
15 Defunct (4)
17 Request (3,3)
19 Church officer in charge of sacred objects (6)
20 Small anchor with several claws or arms (7)
21 Group of warships (5)
22 Cut thinly (5)

Down

1 Confine to a place by cutting off a means of escape (4,2)
2 Inclined towards or displaying love (7)
3 Flexible part of a whip (5)
5 In a foreign country (6)
6 Part of the eye (6)
8 Containing too many words (7)
11 Naturally effervescent mineral water (7)
13 Stan ____, film partner of Oliver Hardy (6)
14 Capital of modern Macedonia (6)
16 River bordered by Vienna, Budapest and Belgrade (6)
18 Object that has survived from the past (5)

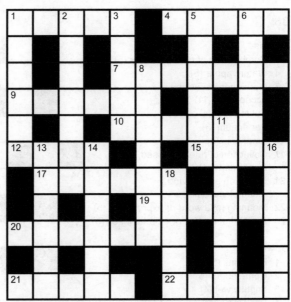

49

95

Across

1 Prince who abducted Helen of Troy (5)
4 Religious song (5)
7 Digit (7)
8 Stringed instrument (5)
10 Act of washing and dressing oneself (8)
13 Large and hurried swallow (4)
15 Elegant or stylishly luxurious (coll) (4)
17 In use (8)
19 Formal title used when addressing a woman (5)
20 Japanese art of flower arranging (7)
21 Forepart (5)
22 Merits, deserves (5)

Down

1 Demonstrates the truth of by evidence or argument (6)
2 Like the unthinking functioning of a machine (7)
3 Egyptian peninsula (5)
5 Climbing garden plant with fragrant flowers (5,3)
6 Organs of photosynthesis and transpiration (6)
9 Small house built of wood (3,5)
11 Circuit (3)
12 Child learning to walk (7)
14 Employee (6)
16 People (6)
18 Iconic mental representation (5)

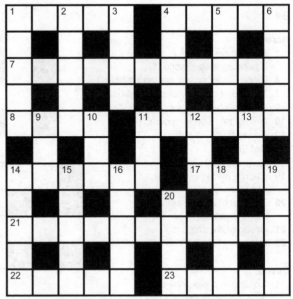

96

Across

1 Combination of musical notes (5)
4 Water vapour (5)
7 Mentioned as worthy of acceptance (11)
8 Put in order (4)
11 Per annum (6)
14 Emphasis (6)
17 Collection of rules imposed by authority (4)
21 Based on or involving resemblance (11)
22 Meaning (of a word or expression) (5)
23 Drained of energy or effectiveness (5)

Down

1 Restrains (5)
2 Come about (5)
3 Slightly wet (4)
4 Panorama (5)
5 Tree that produces berries in autumn (5)
6 Clouded as with sediment (5)
9 Available (3)
10 Definite article (3)
11 Affirmative answer (3)
12 Completely (3)
13 Gloomy, down (3)
14 Hosiery items (5)
15 Resident of the capital of Italy (5)
16 Relative magnitude (5)
18 Similar (5)
19 Cleaned with a broom (5)
20 Flexible containers (4)

97

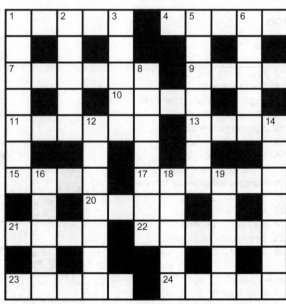

Across

1 Barely noticeable (6)
6 Indian side dish of yogurt and chopped cucumbers (5)
7 Very small (3)
8 Jobs that must be done (5)
10 Root vegetable (5)
12 Pinnacle (3)
14 ___ and buts, objections (3)
15 Existed, lived (3)
16 Love affair (5)
17 Large northern deer (5)
20 Vat (3)
21 Concentrate (5)
22 Showing determination and a lack of fear (6)

Down

1 Condiment, sodium chloride (4)
2 Establishments where alcoholic drinks are served (4)
3 State of mild depression (3,7)
4 Mould (6)
5 Young cattle (6)
6 Put back together again (10)
9 Particle (4)
11 Platform (4)
12 Government tax on imports or exports (6)
13 Law force (6)
18 Probabilities (4)
19 Posing no difficulty (4)

98

Across

1 Abnormal swellings on the body (5)
4 Desert animal (5)
7 Argentine plain (6)
9 Roster of names and tasks (4)
10 Eastern staple foodstuff (4)
11 Layered (6)
13 Exclamation expressive of sorrow (4)
15 Source of illumination (4)
17 Cinnamon-yielding tree (6)
20 Gemstone (4)
21 Foreman (4)
22 Corpulent (6)
23 Artist's tripod (5)
24 Short simple song (5)

Down

1 Upper-case letter (7)
2 Battleground of World War I (5)
3 Trap for birds or small mammals (5)
5 State of being behind in payments (7)
6 Additional (5)
8 Conveyance attached to a motorcycle (7)
12 Quick-witted retort (7)
14 Substitute on hand (5-2)
16 Distinctive smell (5)
18 Audibly (5)
19 Transfer to another track, of trains (5)

99

Across

1 Three-handed card game played with 32 cards (4)
3 Artefacts perceived as being of poor quality, especially when garish or sentimental (6)
5 Time period (3)
6 Grassy garden area (4)
7 Nuts or fruit pieces in a sugar paste (6)
9 Gymnastic moves (10)
14 Folding portable aid to climbing, hinged at the top (10)
17 Stroke lovingly (6)
19 Manufactured (4)
20 High mountain (3)
21 Decapitate (6)
22 Time assigned on a schedule or agenda (4)

Down

1 Muslim form of salutation (6)
2 It takes two to do this dance, according to a saying (5)
3 Understand (Scots) (3)
4 Lads (5)
8 Israeli submachine-gun (3)
10 Informer (3)
11 Be unwell (3)
12 Food of a ruminant regurgitated to be chewed again (3)
13 Characterised by strong enthusiasm (6)
14 Remove body hair (5)
15 Augment (3)
16 Throws away as refuse (5)
18 Distressing (3)

100

Across

1 Boasts (5)
4 Fruit of the oak (5)
7 Constricted (6)
9 Expel (gases or odours) (4)
10 Unit of heredity (4)
12 Submerge in a liquid (4)
13 Facing of a jacket (5)
15 High mountain (3)
17 ___ Island, New York Bay area (5)
19 Number indicated by the Roman V (4)
21 Estimation (4)
23 Osculate (4)
24 Making an attempt (6)
25 Leaves of a book (5)
26 Take an oath (5)

Down

1 Cast out (6)
2 Postal service for overseas (7)
3 Mixture of fog and smoke (4)
5 Slink (5)
6 Short letter (4)
8 Strongly built, sturdy (4-3)
11 Forty winks (3)
14 Large imposing building (7)
15 Be of service (3)
16 Pauper (6)
18 Strong, tightly twisted cotton thread (5)
20 Gait in which steps and hops alternate (4)
22 Painting, sculpture, music, etc (4)

101

Across
1 Inventories (5)
4 Position of professor (5)
7 Pompous or pretentious talk or writing (7)
8 Time of life between the ages of 13 and 19 (5)
10 Make a mistake (3)
11 Artful (3)
13 Residence of a clergyman (5)
14 Cry (3)
16 Gelid (3)
18 Disorderly outburst (coll) (3-2)
19 Extreme greed for material wealth (7)
20 Glue (5)
21 Spotted or calico horse (5)

Down
1 Espresso coffee with milk (5)
2 Conduit for carrying off waste products (5)
3 Being on topic and prompting thought (11)
4 Pile of manure and rotting vegetation for use in the garden (7,4)
5 Richard ___, author of *Watership Down* and *The Plague Dogs* (5)
6 Bad-tempered and irritable (coll) (5)
9 Consequently (4)
12 Scottish lake (4)
14 Skin covering the top of the head (5)
15 Pulse vegetables (5)
16 Native of Des Moines, for example (5)
17 Popular web portal (5)

102

Across
1 Shallow baskets used when gardening (5)
4 Clothes drier (5)
7 Chest bones (4)
8 Strainer (5)
9 Mosque official (4)
10 Hard fruits (4)
12 Study intensively for an exam (4)
15 Spinning toys (4)
17 Highway (4)
19 Walking-stick (4)
20 Happen again (5)
22 Brand name of a ballpoint pen (4)
23 Heavenly being (5)
24 Root vegetable (5)

Down
1 Flings up, as with a coin, for example (6)
2 Strong restless desire (4)
3 Alarm (5)
5 Take a firm stand (6)
6 Pitch tents (6)
11 Large nation (inits) (3)
13 Lessen the strength of (6)
14 High-pitched (6)
16 Place of worship associated with a sacred thing or person (6)
18 Worthless material (5)
21 Fuel produced by the distillation of coal (4)

103

Across

1 Bone cavity (5)
4 Person undergoing training for the armed forces (5)
7 Carry out in practice (7)
8 Expert (3)
9 Follow on from (5)
11 Lie in ambush (5)
12 Frighten away (5)
14 Marine crustaceans (5)
16 Allow (3)
17 Climb awkwardly (7)
19 Sloping mass of loose rocks at the base of a cliff (5)
20 Square root of sixty-four (5)

Down

1 Ordered series (5)
2 Mesh (3)
3 Person held in servitude (5)
4 Popular board game (5)
5 Bram Stoker's vampire (7)
6 Adjust finely (5)
10 Electric motor for bringing an engine to life (7)
12 Cut-price events (5)
13 Compere (coll) (5)
14 Go after with the intent to catch (5)
15 Lofty proud gait (5)
18 Appropriate, seize (3)

104

Across

4 Slow speech with prolonged vowels (5)
7 In the current fashion or style (1,2,4)
8 Rough calculation based on very little knowledge (coll) (11)
12 Armistice, truce (9)
15 Option (11)
20 Define clearly (7)
21 Opposing military force (5)

Down

1 Evelyn ____, English novelist (1903–66) (5)
2 Arrived (4)
3 Curtsies (4)
4 Type of food shop (abbr) (4)
5 Halo of light (4)
6 Compare (5)
9 Partial darkness (5)
10 Link up, connect (3,2)
11 Slightly wet (5)
13 Emblem (5)
14 Mineral of which emerald and aquamarine are varieties (5)
16 Periodic rise and fall of sea level (4)
17 Pink-tinged (4)
18 Not many (1,3)
19 Coloured part of the eye (4)

105

Across

1 Temporary police force (5)
4 Addition, subtraction, division, multiplication, etc (abbr) (5)
7 Social outcast (6)
9 British nobleman (4)
10 Gas used in lighting (4)
11 Crack in a lip caused usually by cold (4)
12 Metal ring that opens a can (3)
15 Stitch back (3)
17 Introduce to solid food (4)
19 "Beware the ___ of March", advice given to Julius Caesar (4)
21 Arabian ruler (4)
22 Three times (6)
23 Marked by aggressive ambition (5)
24 Assignation between lovers (5)

Down

1 Tenure of office of a pope (6)
2 Family appellation (7)
3 Distinctive and stylish elegance (4)
5 Representative (5)
6 Alone, unaccompanied (4)
8 Pair of earphones (7)
13 Convenient facility (7)
14 Inoculate by using a needle (6)
16 Gleefulness (5)
18 Gather, as of crops (4)
20 Fired a bullet at (4)

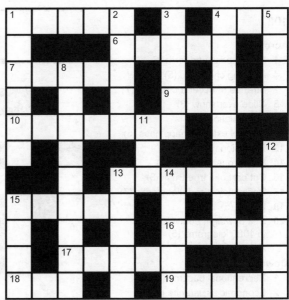

106

Across

1 Gasps for breath (5)
4 Weep (3)
6 Relating to them (5)
7 African antelope (5)
9 Suffered something unpleasant (5)
10 Ailment (7)
13 Abominate (7)
15 Pair of game birds (5)
16 Put up (5)
17 Give rise to (5)
18 Gaming cube (3)
19 Small natural hill (5)

Down

1 Expert in a particular field who often presents views to the media (6)
2 Money risked on a gamble (5)
3 Graves (5)
4 Reticent (9)
5 Digestive juice secreted by the liver (4)
8 Leeway (9)
11 Catch sight of (3)
12 Relating to the teeth (6)
13 Correct errors in computer program code (5)
14 Glossy, smooth (5)
15 Lacking hair (4)

107

Across

1 Pouch in a bird's gullet where food is stored (4)
3 Narrative poem of popular origin (6)
5 Muhammad ___, former boxer (3)
6 Cousin's mother (4)
7 Rich and elaborate cake (6)
9 Attempt to anticipate or predict (6-5)
14 Small paving slab with a curved top, once used to make roads (11)
18 Scattered wreckage (6)
20 Distinguishing symbol (4)
21 Fruit of a rose plant (3)
22 Soft decayed area in a tooth (6)
23 Row or layer (4)

Down

1 Timeless (7)
2 Paved area that adjoins a house (5)
3 Above average in size (3)
4 Nicola ___, boxer who won a gold medal at the 2012 Olympics (5)
8 19th letter of the Greek alphabet (3)
10 Adult male swan (3)
11 Female deer (3)
12 Self-importance (3)
13 Canvas shoe with a pliable rubber sole (7)
15 Drama set to music (5)
16 Exclude (3)
17 Entice (5)
19 Diffident (3)

108

Across

1 Moved back and forth (5)
4 Drinking chocolate (5)
7 Strange or eccentric person (7)
8 Glide over snow (3)
9 Appreciation (5)
11 State of extreme happiness (5)
12 Explosion (5)
14 Heavy open wagons (5)
16 Cut part of a tree trunk (3)
17 Deficiency of red blood cells (7)
19 Heave (5)
20 Unit of weight equivalent to 1000 kilograms (5)

Down

1 Recreational pastime (5)
2 Economic assistance (3)
3 Clear space in an area of woodland (5)
4 Famous person (abbr) (5)
5 Bank teller (7)
6 Haywire (5)
10 Walk as if unable to control one's movements (7)
12 South American missile consisting of stones connected by strong cord (5)
13 Faintly detectable amount (5)
14 Shore of a sea (5)
15 Frighten away (5)
18 Adult male person (3)

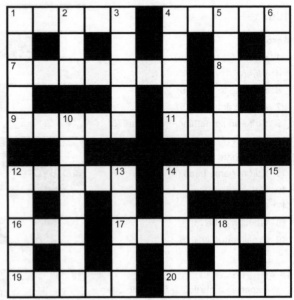

109

Across

1 Package of several things tied together (5)
3 Gush forth in a sudden stream or jet (5)
7 Admission (6)
9 Stitches together (4)
10 Aggravate, worsen (10)
13 Rule or directive made and maintained by an authority (10)
16 As well (4)
17 Largest digit of the foot (3,3)
19 Multiplication (5)
20 Well turned-out (5)

Down

1 Ocean floor (6)
2 Imitate (3)
4 Tagliatelle or ravioli, for example (5)
5 Examination (4)
6 Early form of sextant (9)
8 Go after with the intent to catch (5)
11 Contaminate (5)
12 Inoculate by using a needle (6)
14 Small plantation of trees (5)
15 Cobbler's stand (4)
18 Tissue that surrounds a tooth (3)

110

Across

1 Product of seabirds, used as a fertiliser (5)
5 Rechewed food (3)
7 Cause to be embarrassed (5)
8 Goes along at great speed (5)
9 Deserving of a scratch (5)
12 Collapse caused by exposure to high temperature (10)
16 Plant family that includes the maple (4)
17 Bold and impudent behaviour (4)
19 Item associated with King Arthur (5,5)
22 Protrude outwards (5)
23 Means of communication (abbr) (5)
24 Domestic birds (5)
25 Lad (3)
26 Skimmed (5)

Down

1 Nepalese soldier (6)
2 Study of ancient people through their material remains (11)
3 Desert garden (5)
4 Muslim or Hindu mendicant monk (5)
5 Crammed full of people or things (coll) (5-1-5)
6 Confront with resistance (4)
10 Roman cloak (4)
11 The Underworld (4)
13 Colour of unbleached linen (4)
14 Shallow basket used when gardening (4)
15 Small amount (3)
18 Fable (6)
20 At no time (5)
21 Narrow to a point (5)
22 Rear-facing point on an arrow (4)

111

Across

1 Spain's head of state from 1939–75 (6)
6 Twelve noon (6)
7 Fit for cultivation (6)
9 Ultimate client for which a thing is intended (3,4)
13 Individual units in a list (5)
14 Capacious (5)
15 Male child (3)
16 Furze (5)
19 Insectivorous terrestrial lizard (5)
20 Watch attentively (7)
22 Surname of Roseanne Barr's ex-husband Tom (6)
23 Appraise (6)
24 Pencil rubber (6)

Down

1 Pink wading bird (8)
2 Non-professionals (8)
3 Portent (4)
4 Hate coupled with disgust (5)
5 Honey-badger of Africa and southern Asia (5)
8 Smaller in amount (6)
10 Hazard (6)
11 Plausible but false (8)
12 Tubular wind instrument with eight finger holes (8)
17 Rotund, extremely chubby (5)
18 Set or keep apart (5)
21 Jar for flowers (4)

112

Across

1 Greek 'L' (6)
6 Gorge (6)
8 Traditions (7)
9 Former hereditary monarch of Iran (4)
10 Will (5)
13 Afternoon meal (3)
14 Unwanted discharge of a fluid (7)
16 Unit of sound intensity (3)
17 French queen, wife of Louis XVI, ___ Antoinette (5)
19 Pip (4)
21 Leisurely walk (7)
22 General condition of body and mind (6)
23 Greater (6)

Down

1 Is without (5)
2 Armed fight (6)
3 Official symbols of a family, state, etc (4)
4 Device for kindling a fire (7)
5 Country, capital Nairobi (5)
7 Place of religious retreat for Hindus (6)
11 Made up of famous top performers (3-4)
12 Most recent (6)
15 Gather, as of crops (6)
16 Cleanse the entire body (5)
18 Inadvertent incorrectness (5)
20 Roald ___, author of *Charlie and the Chocolate Factory* (4)

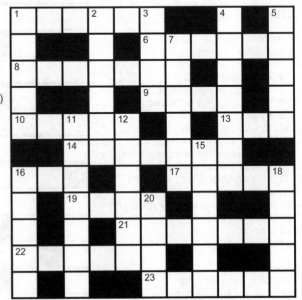

113

Across
1 Expected and wished (5)
4 Addenda (5)
7 US musician and record producer, ___ Turner (3)
8 US state (5)
10 Consciousness of one's own identity (3)
11 Body of water (4)
12 Tubes (5)
14 Disgrace (5)
15 Censure severely (5)
16 Arm off of a larger body of water (5)
19 Measure (out) (4)
20 Appropriate (3)
21 Due (5)
23 Moldovan monetary unit (3)
24 Dish out (5)
25 Coil of knitting wool (5)

Down
1 Stirred emotionally by anger or excitement (coll) (3,2)
2 Contagious disease characterised by purulent skin eruptions (3)
3 Take apart (11)
4 Impoverished, destitute (11)
5 Foot digit protector (7)
6 Fume (5)
9 Alcoholic beverage (3)
13 Device attached to a computer (7)
15 Uncouth (5)
17 Novel (3)
18 Offspring of a male tiger and a female lion (5)
22 Coat a cake with sugar (3)

114

Across
1 Flower associated with Remembrance Sunday (5)
3 Reddish-brown tint (5)
6 Coniferous tree (4)
8 King who allegedly burned the cakes (6)
9 Vehicle from another world (inits) (3)
11 Beat with a piece of leather (5)
12 Greetings (5)
14 Appearance of a place (7)
15 Curl of the lip (5)
16 Unsuccessful person (5)
18 Penultimate Greek letter (3)
19 Loveliness (6)
20 Small area of land (4)
21 Passenger (5)
22 Furious (5)

Down
1 Conduits used to convey liquids or gases (5)
2 Short introductory essay preceding the text of a book (7)
3 Doing things without the assistance of others (4-4)
4 Loss of the ability to move a body part (9)
5 Relating to sound (5)
7 Nanny (9)
10 Telephone switchboard assistant (8)
13 Wearing away (7)
15 Not affected by alcohol (5)
17 High, thin in tone (5)

115

Across

1 Design made of small pieces of coloured stone (6)
6 Lessen the density or solidity of (6)
8 Store selling children's playthings (7)
9 Try out (6)
10 Make free of ice (7)
13 Flow back (3)
14 Conspicuous success (3)
17 Timidity (7)
20 Island to the north of Java (6)
21 Daybreak (7)
22 Not if (6)
23 Firstborn (6)

Down

1 In a softened tone (5)
2 Assimilate or take in (6)
3 Emblem of Christianity (5)
4 Notwithstanding (7)
5 ___ Cup, golf tournament played every two years (5)
7 Absence of emotion or enthusiasm (6)
11 Feverish (7)
12 Be constantly talking or worrying about something (6)
15 Hardened to (6)
16 Around (5)
18 Accommodate (5)
19 Smell (5)

116

Across

1 Light violet colour (5)
3 Be overcome by a sudden fear (5)
7 Mother (4)
8 Showing self-interest and shrewdness (5)
9 Faithful (5)
11 Farming (11)
14 Narrator (11)
16 Gains victory over (5)
19 Financial institutions (5)
20 Cook slowly and for a long time in liquid (4)
21 Develop fully (5)
22 Number indicated by the Roman XL (5)

Down

1 Birthplace of Muhammad (5)
2 Basic French dressing for salads (11)
3 Mate (3)
4 Pale medium-dry Spanish sherry (11)
5 Word indicating a negative answer (3)
6 Bear a young cow (5)
10 Apartment consisting of a series of connected rooms (5)
12 Intestine (3)
13 Fish eggs (3)
14 Not affected by alcohol (5)
15 Impaired in skill by neglect (5)
17 Type of cobra (3)
18 One-hundredth of a yen (3)

117

Across

1. Cylindrical container (4)
3. Scour (5)
6. Elegant and stylish (4)
7. Hasten (4)
9. Madame de ___, French noblewoman who was the lover of Louis XV (9)
11. Augment (3)
12. Dead and rotting flesh (7)
14. Invest with a knighthood (3)
16. Lose water due to heating (9)
18. By word of mouth (4)
19. Academic test (abbr) (4)
20. Drained of energy or effectiveness (5)
21. Formal offers at an auction (4)

Down

1. Abrupt (5)
2. Reverberate (4)
3. Type of neuralgia that affects the hips (8)
4. Quick and witty response (9)
5. Facial hair (5)
8. Elaborate and remarkable display on a lavish scale (9)
10. South American monkey with claws instead of nails (8)
13. Gains victory over (5)
15. Large pill used in veterinary medicine (5)
17. Sepulchre (4)

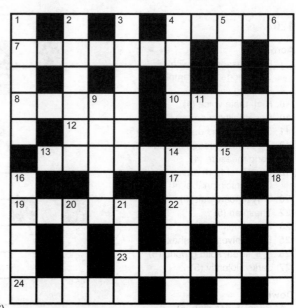

118

Across

4. Floor consisting of open space at the top of a house (5)
7. Computer generated image (7)
8. Overgrown with a clinging plant (5)
10. Radial member of a wheel joining the hub to the rim (5)
12. Reverential salutation (3)
13. Transversely (9)
17. Immeasurably long period of time (3)
19. Projecting bay window (5)
22. Hurray! (5)
23. Literate people (7)
24. Kinswoman (5)

Down

1. One more time (5)
2. Salted roe of a sturgeon (6)
3. Largest of the Dodecanese islands (6)
4. Top cards (4)
5. Country, capital Lomé (4)
6. Blanket (5)
9. Call forth (5)
11. Beforehand (5)
14. Internet photographic equipment (6)
15. Moves along a winding path (6)
16. Adult female (5)
18. Brag (5)
20. Unused (4)
21. Entice (4)

119

Across
1 Falls away (5)
3 Couple (5)
7 Keen on (4)
9 Domesticated llama (6)
11 Leisurely walk (5)
13 Body (5)
14 Mix up or confuse (5)
15 Pallid, weak (3)
16 Public announcement of a proposed marriage (5)
17 North African port (5)
20 Run off to marry (5)
22 Farmyard manure in fluid form (6)
23 Border (4)
24 Burn with steam (5)
25 Full-grown (5)

Down
1 Bird that resembles a swallow (5)
2 Formal school or college balls held at the end of a year (5)
4 Deserted (9)
5 Fill with high spirits (5)
6 Diminutive of Henry (3)
8 Large hairy tropical spider (9)
10 Rough shelter at the side of a house (4-2)
12 Light tanker for supplying water or fuel (6)
16 Footing (5)
18 Flip to a vertical position (2-3)
19 Perfume (5)
21 Caustic washing solution (3)

120

Across
1 Boats associated with Cambridge, for example (5)
4 Drinking vessel (5)
9 High male voice (4)
10 Resembling a dream (7)
11 Spring-loaded door fastener (5)
12 Block the passage through (6)
15 Land measure (4)
18 Character from an ancient Germanic alphabet (4)
20 Playing card suit (6)
22 Thespian (5)
23 Faced boldly (7)
25 Fit of shivering or shaking (4)
26 ___ firma, solid ground (5)
27 Jerks violently (5)

Down
1 Spanish rice dish (6)
2 Help to develop and grow (7)
3 Japanese dish (5)
5 Food store (6)
6 Alcoholic beverage (3)
7 Flower part (6)
8 Roman god of the Sun (3)
13 Rug (3)
14 Trash can (7)
16 Price for some service (6)
17 Breadwinner (6)
19 Emergence (6)
21 Unhappily (5)
23 Overweight (3)
24 Belonging to us (3)

121

Across

1 Colour of the rainbow (5)
3 Country, capital Niamey (5)
7 City formerly called Bombay (6)
9 Symbol (4)
10 Travel across snow (3)
11 Transparent optical device (4)
13 Overnight condensation (3)
15 Transporter (7)
17 For every (3)
18 Pro ___, in proportion (4)
20 Light touch or stroke (3)
21 Not in favour of (4)
22 Exit a computer (3,3)
24 Drying cloth (5)
25 Aberdeen ___, cattle breed (5)

Down

1 Take a chance (6)
2 Flow back (3)
4 Person in an organisation who is privy to information unavailable to others (7)
5 Loop (4)
6 Extremely unhappy (9)
8 Cut into small pieces (5)
12 Small fish (7)
14 Greek muse of love poetry (5)
16 Prickly desert plant (6)
19 Cobbler's stand (4)
23 Alcoholic spirit (3)

122

Across

1 Armistice (5)
4 Wrinkled (5)
8 Poker stake (4)
9 Hydrophobia (6)
10 Hour at which something is due (inits) (3)
11 Not this! (4)
13 Flightless bird of South America (4)
14 Female spirit of Irish folklore, whose wailing warns of death (7)
15 Water-dwelling creature (4)
16 Of champagne, dry (4)
17 Be indebted to (3)
18 Emergency (6)
19 Arrive (4)
21 Subdivision of an act of a play (5)
22 Young sheep (5)

Down

2 Dashed (3)
3 World's swiftest mammal (7)
5 Not one nor the other (7)
6 Take to pieces (9)
7 Change the order or arrangement of (9)
8 Man-made objects of cultural or historical interest (9)
12 Chop off (7)
13 Daphne du Maurier novel (7)
20 Association of criminals (3)

123

Across

3 Accomplish (7)
6 Natives of Ankara, for example (5)
7 Grazing land (7)
8 Speak (about unimportant matters) rapidly and incessantly (5)
10 Given to sympathy or gentleness (6)
12 Stun (4)
14 Bird's construction (4)
17 Compositor (6)
19 Repeat performance (5)
20 Person who makes and serves coffee (7)
21 Twilled woollen fabric (5)
22 Native to the UK (7)

Down

1 Without much intelligence (6)
2 Inferior substitute (6)
3 Trembling poplar (5)
4 Person who is held captive (8)
5 Against (6)
9 Close-fitting casual top (3,5)
11 Point (3)
13 Liaison, romantic intrigue (6)
15 Mistakes (6)
16 Bicycle for two (6)
18 Rubbish (5)

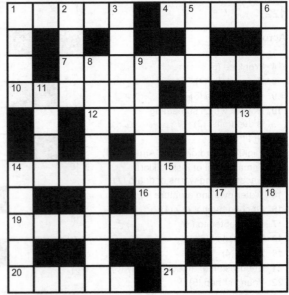

124

Across

1 Packs to capacity (5)
4 Does as one is told (5)
7 Lack of knowledge or education (9)
10 Formerly the basic unit of money in Spain (6)
12 Noteworthy scarcity (8)
14 Canadian province (8)
16 Shrouds (6)
19 Scattered in small drops or particles (9)
20 Dispel gloom (5)
21 Despatches (5)

Down

1 Cut with an axe (4)
2 Bloc (4)
3 Father Christmas (5)
5 Sudden inspiration or bright idea (coll) (9)
6 Cooks slowly and for a long time in liquid (5)
8 Agent that destroys disease-carrying microorganisms (9)
9 Holder on a boat that acts as a fulcrum for rowing (7)
11 Island associated with Napoleon (4)
13 Mark left by a wound (4)
14 Melodious sounds (5)
15 Screws, rivets (5)
17 Garden of Adam and Eve (4)
18 Performs an act of transgression (4)

125

Across

1 Machine for bundling hay (5)
4 Thoroughly unpleasant (5)
7 Vanguard (9)
9 Particular items (5)
10 Tiny morsel of bread or cake (5)
12 Dried-up riverbed (4)
14 Comes to the assistance of (4)
16 Hungarian composer of classical music (5)
18 Lubricated (5)
20 Degeneration (9)
21 Number of players in a netball team (5)
22 Implement with a shaft and barbed point (5)

Down

1 Confer, grant a right or title (6)
2 Course of existence of an individual (4)
3 Less common (5)
5 Vigorously active, gymnastically (9)
6 Canned (6)
8 Swing from side to side regularly (9)
11 Device ensuring continuous electricity (inits) (3)
13 Unit of electric current (6)
15 Seat for the rider of a horse (6)
17 Divided into regions (5)
19 Lacking excess flesh (4)

126

Across

1 Elephant's proboscis (5)
3 Large parrot (5)
7 Popular carbonated drink (4)
8 Partially melted snow (5)
9 Measure the depth of something (5)
11 Breakfast food (6)
13 Device in which pepper is ground (4)
14 Cassette (4)
15 Rub elbows with (coll) (6)
17 Name of several kings of England (5)
20 Mythical monster similar to a vampire (5)
21 Witnessed (4)
22 Outstanding players in a tournament (5)
23 Fed up, tired (5)

Down

1 International games, especially in cricket (4,7)
2 Birds' homes (5)
3 Cleaning implement (3)
4 Completely (3)
5 Warning (7)
6 Australian musical instrument, played by holding in both hands and flexing (6,5)
10 Period of darkness (5)
12 Wide scope (7)
16 Hurray! (5)
18 Colour (3)
19 Affirmative answer (3)

127

Across

3 Dissent (7)
6 Scavenging carnivore (5)
7 Cocktail made of orange liqueur, lemon juice and brandy (7)
8 Fees levied for the use of roads or bridges (5)
9 All the time (4)
11 ___ and ends (4)
14 Girdle (4)
17 Partly open (4)
19 Entomb (5)
20 V-shaped sleeve badge indicating military rank (7)
21 Military blockade (5)
22 Ancient Greek or Roman warship (7)

Down

1 Residential district, often run-down (6)
2 Stripped of rind or skin (6)
3 No longer fashionable (5)
4 Belonging to those people (6)
5 Trousers for casual wear (6)
10 By means of (3)
12 Stylish person (coll) (6)
13 Tray for serving food or drinks (6)
15 Song of devotion or loyalty (6)
16 Become set (6)
18 Use water to remove soap (5)

128

Across

1 Apostolic (5)
4 Drizzle (4)
6 ___ Major, the Great Bear constellation (4)
8 Deflect, fend off (5)
9 Time starting when travel in the region beyond the earth's atmosphere became possible (5,3)
12 Yours and mine (4)
13 Enlist (5)
15 Bout, period of indulgence (5)
17 Boorish (4)
19 Giving delight and satisfaction (8)
21 Longs for (5)
22 Genuine (4)
23 Deprivation (4)
24 End resistance (5)

Down

1 Items used to secure washing to a line (4)
2 Colourful rice (5)
3 Enticements (5)
4 Very, very hungry (8)
5 Of birth (5)
7 Aromatic grey-green herb (4)
10 Grandeur (4)
11 Spreading plants such as ivy or periwinkle (8)
14 Kitchen appliance (4)
15 Floral leaf (5)
16 If not, then (4)
17 Large gathering of people (5)
18 Nickname for the southern USA (5)
20 Precious metal, symbol Au (4)

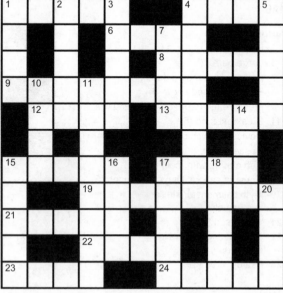

129

Across

1 Month of the year (5)
4 Steal from a person (3)
6 Wayside plant with daisy-like flowers (2-3)
7 Step (5)
9 Boxlike containers in a piece of furniture (7)
11 Ask earnestly (7)
13 Love affair (7)
15 Enduring strength and energy (7)
16 Downright (5)
17 Capital city of Japan (5)
18 Number in a brace (3)
19 Easily agitated or alarmed (5)

Down

1 Failed to hit (6)
2 Large crowd of people (5)
3 Influence by corruption (3,2)
4 Allusion (9)
5 Rubbish receptacles (4)
8 Course of appetisers in an Italian meal (9)
10 Synthetic silk-like fabric (5)
12 Deliver to an enemy by treachery (6)
13 Takes a chance (5)
14 Craftsman who works with stone (5)
15 Type (4)

130

Across

1 Mineral such as quartz (6)
6 Voucher that can be redeemed as needed (6)
7 Edith ___, French cabaret singer (1915–63) (4)
8 Egotistical, inconsiderate of others (7)
10 Before, poetically (3)
12 International cricket games (4,7)
15 *Much ___ about Nothing*, Shakespeare play (3)
16 Navigational instrument (7)
19 Naked (4)
20 Give all or most of one's time or resources to (6)
21 Impair in force or sensation (6)

Down

1 Seven people considered as a unit (6)
2 Organs of photosynthesis and transpiration (6)
3 Highest level attainable (4)
4 Caramel brown (4)
5 Tightly twisted woollen yarn (7)
8 Lively ballroom dance from Brazil (5)
9 Thin strips of wood, used in plastering, etc (5)
11 Get over an illness (7)
13 Source of danger (6)
14 Dignified and sombre in manner (6)
17 Having little money (4)
18 Wooden vehicle mounted on runners (4)

131

Across

1 Pear-shaped tropical fruit (5)
4 Body embalmed and wrapped for burial (5)
7 Using frugally or carefully (7)
9 News chief (6)
10 Bulge or swelling (4)
11 Mud or small rocks deposited in an estuary (4)
14 Young woman (4)
17 Burden of responsibility (4)
19 Metal paper fastener (6)
20 Entertainer who performs tricks of manual dexterity (7)
21 Republic on the south-western shores of the Arabian Peninsula (5)
22 Squeeze (5)

Down

1 Any leafy plants eaten as vegetables (6)
2 Radio antenna (6)
3 Malicious burning of property (5)
5 Wind off from a spool (6)
6 Insect which rests with forelimbs raised as if in prayer (6)
8 Extravagant, copious (7)

12 Wound (6)
13 Mobile mass of muscular tissue located in the mouth (6)
15 Have a lofty goal (6)
16 Gardening scissors (6)
18 Disrobe (5)

132

Across

1 Very warm (3)
3 Tightly curled and unopened flower (7)
6 Counterpane (9)
8 Lyric poem (3)
10 Woven floor covering (6)
13 Vagrant, tramp (4)
14 Amount by which a salary is increased (5)
16 Blackthorn fruit (4)
17 Writing implement (6)
20 Seventh letter of the Greek alphabet (3)
21 Self-service restaurant (9)
22 Sign of something about to happen (7)
23 Cambridgeshire cathedral city (3)

Down

1 Violent and needless disturbance (5)
2 Fleshy root (5)
3 Arm of the Indian Ocean between Africa and Arabia (3,3)
4 Made of clay (7)
5 Explosion that fails to occur (3)
7 Even if (6)
9 Perennial garden plant with large brightly-coloured flowers (6)

11 General rule regarding moral conduct (7)
12 Give money as a reward for a service (3)
15 Clandestine (6)
18 Discontinue (5)
19 Place for temporary parking (3-2)
21 Artificial covering for a tooth (3)

133

Across

1 Fraudulent business scheme (4)
3 Small and delicate (5)
6 Brings to a close (4)
7 Pen tips (4)
9 Biblical first woman (3)
10 Ease or lessen (7)
12 For each (3)
13 Compete (3)
14 Substitute (7)
15 School group (inits) (3)
16 Free (3)
18 Woven floor coverings (7)
20 French vineyard or group of vineyards (3)
21 Ale (4)
22 Cliff-dwelling, gull-like seabird (4)
23 Squads (5)
24 Fully developed (4)

Down

1 Dawn (3-2)
2 Clutter (4)
3 Mischievous adventure (8)
4 Poetry that does not rhyme or have a regular rhythm (4,5)
5 Daughter of a sibling (5)
8 Spiny-finned fish (9)
11 Inhibit (8)
15 Looped edging on a ribbon (5)
17 Hymn of mourning (5)
19 Strap with a crosspiece on the upper of a shoe (1-3)

134

Across

1 Omar ___, stage name of Michael Shalhoub (6)
6 Elbow-room (6)
7 Not mature (of fruit) (6)
9 Meeting for boat races (7)
10 Brandy measure (3)
12 Device used to measure a vehicle's rate of travel (11)
17 Earlier in time than, poetically (3)
18 Quandary (7)
20 Compound capable of turning litmus blue (6)
21 Compulsory force or threat (6)
22 Thin layers of rock used for roofing (6)

Down

1 Dangerous, attention-grabbing feats (6)
2 Supply or impregnate with oxygen (6)
3 Run away quickly (4)
4 Turned into (6)
5 At a more distant point (7)
8 Goad, poke (4)
11 Best amount possible under given circumstances (7)
13 Number represented by the Roman XI (6)
14 Repast (4)
15 One who pays rent (6)
16 Failing in what duty requires (6)
19 Bulk (4)

135

Across

1 Declaration (9)
8 Group of many insects (5)
9 Areas of grass found in gardens (5)
10 Umberto ___, author of *The Name of the Rose* (3)
11 Higher in position (5)
13 Impudent aggressiveness (5)
15 Find repugnant (5)
18 Contagious viral disease (5)
20 Kimono sash (3)
21 Country, capital Beijing (5)
22 Argentinian football manager, ___ Maradona (5)
23 Perform several jobs at the same time (9)

Down

2 Disreputable wanderer (5)
3 Equipment that measures periods (5)
4 Fruit with sweet, juicy flesh (5)
5 More recent (5)
6 Freedom from doubt (9)
7 Action of rising to an important position or a higher level (9)
12 Former name of Tokyo, Japan (3)
14 ___ de Cologne, perfume (3)
16 Japanese verse form (5)
17 Cook in an oven (5)
18 Location of something surrounded by other things (5)
19 Encounters (5)

136

Across

1 Similar things placed in order (6)
6 Revulsion (6)
7 Surface for ice-skating (4)
8 Subdivision (7)
9 Collection of facts (4)
12 Hard glossy coating (7)
15 Slaughtered (4)
16 One who lives in solitude (7)
19 Material frame of a person or animal (4)
20 Bordering (6)
21 Entry (6)

Down

1 Hindu woman's garment (4)
2 Relating to letting of a property (6)
3 Item of footwear (4)
4 Glazed and salted cracker (7)
5 Bough (6)
8 Hollow, flexible structure resembling a bag (3)
10 Newspaper with half-size pages (7)
11 Consortium of companies formed to limit competition (6)
13 Application (3)
14 Far off (6)
17 Long detailed story (4)
18 Colouring substances (4)

137

Across

1 Well-known Italian fashion label (5)
4 Authorisation to go somewhere (4)
6 Lower part of an interior wall (4)
7 Two-winged insect (3)
9 Blow delivered with an open hand (4)
10 Alloy of iron and carbon (5)
11 In existence (5)
13 Tatters (4)
15 Coarse file (4)
17 Boredom (5)
19 Garden tool for cutting grass on lawns (5)
21 Ms Chanel, fashion designer (4)
22 Woman's support garment (abbr) (3)
23 Edward __, British artist and writer of nonsense verse (4)
24 Feast upon (4)
25 In the lead (5)

Down

1 Natural spring that gives out steam (6)
2 Retail establishment serving light refreshments (4)
3 Musical composition that evokes rural life (5)
4 Positioned behind or at the back (9)
5 Shelters from light (6)
8 Land or property that is let for a set period of time (9)
12 Small hotel (3)
14 Nobody specifically (6)
16 Steered into a resting position (6)
18 Darkest part of a shadow (5)
20 Walk through water (4)

138

Across

1 Believing the worst of human nature and motives (7)
7 Set straight or right (5)
9 Extremely ornate (5)
11 Incision (3)
12 Work together on a common project (2-7)
13 Canonised person (5)
14 Supervise (7)
18 Holiday resort island in the Caribbean (5)
20 Dog that can be trained to fetch game (9)
23 In the past (3)
24 Fragrance (5)
25 Small heron (5)
26 Perpetually young (7)

Down

1 Coffee shops (5)
2 Papal legate (6)
3 North American native dog (6)
4 Interweave (4)
5 Type of Greek cheese (4)
6 Common viper (5)
8 Criminal who commits homicide (8)
10 Come together (8)
15 Barbaric (6)
16 Continent (6)
17 Having weapons (5)
19 Natives of Kuwait, for example (5)
21 Weedy annual grass (4)
22 Tiny amount (4)

139

Across

1 Slates (5)
4 Roman god of love (5)
7 The act of coming together again (7)
8 Curious (3)
9 Empty area (5)
11 Fad (5)
12 Accolade (5)
14 Puts up with (5)
16 Singing couple (3)
17 Person or thing whose name does not need to be specified (2-3-2)
19 In a laconic manner (5)
20 Admission (5)

Down

1 Slabs of grass and grass roots (5)
2 Romanian monetary unit (3)
3 Pig, hog (5)
4 Having a shape which tapers from a circular base to a point (5)
5 Proportionately (3,4)
6 Avoid by a sudden quick movement (5)
10 Study of the body (7)
12 Assisted (5)
13 Lit by twilight (5)
14 Make a strident sound (5)
15 Flamboyant (5)
18 Very small circular shape (3)

140

Across

2 Forecast (9)
7 Egg cells (3)
8 Aromatic herb (7)
10 Intellectual person (coll) (7)
12 Simple, bare (4)
13 Speak haltingly (7)
14 Point towards (4)
16 Plant valued for its fragrant tubular flowers (7)
19 Liquorice-flavoured herb (7)
20 Imitate (3)
21 Film equipment operator (9)

Down

1 One stroke over par in golf (5)
2 Twinge (4)
3 Musical instrument (4)
4 Children in ___, annual BBC appeal (4)
5 Drool (6)
6 Plain dough cake, often griddled (5)
9 State of elated bliss (7)
11 Detest (4)
12 Measure (out) (4)
13 Division of a group into opposing factions (6)
14 Former French coin (5)
15 Light brown, nut-coloured (5)
16 Dread (4)
17 Kind of cheese (4)
18 Long-necked bird (4)

141

Across

3 Ray of natural light (7)
6 Biting tools (5)
8 Speed by which the population declines (9)
9 Main (5)
10 Deep serving bowl (6)
13 Musical composition (4)
16 Killed (4)
18 Climb (6)
20 Frameworks for holding objects (5)
22 Careless, inattentive (9)
23 Stir up (a fire) (5)
24 Effigies of human beings or animals (7)

Down

1 Type of plaster applied to exterior walls (6)
2 Boring, monotonous (7)
3 Vertical passage into a mine (5)
4 Commits to a grave (6)
5 Bring into harmony with (6)
7 Quoits target (3)
11 Container for ashes (3)
12 Citizen who has a legal right to vote (7)
14 Father or mother (6)
15 Carve or shape stone (6)
17 Flat disk used as a seal to prevent leakage (6)
19 Clothing (5)
21 Insect (3)

142

Across

1 Block of iron or steel on which hot metals are shaped (5)
3 Transfer to another track, of trains (5)
6 Device used to deviate a beam of light (5)
7 Landed estate of a lord (5)
10 Combined troops and weaponry of a country (5,6)
13 Books that retail in very large numbers (11)
15 At a distance (5)
18 Dome-shaped dessert (5)
19 Lustre (5)
20 Vigilant, awake (5)

Down

1 Greek letter (5)
2 High-ranking police officer (9)
3 Quantity obtained by addition (3)
4 Container for ashes (3)
5 Rolls (5)
8 Person tricked on the first day of the fourth month of the year (5,4)
9 Behind (5)
11 Repent (3)
12 Fruiting spike of a cereal plant (3)
13 Items strung to make a necklace (5)
14 Dish served as the last course of a meal (5)
16 One of four playing cards in a deck (3)
17 Metal container (3)

143

Across
1 Hard slap (5)
5 Pile (5)
8 Outer edge of a plate (3)
10 Concluding part of a performance (6)
11 Cable (4)
14 Young rooster (8)
15 Published volume (4)
16 Cried (4)
17 Chief port of Yemen (4)
20 Divisible by two (4)
21 Fearless daring (8)
23 Faithful (4)
24 Abundant non-metallic element (6)
25 Glide over snow (3)
26 Give rise to (5)
27 Suggestive of the supernatural (5)

Down
2 Sale or purchase of goods by post (4,5)
3 Fissure (5)
4 One thousand grams (abbr) (4)
6 Chucked (5)
7 Went down on the knees (5)
9 Branch of physics concerned with the motion of bodies (9)
12 Metal-bearing mineral (3)
13 Spicy pork and beef sausage (9)
17 Loft (5)
18 Large flightless bird (3)
19 Depends on (5)
20 Eagle's nest (5)
22 Carry (4)

144

Across
1 List of contents of a book (5)
3 Writing tables (5)
6 Procrastinate (5)
7 United Nations agency (inits) (3)
8 Capital of the Maldives (4)
9 Revised (7)
12 Lacking moisture (3)
14 Devoured (3)
15 Colouring agent (3)
17 Going by, overtaking (7)
20 Carpentry pin (4)
21 Demented (3)
22 Rectangular containers (5)
23 In an unfortunate manner (5)
24 Perceives sound (5)

Down
1 Country in which Mumbai is situated (5)
2 Rub out (5)
3 Periods of ten years (7)
4 Used a needle and thread (5)
5 Chronicle (5)
8 Chemical element that can be formed into sheets (5)
10 Not of the clergy (3)
11 Very fast (7)
13 Dashed (3)
15 Hemispherical roofs (5)
16 Brought to a conclusion (5)
18 Weight equivalent to 14 pounds (5)
19 Oxygen and nitrogen, for example (5)

145

Across

1 Great gap (5)
4 State of conflict between colours (5)
7 Brother of George Gershwin (3)
8 Dental thread (5)
9 Milky-white gem made by an oyster (5)
10 Golf peg (3)
11 Of questionable taste or morality (5)
14 Dangerous (5)
17 Red dye (5)
20 Fourth letter of the Greek alphabet (5)
23 Bruce ___, expert kung fu
  actor who died in 1973 (3)
24 Left-hand page (5)
25 Mood disorder (5)
26 To and ___ (3)
27 Slumbered (5)
28 Capital of Switzerland (5)

Down

1 Turned-back hems at the
  ends of sleeves (5)
2 Forum in ancient Greece (5)
3 Hazy (5)
4 Frolic, cavort (5)
5 Natives of Iraq or Jordan,
  for example (5)
6 Mountainous (5)
12 Complexion (3)
13 Hideout (3)
15 Extreme anger (3)
16 Equipment (3)
17 Homes for bees (5)
18 Hospital worker (5)
19 At great height (5)
20 Retire from military
  service (5)
21 Moon-related (5)
22 Wide open (5)

146

Across

1 Sharp part of a knife (5)
4 Make sore by rubbing (5)
8 Angle between a stem and a leaf (4)
9 Hollow under the upper limb where
  it is joined to the shoulder (6)
10 Hostel (3)
12 Largest province of Canada (6)
14 Elaborate song for a solo voice (4)
15 Bureaucratic procedure (3,4)
17 In the Roman calendar; the day that
  marked the middle of the month (4)
18 Remove an electrical device
  from a socket (6)
19 Yes (3)
20 Mariner (6)
21 ___ Lang Syne, Scottish song (4)
23 Discharge, throw out (5)
24 Gemstone (5)

Down

2 Casual (3)
3 French composer of operas
  such as Lakme (1836–91) (7)
5 Attire (7)
6 Alienated (9)
7 Shelter from danger, refuge (9)
8 Express agreement (9)
11 ___ Kelly, famous 19th
  century Australian
  bushranger (3)
13 Christian recluse (7)
14 Gain the good
  will of (7)
16 None in particular (3)
22 Be in a horizontal
  position (3)

147

Across

1 Squeeze or press together (9)
8 Sound (5)
9 Genetic copy (5)
10 Historical period (3)
11 Inflexible (5)
13 Fragment (5)
15 Foot traveller (5)
18 Attack on all sides (5)
20 Rapid bustling commotion (3)
21 Mark ___, US swimmer who won seven gold medals in the 1972 Olympic Games (5)
22 Patty Bouvier's twin sister in TV's *The Simpsons* (5)
23 Spiritual leader of the Christian Church (9)

Down

2 Due (5)
3 Rate of travel (5)
4 Provide a brief summary (5)
5 Struggle for breath (5)
6 Political theory favouring the abolition of governments (9)
7 Heavenly (9)
12 Water in a solid state (3)
14 US musician and record producer, ___ Turner (3)
16 Small creatures eaten by whales, etc (5)
17 Sharp instrument used for hair removal (5)
18 Domineering (5)
19 Spicy sauce to accompany Mexican food (5)

148

Across

1 Distance covered by a step (6)
4 Makes a knot (4)
6 Person who undertakes various small tasks (3-3,3)
8 Behave (3)
10 Attach, do up securely (6)
13 ___ Pound, poet (4)
14 Last letter of the Greek alphabet (5)
16 Prickly seedcase (4)
17 Savagely cruel (6)
20 A person in general (3)
21 Flag hoisted when a ship is about to sail (4,5)
22 Fine specks of detritus (4)
23 Female parent (6)

Down

1 Bundle, of straw for example (5)
2 Colloquial term for one's ancestry (5)
3 Bumper car (6)
4 Group of people attractively arranged (7)
5 Earth's nearest star (3)
7 Pilot of a plane (6)
9 Free-and-easy (6)
11 Rushing flow (7)
12 Bird's beak (3)
15 Small cave with attractive features (6)
18 Portable light (5)
19 Large-eyed, arboreal prosimian having a foxy face (5)
21 Partially opened flower (3)

149

Across

3 Feel of a surface (7)
6 Compass point at 0 or 360 degrees (5)
7 Monarchy (7)
8 Get the better of (5)
9 Machine for extracting water from washed clothes (7)
13 Break (4)
16 Withered (4)
17 Repletion (7)
19 Elated (2,3)
20 Flat highland (7)
21 Interprets words (5)
22 Acquiesces (7)

Down

1 Within the confines of a building (7)
2 Complain (7)
3 Chuck (5)
4 Vehicles that run on tracks (6)
5 Somewhat (6)
10 Bunkum (3)
11 Rapid escape (7)
12 Put down by force or intimidation (7)
14 Sharp-eyed birds (6)
15 Walk silently (6)
18 ___ sincerely, letter ending (5)

150

Across

1 Clause appended to a legislative bill (5)
4 Distinctive smell (5)
7 Dirty washing (7)
8 Military fabric (5)
9 Climbing plant (7)
13 Yugoslavian leader who died in 1980 (4)
16 Dandy (4)
17 Child's two-wheeled vehicle (7)
19 Divisions of quantity (5)
20 Source of illumination that burns a fuel derived from coal (3,4)
21 Wild animal (5)
22 Mr Wise, former showbiz partner of Eric Morecambe (5)

Down

1 Childhood disease caused by deficiency of vitamin D (7)
2 Actual, if not rightful or legally recognised (2,5)
3 Historical object (5)
5 Hired (6)
6 Branded (6)
10 Cereal crop (3)
11 Person excessively concerned about propriety and decorum (7)
12 Print anew (7)
14 Implement used by mountain-climbers to cut footholds in compacted snow (3,3)
15 Lots and lots (coll) (6)
18 Indian currency unit (5)

151

Across

1 Casts off (5)
3 Eject the contents of the stomach through the mouth (5)
6 Heather (5)
7 Kingdom in the South Pacific (5)
10 Able to produce the result intended (11)
13 Autonomous (4-7)
15 Gangway (5)
18 Farm outbuildings (5)
19 Deep and harsh sounding (5)
20 Settle (a loan) (5)

Down

1 Mr Davis, former Snooker World Champion (5)
2 Double-dealing, intending to mislead (9)
3 Charge levied on goods or services (inits) (3)
4 Adult males (3)
5 Common amphibians (5)
8 Bring into being (9)

9 Place of safety or sanctuary (5)
11 Enemy (3)
12 Container for ashes (3)

13 Swayed back and forth (5)
14 Easily irritated (5)
16 Small coin (3)
17 Brownie (3)

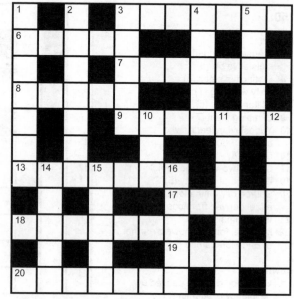

152

Across

3 Love story (7)
6 Small fluid-filled sac located in the joints (5)
7 Schematic or technical drawing (7)
8 Hindu religious teacher (5)
9 Pastoral (7)
13 Wedging, implanting (7)
17 Should (5)
18 Fairground ride (7)
19 Complain peevishly (5)
20 Apply (paint) in small touches (7)

Down

1 Extremely bad, appalling (7)
2 Greatly feared (7)
3 Spokes (5)
4 Small, brightly coloured tropical fish (5)
5 American raccoon (5)
10 Cacophony (3)
11 Lackadaisical (7)

12 Workers' dining hall (7)
14 Abstract form of painting that produces dramatic visual effects (2,3)

15 Rise to one's feet (3,2)
16 Overeat (5)

153

Across

1 Talk (5)
3 Aromatic substance used to add flavouring (5)
7 Plant family that includes the maple (4)
9 Blazing (6)
10 One-hundredth of a dollar (4)
11 Having a strong healthy body (4)
12 Extension to a main building (5)
15 Ancient upright stone slab bearing markings (5)
17 Soft creamy French cheese (4)
19 Without blemish or contamination (4)
20 Chronological accounts of events (6)
21 Speck (4)
22 Went out with, courted (5)
23 Indicate (5)

Down

1 Sailor (6)
2 Concur (5)
4 Tower supporting high-tension wires (5)
5 Divisible by two (4)
6 State where one is more or less completely incapacitated (9)
8 Ceremonial elegance and splendour (5)
13 Heron (5)
14 Solitary man (6)
16 Wipe off (5)
17 Hurray! (5)
18 Stripe of contrasting colour (4)

154

Across

1 Meat pie (5)
4 Provide a brief summary (5)
8 Ship's wheel (4)
9 UK city in which the Met Office is based (6)
10 Green vegetable (3)
12 Utensil used to shred cheese, etc (6)
14 Skim (4)
15 In the middle (7)
17 Titled peer of the realm (4)
18 Small ornamental case worn on a necklace (6)
19 Continuing in the same way (abbr) (3)
20 Secretory organs (6)
21 Paddles (4)
23 Post a short message on the internet site Twitter (5)
24 Recognised (5)

Down

2 Yes (3)
3 Had an inclination to do something (7)
5 Narrow platform along which models parade (7)
6 Spreads or diffuses through (9)
7 Callous (9)
8 Make more prominent (9)
11 To the full extent (poetically) (3)
13 Land area, especially of a farm (7)
14 Nocturnal mammal native to North America (7)
16 Decay (3)
22 Angry dispute (3)

155

Across

1. Sash worn by an expert in judo (5,4)
8. Acts to arouse action (5)
9. Brother of one's father (5)
10. Rocky peak or hill (3)
11. Loiter, delay (5)
13. Emblem (5)
15. Printer's mark, indicating an insertion (5)
18. Garment fold (5)
20. Mr Geller, spoon-bender (3)
21. Expression of dislike (5)
22. Form of civil disobedience (3-2)
23. Gain courage (4,5)

Down

2. Sufferer from Hansen's disease (5)
3. Marked by malice (5)
4. Descriptive statement seen on the back of a book (5)
5. Clear (5)
6. Clever joke (9)
7. Going back to a previous state (9)
12. Repent (3)
14. Every one (3)
16. Dry red table wine from Spain (5)
17. Fine net used for tutus (5)
18. Ski run densely packed with snow (5)
19. Enrol (5)

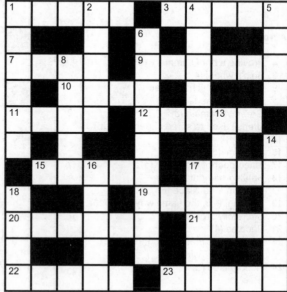

156

Across

1. Sun-dried brick (5)
3. Crouch, bow (5)
7. Poems (4)
9. Cause (6)
10. Four-wheeled motor vehicle (4)
11. Incinerate (4)
12. Saline (5)
15. Awry (5)
17. Symbol of the zodiacal sign Leo (4)
19. Eric ___, member of the Monty Python team (4)
20. Physical science relating to light (6)
21. A long way off (4)
22. Walked up and down (5)
23. Unsatisfactorily (5)

Down

1. Single-celled, water-living protozoon (6)
2. Petty officer on a merchant ship who controls the work of other seamen (5)
4. Drag behind (5)
5. Cooking utensils (4)
6. Transversely (9)
8. Merits, deserves (5)
13. Burglar (5)
14. Exertion of force (6)
16. Item of cutlery (5)
17. Andean mammal (5)
18. Closed circuit (4)

157

Across
4 Shatter (5)
8 Small Australian parrot (9)
9 Local time at the 0 meridian passing through Greenwich (inits) (3)
10 Semi-precious stone (5)
13 Devices used by anglers (5)
14 Couple (4)
15 Extremely harsh (9)
19 Cuckoo pint, for example (4)
21 Drivers' stopover (5)
24 Dish (5)
25 Mineral (3)
26 Insularity (9)
27 Dave ___, Irish comedian who died in 2005 (5)

Down
1 Junk (5)
2 Finger-shaped cream cake (6)
3 ___ Austen, author (4)
4 Sound expressive of relief (4)
5 Commemoration (8)
6 Lowest female singing voice (4)
7 Hermann ___, author of *Steppenwolf* (5)
11 Wander aimlessly (3)
12 Cross (8)
16 Saudi ___, country (6)
17 Hexagonal fastener (3)
18 Darkest part of a shadow (5)
20 Implied (5)
22 Labour (4)
23 ___ Brittan, former Home Secretary (1983–85) (4)
24 Summit (4)

158

Across
1 People employed to show tourists around places of interest (6)
6 Government tax on imports or exports (6)
8 Attack by planes (3,4)
9 Give expression to (6)
10 Wide scope (7)
13 Flightless Australian bird (3)
14 Common rodent (3)
17 Completely enveloping (7)
20 Bathing costume (6)
21 Deep red (7)
22 Small box for holding valuables (6)
23 Aircraft shed (6)

Down
1 Tomb (5)
2 Cathedral city (6)
3 Pigpens (5)
4 Intermediate between peat and bituminous coal (7)
5 Frequently (5)
7 Part of speech (6)
11 Somewhat hungry (7)
12 Subtle difference in meaning (6)
15 Pilot of a plane (6)
16 By surprise (5)
18 Gleefulness (5)
19 Adult male singing voice (5)

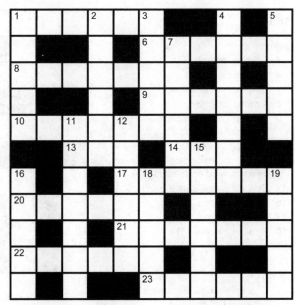

159

Across

1 Roman god of love (5)
4 Sir Walter ____, British author (1771–1832) (5)
7 Inspiring amazement or wonder (7)
9 Cover against loss or damage (6)
10 Sheep's coat (6)
12 Clothing (4)
15 Unit of language (4)
17 Pressure line on a weather map (6)
19 Area (6)
20 Bites off very small pieces (7)
21 Ball-shaped (5)
22 Main part of the human body (5)

Down

1 Providing a remedy (6)
2 Celestial bodies that emit regular bursts of radio waves (7)
3 Make appear small by comparison (5)
5 Kidney-shaped nut (6)
6 Moderate (6)
8 Provision of economic assistance to persons in need (7)
11 Evergreen tree or shrub (7)
13 Japanese martial art, a form of wrestling (6)
14 Reel, spool (6)
16 Generator (6)
18 Adjust again after an initial failure (5)

160

Across

1 Caprine animals (5)
4 Implore (5)
7 Commander of a fleet (7)
8 Kimono sash (3)
9 Worked into an emotional fever (coll) (3,2)
11 Object (5)
12 Husks of corn or other seed separated by winnowing or threshing (5)
14 Second planet from the Sun (5)
16 Deciduous tree (3)
17 Violation (7)
19 Roofing material (5)
20 Appetising (5)

Down

1 Chart showing the relationship between things (5)
2 Direct (3)
3 Sweet sticky liquid (5)
4 Aviator (5)
5 Wearing away (7)
6 Expiring (5)
10 Tube that conveys air in and out of the lungs (7)
12 Packs to capacity (5)
13 Crystal of snow (5)
14 Go to see (5)
15 Grilled food on a skewer, served with peanut sauce (5)
18 Raises (3)

161

Across
1 Provided with a particular motif (6)
6 Cause to regain consciousness (6)
8 State of conflict between Britain and South Africa (4,3)
9 Filled tortilla (4)
10 Wayside plant with daisy-like flowers (2-3)
13 Archaic form of the word 'your' (3)
14 Swiss cheese with very small holes (7)
16 Domestic swine (3)
17 Reddish colour often associated with good health (5)
19 Drag (4)
21 Corroborate (7)
22 Demises (6)
23 Being wet with perspiration (6)

Down
1 Prohibited (5)
2 One who suffers for the sake of principle (6)
3 Mild expletive (4)
4 Blindly and obstinately attached to some creed or opinion (7)
5 Boat used to transport people and cars (5)
7 Pencil rubber (6)
11 Intellectual person (coll) (7)
12 Harem guard (6)
15 Disturb the smoothness of (6)
16 Bamboo-eating mammal (5)
18 Childish word for scrumptious (5)
20 Deprivation (4)

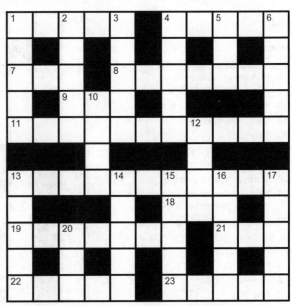

162

Across
1 Three-dimensional shape (5)
4 In accompaniment or as a companion (5)
7 Grow old (3)
8 Book of the New Testament written in the form of a letter (7)
9 Distress signal (inits) (3)
11 Take apart (11)
13 Explained in terms of physical forces (11)
18 To the ___ degree (to the utmost) (3)
19 Goat-like antelope (7)
21 Lamb's mother (3)
22 Gleamed (5)
23 Link up, connect (3,2)

Down
1 Rise to one's feet (5)
2 Silt deposited by the wind (5)
3 Frock (5)
4 *A Town Like ___*, Nevil Shute novel later made into a film (5)
5 Known (3)
6 Web-footed, long-necked birds (5)
10 Solemn promise (4)
12 Ground fog (4)
13 Protective secretion of bodily membranes (5)
14 Roused from slumber (5)
15 Gusset (5)
16 In that place (5)
17 Dirt-free (5)
20 Flurry (3)

163

Across

1 Small group of people with a common task (5)
4 Flush (5)
7 Carl ___, German composer (1895–1982) (4)
8 Snatches (5)
9 Domesticated bovine animals (4)
10 Deal, trade (4)
12 Yob deterrent (inits) (4)
15 Muck, filth (4)
17 Incandescent lamp (4)
19 Basic rhythmic unit in a piece of music (4)
20 Fish with a hook and line (5)
22 Large pots for making tea (4)
23 Light brown, nut-coloured (5)
24 Opaque gems (5)

Down

1 Mark of disgrace (6)
2 Waste product useful as a fertiliser (4)
3 Worthless material (5)
5 Wrap (6)
6 Make attractive or lovable (6)
11 Old cloth measure (3)
13 Long jagged mountain chain (6)
14 Lacking in insight (6)
16 Belonging to those people (6)
18 Adult male voice (5)
21 'Lady' whose real name is Stefani Joanne Angelina Germanotta (4)

164

Across

1 Exaggerate to an excessive degree (6)
6 Victorious contestant (6)
7 Render unable to hear (6)
10 Area in which lessons take place (9)
12 Less common (5)
13 Tiny (3)
15 Rigidly formal (5)
18 Large reddish-brown ape (5-4)
20 North African desert (6)
21 Person who leaves one country to settle in another (6)
22 Drag the bottom of a lake (6)

Down

1 Instruction (5)
2 Type of gun (5)
3 Has (4)
4 Asian peninsula that includes Burma, Cambodia, Laos, Malaysia, Thailand and Vietnam (4-5)
5 First in rank or degree (5)
8 Vigorously active, gymnastically (9)
9 Common garden insect (6)
11 Nap in the early afternoon (6)
14 Fist fighter (5)
16 Lake and popular resort area of Nevada, USA (5)
17 Candle light (5)
19 Employed (4)

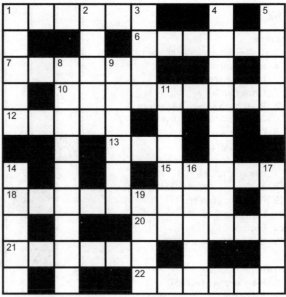

165

Across

1 Of large size compared to weight (5)
3 Latin for 'about' (5)
6 Kitchen appliance (4)
8 Doglike (6)
10 Finnish steam bath (5)
12 River that flows through Kelso (5)
14 Transporter (7)
15 Glisten (5)
16 Play for time (5)
18 Astonished (6)
19 Despatch (4)
20 Moves in large numbers, swarms (5)
21 Line on which music is written (5)

Down

1 Footwear items (5)
2 Family (3)
3 Censure severely (8)
4 Say again (9)
5 Set straight or right (5)
7 Make clear and (more) comprehensible (9)
9 Slipshod (8)
11 Grandmother (3)
13 Drenched with water (3)
15 Astute (5)
17 Deep serving spoon (5)
19 Relax in a chair (3)

166

Across

1 Delicate, powdery surface deposit (5)
4 Cringe in fear (5)
7 Beetle considered divine by Ancient Egyptians (6)
9 Subjected to great tension (4)
10 Office note (abbr) (4)
11 Dissertation (6)
13 Aristocrat (4)
15 Country, capital Lima (4)
17 Darted (6)
20 Open vessel with a handle and a spout (4)
21 Female pantomime character (4)
22 Mentally or physically infirm with age (6)
23 Painful eyelid swellings (5)
24 Victoria Beckham's former surname (5)

Down

1 Place where vehicles halt to discharge and take on passengers (3,4)
2 Rounded like an egg (5)
3 ___ Vice, TV series (5)
5 Eight-armed creature (7)
6 Evade (5)
8 In addition (7)
12 Compress (7)
14 Make amends for, remedy (7)
16 Perform as if in a play (5)
18 Central area of an ancient Roman amphitheatre (5)
19 Port in north-western Israel on the Bay of Acre (5)

167

Across

3 Coalminer (7)
6 Lightweight triangular scarf (5)
7 Having a connection (7)
8 Domains (5)
9 Duelling sword (4)
11 Posing no difficulty (4)
14 Journey in a vehicle (4)
17 Material effigy worshipped as a god (4)
19 Garret (5)
20 Mechanical device that connects the ends of adjacent objects (7)
21 Organised groups of workmen (5)
22 Capital of Sicily (7)

Down

1 Remove completely from recognition or memory (6)
2 Fasteners with threaded shanks (6)
3 Evil spell (5)
4 Person who inspires others (6)
5 Protective fold of skin (6)
10 For, in favour of (3)
12 Break of day (6)
13 Exclamation of joy or victory (6)
15 Aim, purpose (6)
16 Overabundance (6)
18 *Key ___*, 1948 film (5)

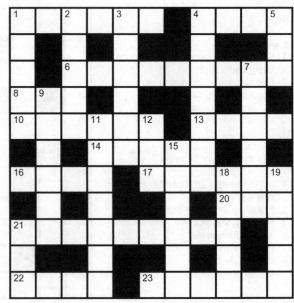

168

Across

1 Loud laugh suggestive of the noise made by a hen (6)
4 Very dry (4)
6 Grant clearance for (9)
8 Feverish cold (abbr) (3)
10 Decorative bunch of cords (6)
13 Cleansing agent (4)
14 Have faith in (5)
16 Bill of fare (4)
17 Piece of material inset to enlarge a garment (6)
20 Fuss (3)
21 A movement upward (9)
22 Barley used in brewing (4)
23 Make steady (6)

Down

1 Small farm (5)
2 See 18 Down (5)
3 Component of a word (6)
4 Takes into custody (7)
5 Owing (3)
7 Ocean floor (6)
9 Continuation of the collar of a jacket or coat (6)
11 Scholarly person (7)
12 Pull (3)
15 Lying face upward (6)
18 and 2 Down Father Christmas (5)
19 ___ pole, tribal emblem (5)
21 Branch (3)

169

Across
1 Stretching out (5)
3 Pseudonym (5)
7 Large gun (6)
9 Shaft on which a wheel rotates (4)
10 Propensity, natural inclination (10)
15 Common name for the English hawthorn (3)
16 None in particular (3)
18 Vehicle which carries people and equipment to the scene of a conflagration (4,6)
21 Cause the ruin or downfall of (4)
22 Flow with a bubbling noise (6)
24 Dried plum (5)
25 Church associated with a convent (5)

Down
1 Not including (6)
2 Female member of a religious order (3)
4 Foremost (7)
5 Pip (4)
6 Opposed to (4)
8 Old Testament mother-in-law of Ruth (5)

11 Satirical drawing published in a newspaper (7)
12 Caustic washing solution (3)
13 Delivery vehicle (3)
14 Attaching (5)
17 Salad vegetable (6)
19 Being in a tense state (4)
20 Bicycle accessory (4)
23 Chafe (3)

170

Across
1 Crustlike surfaces of healing wounds (5)
4 Dispense with, forgo (5)
7 Inactive (4)
8 Disperse (6)
9 Ninth month of the year (abbr) (4)
10 Tight-fitting hats (4)
12 Mix (4)
13 Say again, repeat (7)
14 Cast off (4)
15 Make (4)
16 Bundle of straw or hay (4)
17 Beast (6)
18 Predatory freshwater fish, with elongated body (4)
20 Changes direction (5)
21 Twelve as a fraction of 120 (5)

Down
2 Important North Atlantic food fish (3)
3 Sanctified (7)
4 Cried (4)
5 Popular chilled beverage (4,3)
6 Power to withstand hardship or stress (9)
7 Ceaseless, constant (9)
8 Relating to extent (7)
11 First in rank or degree (7)
12 Church tower (7)
16 Lowest adult male singing voice (4)
19 Equipment (3)

171

Across
1 Barrage balloon (5)
5 Concession given to mollify (3)
7 Sophisticated, refined (6)
8 Australian wild dog (5)
10 Bundle of fibres that transmits a signal to the brain (5)
11 Ardently serious (7)
14 Extremely poisonous substance (7)
16 Final Greek letter (5)
17 Biting tools (5)
19 Plug for a bunghole in a cask (6)
20 Biblical character whose wife was turned into a pillar of salt (3)
21 One who drives cars at high speeds (5)

Down
1 Carnivorous burrowing mammal (6)
2 Drinking vessel (3)
3 Dig into (5)
4 Lose consciousness (5)
5 Reticent (9)
6 Catholic Holy Father (4)
9 English region around Northumberland and Durham (5,4)
12 Put into words (3)
13 Located beneath something else (6)
14 Small house in the woods (5)
15 Thespian (5)
16 Elliptical (4)
18 Hour at which something is due (inits) (3)

172

Across
1 Turned-back hems at the ends of sleeves (5)
4 Reproductive body produced by plants such as the fern (5)
7 Carry out in practice (7)
8 Terminate (3)
9 Freedom from disputes (5)
11 Float aimlessly (5)
12 Pig food (5)
14 Lads (5)
16 Choose or show a preference (3)
17 Wheeled vehicle that can be pulled by a car (7)
19 Curt, brusque (5)
20 Raise, erect (3,2)

Down
1 Car wheel immobilising device (5)
2 Overweight (3)
3 Form (5)
4 Position (5)
5 Egg-shaped and flutey-toned musical instrument (7)
6 Happening (5)
10 Aircraft pilot (7)
12 Grunt (5)
13 Supple (5)
14 Fastener (5)
15 Undress (5)
18 Allow (3)

173

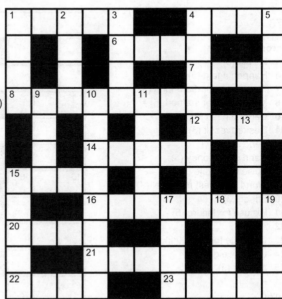

Across

1 Similar things placed in order (6)
6 Orange root vegetable (6)
7 Dry ground (4)
8 One more (7)
9 More docile (5)
11 In an aroused state (7)
16 Similar (5)
17 Young tree (7)
19 Bullets, etc (abbr) (4)
20 At the back of (6)
21 Lancashire town which gave its name to a cake (6)

Down

1 Military greeting (6)
2 Give a new title to (6)
3 Examine hastily (4)
4 Glazed and salted cracker (7)
5 Legal tender (5)
8 Continuous portion of a circle (3)
10 Manipulate to one's advantage (7)
12 Label (3)
13 Gloomy (6)
14 Noughts (6)
15 Bird associated with the Tower of London (5)
18 Bulge or swelling (4)

174

Across

1 Trinket (5)
4 Angling implements (4)
6 Small opening in the skin (4)
7 Verdi opera with an Egyptian theme (4)
8 Official who evaluates property for the purpose of taxing it (8)
12 Walk through water (4)
14 Norse goddess (5)
15 Dandy (4)
16 Loud (8)
20 Cab (4)
21 Weathercock (4)
22 Pale yellowish-green colour (4)
23 Push roughly (5)

Down

1 Spanish sparkling white wine (4)
2 Oil platforms (4)
3 Musical composition (4)
4 At the back (8)
5 No longer new, uninteresting (5)
9 Open skin infection (4)
10 Gushing (8)
11 Curl of the lip (5)
13 Daybreak (4)
15 Asian pepper plant (5)
17 "Beware the ___ of March", advice given to Julius Caesar (4)
18 Basic unit of currency in Germany (4)
19 Melody (4)

175

Across

1 Lines where pieces of fabric are sewn together (5)
3 Sketches (5)
7 Cleared of weapons such as H-bombs, etc (7,4)
8 Concerned with religion (6)
10 Use a container to remove water flooding a vessel (4)
11 Jimmy ____, host of TV's *8 Out of 10 Cats* (4)
12 Leave in the lurch (6)
15 Piece of armour covering the chest (11)
16 Spring-loaded door fastener (5)
17 Method of producing designs on cloth by covering with wax, then dyeing (5)

Down

1 Drops down (5)
2 Tooth with a broad crown (5)
4 Price of a plane ticket (3,4)
5 Hard outer covering (5)
6 Nominee (9)
9 Belonging to the present time (7)
11 Clique (often secret) that seeks power usually through intrigue (5)
13 Patty Bouvier's twin sister in TV's *The Simpsons* (5)
14 Adjust finely (5)

176

Across

1 Insipid (5)
4 Happen again (5)
7 Slang term for diamonds (3)
8 Makes dirty or stained (5)
10 Car crash (sl) (5)
11 Desired result (3)
12 Send away (7)
13 Hand over money (3)
15 Pulse vegetable (3)
17 World's swiftest mammal (7)
20 Epoch (3)
21 Excuse for failure (5)
22 Alarm (5)
23 Compete for something (3)
24 Unit of weight (5)
25 Journal (5)

Down

1 Assigned to a station (5)
2 Compounds capable of turning litmus red (5)
3 Serving to identify a species or group (11)
4 Claimed back (11)
5 Gripping device (5)
6 Ball game (5)
9 Delayed, postponed (2,3)
14 Cognisant (5)
15 Greek philosopher (ca 427–347 BC) (5)
16 Foreigner, stranger (5)
18 ____ firma, solid ground (5)
19 Convenient (5)

177

Across

2 Pupa (9)
6 John ___, film actor who played tough heroes (5)
7 Forays (5)
9 Robert E ___, general in the US Civil War (1807–70) (3)
10 ___ faithfully, letter ending (5)
12 Appliance that removes moisture (5)
14 Select by a vote (5)
17 Scent trail of an animal (5)
19 Young newt (3)
20 Chair used as a carriage (5)
21 Sign of the zodiac, the Ram (5)
22 Keep on striving (9)

Down

1 Honeymooners (9)
2 Beaver-like animal (5)
3 Staggers (5)
4 Cut finely (5)
5 Everyone except the clergy (5)
8 Takes unawares (9)
11 Legendary bird (3)
13 Gentle blow (3)
15 Duck valued for its soft down (5)
16 Unrelaxed, taut (5)
17 Assert (5)
18 Popeye's girlfriend (5)

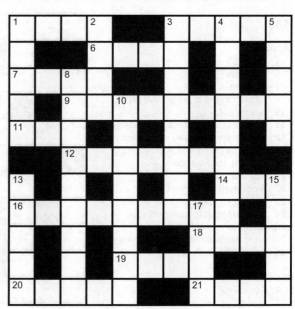

178

Across

1 Young of a cow (4)
3 River flowing into the North Sea (5)
6 Actor's portrayal of someone (4)
7 Insect between larva and adult stage (4)
9 Adopt rural ways or practices (9)
11 General name for beer (3)
12 Any domain of knowledge accumulated by systematic study (7)
14 Aspire (3)
16 Citadel in ancient Greek towns (9)
18 Costly (4)
19 English flower, also a girl's name (4)
20 Religious righteousness (5)
21 Certain (4)

Down

1 Coconut meat (5)
2 Married German woman (4)
3 Characteristic of a particular area (8)
4 Unsure and constrained in manner (3,2,4)
5 Young of an eel (5)
8 Authorise use of medicine (9)
10 Tending to cause things to slide (8)
13 Consume (3,2)
15 Integrate (5)
17 *The ___ of March*, 2011 film (4)

179

Across

4 Flake of dead skin (5)
7 Attempt to equal or surpass (7)
8 Drink usually served with the final course of a meal (7,4)
12 Most visually attractive (9)
15 Untimely (11)
20 Capable of being stretched (7)
21 Breathe noisily during sleep (5)

Down

1 Child's toy bear (5)
2 Purchases (4)
3 Container for a bird (4)
4 Despatched (4)
5 Tangerine/grapefruit hybrid (4)
6 Cooked in oil (5)
9 Exorbitant (5)
10 Relative magnitudes of two quantities (5)
11 Cereal crop (5)
13 Married women (5)
14 Barrier constructed to keep out the sea (5)
16 Collection of miscellaneous things (4)
17 Savoury meat paste (4)
18 Basic unit of money in South Africa (4)
19 Division of quantity accepted as a standard of measurement (4)

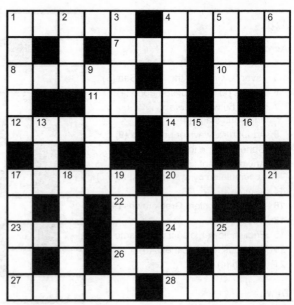

180

Across

1 Bush (5)
4 Wanderer (5)
7 Be obliged to repay (3)
8 Edible organs of an animal (5)
10 Is able to (3)
11 Hindu or Buddhist religious leader (4)
12 Mr Presley, rock and roll legend (5)
14 Unstable (5)
17 ___ out, dwindle (5)
20 Not sharp (5)
22 Woodwind instrument (4)
23 Hold at an angle in order to pour (3)
24 ___ Cup, golf tournament (5)
26 Stand for a golf ball (3)
27 Aromatic plants used in cookery (5)
28 Cover with cloth (5)

Down

1 Twenty (5)
2 Branch of the armed forces (inits) (3)
3 Large pill used in veterinary medicine (5)
4 Connected series or group (5)
5 Birthplace of Muhammad (5)
6 Dismal (5)
9 Nimble (5)
13 Prevarication (3)
15 Bill ___, singer with The Comets (5)
16 Understand (Scots) (3)
17 Eye covering (5)
18 Heavy drinker (5)
19 Sources (5)
20 Pierced with a drill (5)
21 Laconic (5)
25 Chemical that carries genetic information (inits) (3)

181

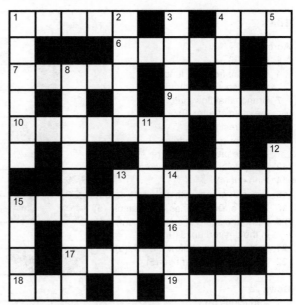

Across

1 Bulgarian capital (5)
4 Scorch (4)
7 Headdress worn by a bishop (5)
8 Craft considered to have extraterrestrial origins (inits) (3)
10 Consequently (4)
11 Popular spice (6)
13 Expect, believe (7)
16 Country, capital Rome (5)
17 Medicine used to relieve pain (7)
18 Dull-witted, foolish (6)
21 Motor vehicle (4)
23 Beam of light (3)
24 Extremely sharp (5)
25 Ancient city in Asia Minor (4)
26 Closely packed (5)

Down

1 Ostracise (4)
2 Measure of 12 inches (4)
3 General pardon (7)
4 ___ crawly, insect (6)
5 That girl (3)
6 River that rises in the Swiss Alps (5)
9 Cotton-stuffed mattress originating in Japan (5)
12 Product of seabirds (5)
14 Having folds (7)
15 US composer of military marches (1854–1932) (5)
16 Foolishness (6)
17 Nautical term meaning to hold firm or stop (5)
19 Islamic republic (4)
20 Blatant promotion (4)
22 Ultimate principle of the universe (3)

182

Across

1 Titan forced by Zeus to bear the sky on his shoulders (5)
4 Waterproof raincoat (abbr) (3)
6 Piece of pipe that bends backwards on itself (1-4)
7 Rise in bodily temperature (5)
9 Bring dishonour upon (5)
10 One who assists a priest in a liturgical service (7)
13 Confined, imprisoned (7)
15 Game with numbered balls (5)
16 Organs located in the chest (5)
17 Pimples (5)
18 Piece of metal held in a horse's mouth by reins (3)
19 William Butler ___, Irish poet (5)

Down

1 Altercation (6)
2 Inclined to anger or bad feelings (5)
3 Heartbeat (5)
4 Award for winning a championship (9)
5 Informal restaurant (4)
8 Fiddler (9)
11 Drink made by infusing dried leaves (3)
12 Against (6)
13 Part of the large intestine (5)
14 Condition marked by uncontrollable tremor (5)
15 Explosive device (4)

183

Across

4 Natives of Ankara, for example (5)
7 Abusive attack on a person's good name (7)
8 Piece of scrap material (3)
10 Farewell (5)
12 Excessively fat (5)
13 Border (4)
15 Kind of gelatin used for fining real ale (9)
19 Anise-flavoured Greek liqueur (4)
21 Cetacean mammal (5)
24 Means for communicating information (5)
25 Common cyst of the skin (3)
26 Observers (7)
27 Place for temporary parking (3-2)

Down

1 Scarper (5)
2 Friendly nations (6)
3 Attack as false or wrong (6)
4 Novice (4)
5 Fury (4)
6 Alloy of iron and carbon (5)
9 On fire (6)
11 Fit to be eaten (6)
14 Self-importance (3)
16 Wood that has been prepared for building (6)
17 Saturated (6)
18 Expand abnormally (5)
20 Intermission (5)
22 Not at home (4)
23 Feeling of desire (4)

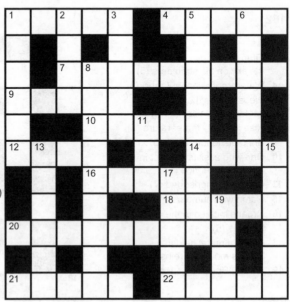

184

Across

1 Fools (5)
4 Expel air from the lungs with a sudden sharp sound (5)
7 Branch that flows into the main stream (9)
9 Lay to rest (5)
10 Pungent spice, popular in apple pies (5)
12 Movable barrier in a fence or wall (4)
14 Fine grit (4)
16 Dress or groom with elaborate care (5)
18 Native of Des Moines, for example (5)
20 Mark (the scale of an instrument) in the desired units (9)
21 Part of the face below the eye (5)
22 Long-legged water bird (5)

Down

1 Audacious (6)
2 Try to hit a golf ball into a hole by striking it gently (4)
3 Eddy (5)
5 Immediately, without delay (2,3,4)
6 Native of Berlin, for example (6)
8 Open to arguments, ideas or change (9)
11 Judo belt (3)
13 Fix together (6)
15 Performer who moves to music (6)
17 Sound made by a cat (5)
19 Unwanted plant (4)

185

Across

1 Capable of being dissolved in liquid (7)
7 Chortle (5)
8 Application (3)
9 Projection at the end of a piece of wood (5)
11 Young seal (3)
12 Field of study dealing with numbers (11)
14 Line of work (3)
15 Pack of cards used for fortune-telling (5)
18 Israeli submachine-gun (3)
19 Pixies (5)
20 Male child of your spouse and a former partner (7)

Down

1 Look good on (4)
2 Grassy garden area (4)
3 Short musket of wide bore with a flared muzzle (11)
4 Very large or ungainly (11)
5 Soft moist part of a fruit (4)
6 Seats (6)

10 Ms Cassidy, singer whose albums include *Songbird* (3)
12 Infuriate (6)
13 Sound made by a dove (3)

14 Lively style of jazz music, swing (4)
16 Tatters (4)
17 Mountain lake (4)

186

Across

1 Points towards (5)
4 Gibe, mock (5)
7 Coming first in a race (7)
8 Crystallised (of fruit) (5)
10 Veteran soldier (8)
13 Health resorts (4)
15 Area equivalent to 4840 square yards (4)
17 Frenzy (8)
19 Modify (5)
20 Decline to vote (7)
21 Desert animal (5)
22 Geoff ___, footballer who scored a hat-trick in the 1966 World Cup Final (5)

Down

1 Parasitic plant (6)
2 Seeds used to flavour a traditional seedcake (7)
3 Conduit for carrying off waste products (5)
5 Artificial cloud created by an aircraft (8)
6 Fireplace frame (6)
9 Music-tape container (8)

11 Garden tool (3)
12 Cause to separate and go in different directions (7)
14 Anxiety disorder (6)

16 Fascinated, enthralled (6)
18 Farm with facilities for livestock (5)

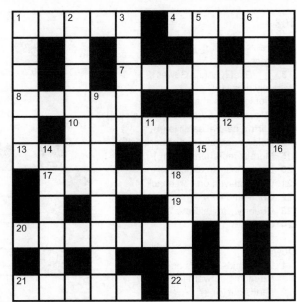

187

Across

1 Forest god (5)
4 Estate to which a wife is entitled on the death of her husband (5)
7 Fleet of warships (6)
9 Russian emperor (4)
11 Native of Zagreb, for example (5)
12 Sample (6)
14 Cattle reared for their meat (4)
16 Charge (4)
19 Treasurer at a college (6)
21 Miraculous food (5)
22 Daddy (4)
23 Cold dessert often served at parties (6)
25 Mechanical bar (5)
26 Functions (5)

Down

1 Electric motor for bringing an engine to life (7)
2 Multiplication (5)
3 Flushed (3)
5 Tenth month of the year (7)
6 Fill with high spirits (5)

8 Circus performer (7)
10 Means of returning something by post (inits) (3)
13 Relating to those 13 to 19 years old (7)
15 Pair of pincers used in medical treatment (7)
17 Affect with wonder (5)
18 Bathroom fixture (3)
20 Less dangerous (5)
24 Tier (3)

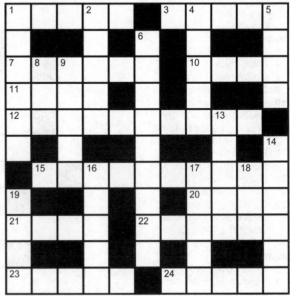

188

Across

1 Reef of coral (5)
3 ___ *Beauty*, Anna Sewell's only novel (5)
7 Pierce with a sharp stake (6)
10 Measure the duration of an event (4)
11 Earth's natural satellite (4)
12 Noisy, energetic and cheerful (10)
15 Morally reprehensible (10)
20 Lively Scottish dance (4)
21 Game played on horseback (4)
22 Come into view (6)
23 Country, capital Sana'a (5)
24 Defect (5)

Down

1 With hands on hips and elbows extending outward (6)
2 Lends out (5)
4 Game in which numbered balls are drawn at random (5)
5 Eager (4)
6 Gained an advantage or profit from (9)
8 Sound made by a cow (3)
9 Balance (5)

13 Natural brown earth pigment (5)
14 Give in, as to influence or pressure (6)
16 Gradient (5)

17 Structure for open-air sports (5)
18 Stage or portion of a journey (3)
19 Nimble (4)

189

Across

1 Melon-like tropical fruit (6)
6 Day nursery for young children (6)
7 Restaurant cook (4)
8 Relating to pottery (7)
12 Magical being (5)
13 Port city of Japan (5)
14 Artificial covering for a tooth (3)
15 An advantageous purchase (5)
18 Fill with optimism (5)
19 Give someone wrong directions or information (7)
21 Desert in central Asia (4)
22 Riposte (6)
23 Keeping back (6)

Down

1 Policy or doctrine of rejecting war (8)
2 Land and the buildings on it (8)
3 Highest level attainable (4)
4 Edgar ____, French painter and sculptor (1834–1917) (5)
5 Arab chief (5)
8 Bike (5)
9 Fastened with a thick cord (5)
10 Pasta in the form of slender tubes (8)
11 Providing food and services (8)
16 Striped cat (5)
17 Tolerate (5)
20 Behaves in a particular way (4)

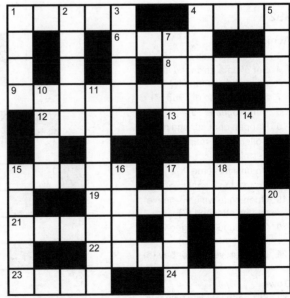

190

Across

1 Draws in by a vacuum (5)
4 Pouches (4)
6 Intimation (4)
8 Sprang up (5)
9 Maintain in unaltered condition (8)
12 Once ___ a time (4)
13 Alleviated (5)
15 Organ enclosed within the skull (5)
17 House attached to one other (4)
19 North American black larch (8)
21 Group of elite soldiers (1-4)
22 US city known for gambling casinos and easy divorce (4)
23 ___ Jones, lead singer with The Monkees who died in March 2012 (4)
24 Agent used in fermenting beer (5)

Down

1 Exchange (4)
2 Weak cry of a young bird (5)
3 Lustre (5)
4 Pennant (8)
5 Pass (time) (5)
7 Body of a church (4)
10 Major industrial and coal mining region in north-west Germany (4)
11 Lone (8)
14 Large-scale (4)
15 Permanent mark made by burning with a hot iron (5)
16 Identify (4)
17 Famous London hotel (5)
18 Island located south of Sicily (5)
20 Standard monetary unit of Burma (4)

191

Across

1 Member of a European light cavalry unit, renowned for elegant dress (6)
6 Land on which food is grown (6)
7 Make less effective (6)
9 Goddess of retribution (7)
13 Titled peers of the realm (5)
14 Land surrounded by water (5)
15 Attack (5)
18 Loom (5)
19 Bad or disorderly government (7)
21 Brass that looks like gold, used to decorate furniture (6)
22 Lay to rest (6)
23 Small stamp or seal on a ring (6)

Down

1 Property in a family for generations (8)
2 Inhibit (8)
3 Infrequent (4)
4 Underground tunnels (5)
5 Golden ____, record popular in past times (5)
8 Being in the original position (2,4)
10 Form of address for a man (6)
11 Reduce speed (4,4)
12 Dreamy, romantic or sentimental quality (8)
16 Fool, twit (coll) (5)
17 Inadvertent incorrectness (5)
20 Propels (an object such as a ball) in a high arc (4)

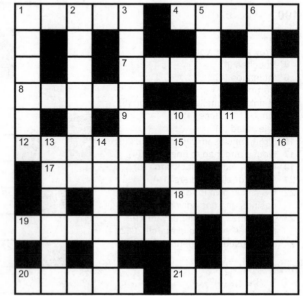

192

Across

1 Hair on the chin (5)
4 Set of data arranged in rows and columns (5)
7 Hitchcock film of 1958 (7)
8 Bring together (5)
9 Happen or occur again (6)
12 Collection of maps (5)
15 Pertain (5)
17 Up until this time (6)
18 Professional cooks (5)
19 Opening to which a sleeve can be attached (7)
20 Compound of oxygen with another element (5)
21 Unassertive man or boy (5)

Down

1 Sturgeon that is a valuable source of caviare (6)
2 Newspaper feature (7)
3 Many and different (7)
5 Clement ____, former Prime Minister (6)
6 Official emissary of the Pope (6)
10 Deal with in a routine way (7)
11 Has an impact upon (7)
13 Part of an insect's body that bears the wings (6)
14 Bowed, curved (6)
16 In a hasty and foolhardy manner (6)

193

Across

1 Large bags (5)
4 Scour vigorously (5)
7 Orderly grouping (11)
8 Amphibian (4)
11 Fried potato slices (6)
14 Country, capital Stockholm (6)
17 Hard fruits (4)
21 Marked by independence and creativity in thought or action (11)
22 Bill ___, of Microsoft fame (5)
23 Puts a name to (5)

Down

1 Outerwear garment (5)
2 Consignment (5)
3 Bathroom fixture (4)
4 Implement with a shaft and barbed point (5)
5 Tall perennial grasses (5)
6 Seizes with the teeth (5)
9 Not processed or refined (3)
10 Deity (3)
11 Metal container (3)
12 Travellers' pub (3)
13 Deep hole (3)
14 Wasp's defence (5)
15 Accurate (5)
16 Departs (5)
18 Applying (5)
19 Paces (5)
20 Fruit preserves (4)

194

Across

1 Turn red with embarrassment (5)
4 Largest city in Nebraska, USA (5)
8 Sean ___, US film actor and director (4)
9 In short supply (6)
10 Mature female deer (3)
11 Military hat with a flat circular top and a peak (4)
13 Very dark, black (4)
14 Setting down (7)
15 Genuine (4)
16 Give up, relinquish (4)
17 Nothing (3)
18 Bureau (6)
19 Compulsion (4)
21 Fit out (5)
22 Beautiful young woman (5)

Down

2 Be prostrate (3)
3 Ornamental timepiece seen in a garden (7)
5 Bring about (7)
6 Gas used chiefly in welding (9)
7 Fictitious name (9)
8 Impassive expression that hides one's true feelings (5,4)
12 Flat highland (7)
13 Consider as part of something (7)
20 Mousse (3)

195

Across

1 Vertical passage into a mine (5)
4 Unfledged, newly hatched pigeon (5)
7 Hollow under the upper limb where it is joined to the shoulder (6)
9 Above, beyond (4)
10 Hit swiftly with a violent blow (4)
12 Light shade of red (4)
13 Fatuous, mindless (5)
15 Bring to a close (3)
17 Birds of prey used in falconry (5)
19 Chronic drinker (sl) (4)
21 Back part of a foot (4)
23 Erstwhile (4)
24 Item of headgear with a tall crown (3,3)
25 Cheap restaurant (5)
26 Deep ravine (5)

Down

1 Large shrimps cooked in breadcrumbs (6)
2 Pungent gas compounded of nitrogen and hydrogen (7)
3 Word denoting a particular thing (4)
5 Prescribed number (5)
6 Master Simpson, cartoon character (4)
8 Matching cardigan and pullover worn at the same time (7)
11 Also (3)
14 Not one nor the other (7)
15 Stretch (3)
16 Baby's knitted footwear item (6)
18 In what place? (5)
20 Affectionate, loving (4)
22 Protracted (4)

196

Across

1 Band of material used to support an injured arm (5)
3 Violent weather condition (5)
6 Killer whale (4)
8 US term for a water tap (6)
9 Mr Garfunkel, singer-songwriter (3)
11 Unkind or cruel (5)
12 US tennis player Chris, who won Wimbledon in 1974, 1976 and 1981 (5)
13 Forename of golfer, Mr Woosnam (3)
14 Colour of the rainbow (5)
15 Bothered (3,2)
18 Sin (3)
19 Accomplish (6)
20 Stun (4)
21 Branchlet (5)
22 Compound leaf of a fern or palm (5)

Down

1 Move with a splashing sound (5)
2 Approaches (5)
3 Collect discarded material (8)
4 Musical group (9)
5 Anthem (5)
7 Woodworker (9)
10 Using one's mind (8)
14 Pasture (5)
16 Arrange (5)
17 Thick woollen fabric (5)

197

Across

1 Gusts (5)
4 Hunt illegally (5)
7 Three-legged support (6)
9 Further, additional (4)
10 Make new (4)
11 Sources of illumination (6)
13 Long narrow opening (4)
15 Collection of facts (4)
17 Country, capital Moscow (6)
20 Plenty (4)
21 Flesh used as food (4)
22 Pliant and flexible (6)
23 Remains in place (5)
24 Pucker or contract (the lips) (5)

Down

1 Within a glass container (7)
2 Due (5)
3 Low in stature (5)
5 Diffusion of liquid through a porous membrane (7)
6 Welsh breed of long-bodied, short-legged dog (5)
8 Arid regions of the world (7)
12 Free from infirmity or disease (7)
14 Acrobat's swing (7)
16 Proficient (5)
18 Commandeer (5)
19 Fabulous, wonderful! (5)

198

Across

1 Cause to wither (5)
3 Take advantage (5)
6 Father (4)
8 Stoneworkers (6)
9 Large pot for making coffee or tea (3)
11 Care for sick people (5)
12 Sends by post (5)
14 Appearing to be (7)
15 Noise (5)
16 Twig (5)
18 Cardinal number (3)
19 Hazard (6)
20 Succeeding (4)
21 Jugs (5)
22 Keep an eye on (5)

Down

1 Visit briefly (3,2)
2 Make less subtle or refined (7)
3 Scaremonger (8)
4 Native Australian (9)
5 Leans (5)
7 Engagement in an activity or course of action (9)
10 Gratuitous (8)
13 Aerial (7)
15 Move furtively (5)
17 Sailing vessel with two masts (5)

199

Across

1 Soothing ointment (5)
3 Higher up (5)
7 Straight sword with a narrow blade (6)
9 Declare formally as true (4)
10 Hen's produce (3)
12 Hitch, unforeseen problem (4)
13 Roll of tobacco (5)
15 Synthetic hairpiece (3)
17 Scottish lakes (5)
19 Hollow in a rock (4)
21 Weeding tool (3)
22 Start again (4)
23 Minuscule (6)
25 Vital organ of the body (5)
26 Equine animal (5)

Down

1 Emphasis (6)
2 Roman numerals for the number seven (3)
4 Melvyn ____, presenter of TV's *The South Bank Show* from 1978–2010 (5)
5 British peer (4)
6 Just as it should be (9)
8 Keyboard instrument (5)
11 Concert (3)
14 At a distance (5)
15 Which person? (3)
16 Harsh, stern (6)
18 Strangle (5)
20 By word of mouth (4)
24 As well (3)

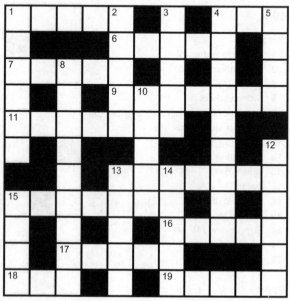

200

Across

1 Extract (metals) by heating (5)
4 Baby's napkin (3)
6 Nocturnal badger-like carnivore (5)
7 Mrs George W Bush (5)
9 Boxlike containers in a piece of furniture (7)
11 Beg (7)
13 Small or minor detail (7)
15 Swaggering show of courage (7)
16 Number of sides of a triangle (5)
17 Acute abdominal pain (5)
18 Prosecute (3)
19 Spare-time activity (5)

Down

1 Showing a brooding ill-humour (6)
2 Commercial exchange (5)
3 Ermine in its brown summer coat (5)
4 Flag hoisted when a ship is about to sail (4,5)
5 Sleeping places (4)
8 Auditory communication (9)
10 Overzealous (5)
12 Hardly, sparsely (6)
13 Masculine (5)
14 Depression scratched into a surface (5)
15 Rubbish receptacles (4)

201

Across

1 Solve crime (6)
4 Pincer (4)
6 Communal dining-hall (9)
8 Unit of electrical resistance (3)
10 Tenant (6)
13 Mosque official (4)
14 Virile sort of chap (2-3)
16 Warm and snug (4)
17 Division of Ireland (6)
20 Strong, angry emotion (3)
21 Agreeing in nature or action (9)
22 Sharp tug (4)
23 Bend the knees and bow in a servile manner (6)

Down

1 Slaver (5)
2 Divisions of the school year (5)
3 Popular beverage (6)
4 Hanging spikes of flowers found on various trees (7)
5 Ironic (3)
7 Peruser of text (6)
9 Brave (6)
11 Merciless usurer in a play by Shakespeare (7)
12 Rod Hull's famous bird (3)
15 Lacking in pigment (6)
18 Taut (5)
19 Give fresh life or strength to (5)
21 Unspecified (object) (3)

202

Across

1 Government of the Roman Catholic Church (6)
4 Barbed spear for landing large fish (4)
6 Hopeless case (4,5)
8 Geological period of time (3)
10 Dish for holding a cup (6)
13 Academic test (abbr) (4)
14 Criticism disguised as praise (5)
16 Hoots with derision (4)
17 Produce incisors, molars, etc (6)
20 Long and slippery fish (3)
21 Litter used as a means of transporting sick people (9)
22 Acquire through effort (4)
23 Swung back and forth (6)

Down

1 Prods (5)
2 Colourful rice (5)
3 More snug or intimate (6)
4 Seductive stare or look at another person (slang) (4,3)
5 Fixed charge for a professional service (3)
7 Enveloping bandage (6)
9 Well-seasoned stew (6)
11 Water tank (7)
12 Bunkum (3)
15 Male relative (6)
18 Former football player and England manager, ___ Venables (5)
19 Large antelope (5)
21 Droop (3)

203

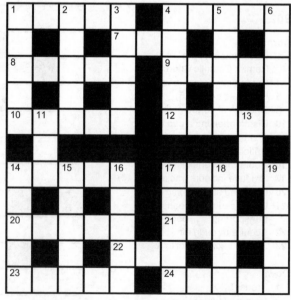

Across

1 Modified leaf of a plant (5)
4 State of danger involving risk (5)
7 Wander about aimlessly (4)
8 Having a sharp inclination (5)
9 Tropical lizard (5)
11 Science or practice of building or flying aircraft (11)
15 Uncertainties, doubtful factors, ___ and buts (3)
16 With intolerance (11)
19 Heartache (5)
21 ___ Allan Poe, author (5)
22 Shared on-line journal (4)
23 Fragrant resin used as incense (5)
24 Comes close (5)

Down

1 Port in southern Iraq (5)
2 Statement of beliefs (5)
3 Toy that can be made to spin (3)
4 Secure with a wooden pin (3)
5 Acknowledgment that payment has been made (7)
6 Facial expressions (5)
10 Secret criminal group in Sicily (5)
12 Cross-current in the sea (7)
13 Egg of a louse (3)
14 Employ (3)
16 Fireplace (5)
17 Gentle poke (5)
18 Tall stories (5)
20 US law enforcement agency (inits) (3)
21 Epoch (3)

204

Across

1 Compact mass, cluster (5)
4 Leisurely walk (5)
7 Spherical object (3)
8 Garden pests that leave trails of slime (5)
9 Relating to the eye (5)
10 Remove unwanted hair (5)
12 Ebbing and flowing (5)
14 Person authorised to act for another (5)
17 Acute insecurity (5)
20 Take in fluids through the mouth (5)
21 Small concavity (5)
22 ___ de Cologne, perfume (3)
23 Goes in front (5)
24 Slack, lax (5)

Down

1 Instances (5)
2 Small pendant fleshy lobe at the back of the soft palate (5)
3 Temporary police force (5)
4 Terminate before completion (5)
5 Held back, as of breath (5)
6 Be superior to (5)
11 Of a female (3)
13 Donkey (3)
14 Foot-operated lever (5)
15 Board used to spell out supernatural messages (5)
16 Exclamation of surprise (5)
17 Abrogate (5)
18 Insectivorous terrestrial lizard (5)
19 Topic (5)

205

Across

1 Fruits of the palm tree (5)
4 Washtubs (5)
7 Dental decay (6)
9 Type of food shop (abbr) (4)
10 Character from an ancient Germanic alphabet (4)
12 Be compliant (4)
13 Tree with edible pods used as a chocolate substitute (5)
15 Do something (3)
17 Dense growth of bushes or trees (5)
19 Thin strand of metal (4)
21 Part of a church that contains the altar (4)
23 God of love, also known as Cupid (4)
24 Higher in rank (6)
25 Person who avoids the company of others (5)
26 Despatches (5)

Down

1 Physician (6)
2 Underwater missile (7)
3 Prophet (4)
5 Type of snake (5)
6 Slide (4)
8 Victory (7)
11 ___ King Cole, jazz pianist and singer (3)
14 Point of view (7)
15 Viper (3)
16 Rubble, dust (6)
18 Out of fashion (5)
20 Deep hole or shaft dug to obtain water (4)
22 Long fishes (4)

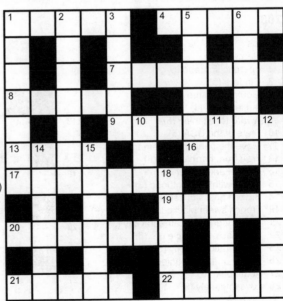

206

Across

1 Primary (5)
4 Coast (5)
7 Aperture or hole leading into a cavity (7)
8 Cooks slowly and for a long time in liquid (5)
9 Cross-brace that supports a rail on a railway track (7)
13 All the time (4)
16 Went on horseback (4)
17 Tightly curled and unopened flower (7)
19 Aquatic creature (5)
20 Extravagantly or foolishly loving and indulgent (7)
21 Division of the year (5)
22 Deep chasm (5)

Down

1 Long pillow (7)
2 Globes, orbs (7)
3 Ill-tempered (5)
5 Physiological need for food (6)
6 Hired (6)
10 ___ Ferrigno, actor who played the Incredible Hulk (3)
11 Assume or act the character of (7)
12 Bottle up (feelings, for example) (7)
14 Religious cult practised chiefly in Caribbean countries (6)
15 Remorse (6)
18 Religious doctrine (5)

207

Across

1 Pain sometimes experienced by divers (coll) (5)
4 Category (5)
7 Pear-shaped fruit (7)
8 Leguminous plant (3)
9 Espresso coffee with milk (5)
11 Kitchen range (5)
12 Port and resort on the west coast of Florida (5)
14 Group of many insects (5)
16 Woman's garment (abbr) (3)
17 Onwards, ahead (7)
19 Motionless (5)
20 Put (pressure) on (5)

Down

1 Noisy altercation (5)
2 Prefix meaning recent or modern (3)
3 Oil-bearing laminated rock (5)
4 Cuts into pieces (5)
5 Ancient jar used to hold oil or wine (7)
6 Person held in servitude (5)
10 Large hemispherical brass or copper percussion instruments (7)
12 Pipes (5)
13 Dreadful, terrible (5)
14 Tennis stroke that puts the ball into play (5)
15 Location of something surrounded by other things (5)
18 Unit of surface area equal to 100 square metres (3)

208

Across

1 Dame Nellie ____, Australian operatic soprano (5)
3 Cinders (5)
7 Moulding, in the form of the letter 'S' (4)
8 Award for winning (5)
10 State of the USA (5)
11 Move the head in agreement (3)
13 Free from harm or evil (6)
15 Biblical ark-builder (4)
16 Invest with a knighthood (3)
18 Broken husks of cereal grains (4)
19 French sweet blackcurrant liqueur (6)
21 Cambridgeshire cathedral city (3)
22 Deposits of valuable ore (5)
25 Presentation, briefly (5)
26 Alone, unaccompanied (4)
27 Acute pain (5)
28 Love intensely (5)

Down

1 Record of things worth recalling (11)
2 Highest peak in the Alps, Mont ____ (5)
3 Yearly assembly of shareholders (inits) (3)
4 Body of water (3)
5 Dreadful (7)
6 Medical instrument (11)
9 At high volume (4)
12 The two in a pack of playing cards (5)
14 Person deemed to be despicable (2-3-2)
17 Indonesian island (4)
20 Church council (5)
23 Long period of time (3)
24 Cunning (3)

209

Across

1 Bulk (4)
3 In a foreign country (6)
5 Shake (3)
6 Measure of medicine (4)
7 Relating to the stars (6)
9 Briefs worn by men and boys (10)
14 Group action in opposition to those in power (10)
17 Frogmen (6)
19 British peer of the highest rank (4)
20 Poem intended or adapted to be sung (3)
21 Narrative poem of popular origin (6)
22 Overwhelming defeat (4)

Down

1 Average, intermediate (6)
2 Root vegetable (5)
3 Turkish commander (3)
4 Natives of Iraq or Jordan, for example (5)
8 Prepare leather (3)
10 Gaming cube (3)
11 Step in dancing (especially in classical ballet) (3)
12 Number (3)
13 Vast, sandy region (6)
14 Indian side dish of yogurt and chopped cucumbers (5)
15 H Rider Haggard novel (3)
16 Britain's only native venomous snake (5)
18 Ground containing a mat of grass and grass roots (3)

210

Across

1 Alcoholic apple drink (5)
4 Give an answer (5)
7 Gave an owl's call (6)
9 Debauchery (4)
10 Exploit (4)
11 Ring road (6)
13 One twelfth of a foot (4)
15 Faucets (4)
17 Plantation (6)
20 Small slender gull with a forked tail (4)
21 Hemispherical roof (4)
22 Give insider information (3,3)
23 Biblical tower intended to reach to heaven (5)
24 Minute (5)

Down

1 Live together (7)
2 Sag (5)
3 Submerged ridges of coral (5)
5 Conceited, self-centred person (7)
6 Art of reasoning accurately (5)
8 Sweet course of a meal (7)
12 Severely simple (7)
14 Attentive (7)
16 Distinctive smell (5)
18 Prunes off small pieces (5)
19 Forum in Ancient Greece (5)

211

Across
1 Undersides of the feet (5)
4 Lofty proud gait (5)
7 Beseech (7)
8 At a great distance (3)
9 Involving danger (5)
11 Device used to deviate a beam of light (5)
12 Bottomless pit (5)
14 Carbonated water containing quinine (5)
16 Strong-scented perennial herb (3)
17 Loss of memory (7)
19 Rubbish (5)
20 Hinged lifting tool (5)

Down
1 One who travels on the piste (5)
2 Circuit (3)
3 Flamboyant (5)
4 Cleaner of chimneys (5)
5 Brutal fellow (7)
6 Make a rhythmic sound with the fingers (5)
10 Timidity (7)
12 Dart (5)
13 Trap for birds or small mammals (5)
14 Article of faith (5)
15 Sharp projections on the paws of an animal (5)
18 ___ City, 2005 film (3)

212

Across
1 Becomes lustreless (4)
3 In a state of uncertainty, perplexed (2,3)
6 Chief Norse god (4)
7 Very dark black (4)
9 Securing in place (9)
11 Civilian clothing (5)
12 Hiding away for future use (7)
15 Large stringed instrument (5)
17 Sudden inspiration or bright idea (coll) (9)
18 Region regularly afflicted by monsoons (4)
19 Wearing footgear (4)
20 Stairs (5)
21 Second wife of Henry VIII, ___ Boleyn (4)

Down
1 Cherished desire (5)
2 Musical composition of three or four movements of contrasting forms (6)
3 Plant grown for its edible seeds and stems (8)
4 Wavy lines (9)
5 Proverb (5)
8 Slight possibility (3-6)
10 Nausea (8)
13 US state in which Las Vegas is located (6)
14 Lies adjacent to (5)
16 Egg-shaped (5)

213

Across

1 Garment hanging from the waist (5)
3 Mood disorder (5)
7 Seethe (4)
8 Eliminate from the body (5)
9 Avoid by a sudden quick movement (5)
11 Country that maintains repressive control over the people by means of secret forces (6,5)
14 Road construction vehicle (11)
16 Be of service (5)
19 Connected with birth (5)
20 Animal's foot (4)
21 Car crash (sl) (5)
22 Informal term for a British policeman (5)

Down

1 Slumber (5)
2 Complete act of breathing in and out (11)
3 Soft wet earth (3)
4 Pale medium-dry Spanish sherry (11)
5 ___ Kelly, famous 19th century Australian bushranger (3)
6 Anoint with oil (5)
10 Facial hair (5)
12 Not at home (3)
13 Definite article (3)
14 Walk heavily (5)
15 Large gathering of people (5)
17 Expression of surprise or sudden realisation (3)
18 Cut part of a tree trunk (3)

214

Across

1 Collect or gather, hoard (5)
4 Dust coat (5)
7 Dirty washing (7)
8 Shows concern (5)
9 Scour a surface (6)
12 Shade of blue tinged with green (4)
15 Jump (4)
17 System of newsgroups on the internet (6)
19 Liquorice-flavoured seeds (5)
20 Comes into possession of (7)
21 Played a part (5)
22 Stupid, daft (5)

Down

1 Tree with sharp thorns (6)
2 Inclined towards or displaying love (7)
3 Latin American dance music, incorporating jazz and rock (5)
5 Handbook (6)
6 Eye part (6)
10 Four-winged insect (3)
11 Unit of relative loudness (7)
13 Canadian province (6)
14 Supply or impregnate with oxygen (6)
16 More than enough (6)
18 Jobs that must be done (5)

215

Across

1 Stooping in submission (6)
6 Coincidence, accord (6)
7 Publishing supervisor (6)
9 Do something to a greater degree (7)
13 Supporting bar (5)
14 Resin-like substance secreted by certain insects (3)
15 Generally incompetent (5)
16 Remove the fastenings from (7)
20 Small carnivore with short legs and an elongated body (6)
21 Vocation (6)
22 Pines (6)

Down

1 Traditional words used when hearing someone sneeze (5,3)
2 Serving woman (8)
3 Eastern teacher (4)
4 Flaccid (4)
5 Spinning toys (4)
8 Stableman or groom at an inn (hist) (6)
10 Directions for cooking something (6)
11 Valuer, estimator (8)
12 Bowling game (8)
17 Less than average tide (4)
18 Having appendages on the feet (4)
19 Lopsided (4)

216

Across

1 Notorious Boston murderer of the 1960s (9)
8 Helicopter propeller (5)
9 Snow leopard (5)
10 Ameliorate (5)
12 Skid (5)
14 Move on hands and knees (5)
17 Ancient unit of length (5)
19 Biblical city known for vice and corruption (5)
20 Cloth woven from flax (5)
21 Apartment on the top floor of a building (9)

Down

2 Name of a book (5)
3 Harsh or corrosive in tone (5)
4 Disgusting, repulsive (5)
5 Boredom (5)
6 Bag with a handle used to carry papers, files, etc (9)
7 Doing again (9)
11 At once (3)
13 ___ Costello, Bud Abbott's film partner (3)
15 Forename of Mr Agassi, tennis champion (5)
16 Boundary (5)
17 Instrument played with a bow (5)
18 Component parts of a skeleton (5)

217

Across
1 Cry of greeting (4)
3 Mariner (6)
5 Be in debt (3)
6 Shed bodily fluid (4)
7 Entwine (6)
9 Appearing as such but not necessarily so (10)
14 Constricting snake (3)
15 Liturgical vestment worn by priests (3)
17 Cost-effective (10)
20 Gambol, play boisterously (6)
22 Caprine animal (4)
23 Misery (3)
24 Red fruit eaten as a vegetable (6)
25 People who belong to the same genetic stock (4)

Down
1 Mix socially, especially with those of a higher social status (coll) (6)
2 Home of a beaver (5)
3 Fixed (3)
4 Mineral source (3,4)
8 Pen point (3)
10 Highest female voice (7)
11 Pitch (3)
12 Glide over snow (3)
13 Science room (abbr) (3)
16 Common insect with hard wingcases (6)
18 Yoko ___, widow of John Lennon (3)
19 Annoyance (5)
21 A couple (3)

218

Across
1 Answer back (6)
5 Puff, pant (4)
7 Well-ventilated (4)
8 Subdivisions of a play (4)
9 Airborne soldier (abbr) (4)
11 Basic unit of money in Albania (3)
14 Made a prediction about (8)
16 Evil (3)
18 System of medical care (inits) (3)
19 Lively (8)
20 Wing of an insect (3)
22 Nearly all (4)
24 Bath powder (4)
25 Adjoin, border (4)
26 Dull (4)
27 Lake on the Swiss-French border (6)

Down
1 Barrier consisting of a horizontal bar and supports (4)
2 Hard durable timber (4)
3 Sane (8)
4 'It is', poetically (3)
5 Pain or discomfort (3)
6 Items of crockery (6)
10 Bath's river (4)
12 Panache (4)
13 Allocate a task to a person (8)
15 Indian dish (4)
16 Employee who serves alcoholic drinks (6)
17 Lodgings (4)
20 Measure of land (4)
21 Continent (4)
23 Metal ring that opens a can (3)
24 Pull sharply (3)

219

Across
1 Extremely ornate (5)
3 The faculty of vision (5)
6 Adored (5)
7 Gone by (3)
8 Examines carefully (4)
9 Designated social position (7)
12 Explode with a bang (3)
14 Hard-shelled seed (3)
15 Old-fashioned affirmative answer (3)
17 Educational establishments (7)
20 Town in south-western England on the River Avon (4)
21 See 10 Down (3)
22 Might (5)
23 Perspiration (5)
24 Arches of hair over the eyes (5)

Down
1 One's parents (5)
2 Peak (5)
3 Fraction equal to approximately 14.2857% (7)
4 Clench, clutch tightly (5)
5 Cavalry unit (5)
8 Give personal assurance, guarantee (5)

10 and 21 Across Band associated with Roger Daltrey and Pete Townshend (3)
11 Immediate (7)
13 Bird which hoots (3)
15 Gapes (5)
16 In a higher position (5)
18 Scent, smell (5)
19 Faces (5)

220

Across
1 Renowned (6)
6 Yellow-flowered tropical tree (6)
8 Showing apprehension (7)
9 Eat hastily without proper chewing (6)
10 Glances over (5)
13 Devoid of practical purpose (7)
16 Cook with dry heat (5)
18 Moves around the border (6)
20 Clearly readable (7)
21 Member of a crowd causing a violent disturbance of the peace (6)
22 Pause uncertainly (6)

Down
1 Becomes bubbly, frothy (5)
2 Pungent bulbs (6)
3 Complacent (4)
4 Port city in southern Kenya (7)
5 Milky plant substance that coagulates on exposure to air (5)
7 Chemical with the same formula but a different structure (6)
11 Accounts checker (7)

12 Resolve (6)
14 Marked by friendly companionship with others (6)
15 Excessive rate of interest (5)
17 Those people's (5)
19 Villein (4)

221

Across
3 Device used to push in a needle when sewing (7)
6 Large family (5)
8 Reed instrument used especially in jazz music (9)
9 Additional (5)
10 Calm, with no emotional agitation (6)
13 Wrongdoing for which an action for damages may be brought (4)
16 Charter (4)
18 Assimilate or take in (6)
20 Narrow shelf (5)
22 Person who brings an action in a court of law (9)
23 Detailed critical inspection (5)
24 Psychics, supernaturalists (7)

Down
1 Thoroughfare (6)
2 Destroy the peace of (7)
3 Lone Star State of the USA (5)
4 Gustav ___, Austrian composer (6)
5 Lime tree (6)
7 Rigid piece of metal (3)
11 Head of corn (3)
12 Necessary for relief or supply (7)

14 Annie ___, famous US sharpshooter (6)
15 Close-fitting pullover or vest (1-5)
17 Colour fabric after knotting it, to produce a pattern (3-3)
19 State of extreme happiness (5)
21 Juvenile newt (3)

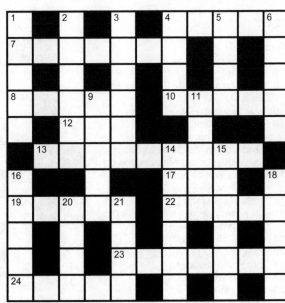

222

Across
4 Protective cover spread on the soil (5)
7 Geographical feature such as Krakatoa (7)
8 Moon-related (5)
10 Occupy (a dwelling) illegally (5)
12 Sleeveless outer garment worn by Arabs (3)
13 Group of musicians playing trumpets, trombones, horns, etc (5,4)
17 Calm central region of a cyclone (3)
19 Kick out (5)
22 ___ Asimov, science-fiction writer (5)
23 Even-tempered (7)
24 Back of a ship (5)

Down
1 Reproductive structure (5)
2 Two-dimensional (6)
3 Former name of the Indian city of Chennai (6)
4 Kate ___, celebrity model (4)
5 Stead (4)
6 Country, capital Port-au-Prince (5)
9 Become less intense (5)

11 Wharves (5)
14 Capital of Lebanon (6)
15 Close at hand (6)
16 Ursine creatures (5)
18 Eight singers who perform together (5)
20 Speed (4)
21 Right to withhold the property of a debtor (4)

223

Across
1 Give rise to (5)
3 Drills a hole (5)
7 Digestive fluid (6)
9 Female operatic star (4)
10 Mr Cruise, star of the 2013 film *Oblivion* (3)
11 Model or pattern regarded as typical (4)
13 Work unit (3)
15 Substance injected to prevent disease (7)
17 Pocket (3)
18 Prepares leather (4)
20 Fodder (3)
21 Gown (4)
22 Figurine (6)
24 Foot traveller (5)
25 Gains victory over (5)

Down
1 Gambling establishment (6)
2 Narrow runner used for gliding over snow (3)
4 Part of a broken set (7)
5 Close with a bang (4)
6 Event resulting in great loss and misfortune (9)
8 Immature insect (5)
12 Large heavy knife (7)
14 Respond to a stimulus (5)
16 Holdings (6)
19 Curved gateway (4)
23 Mature (3)

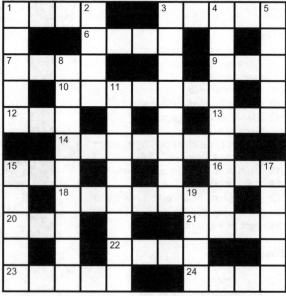

224

Across
1 Sea-going vessel (4)
3 Thong (5)
6 Fourth largest of the Great Lakes (4)
7 Idiots (4)
9 Dignitary (inits) (3)
10 Ornament made of ribbon, given as an award (7)
12 22nd letter of the Greek alphabet (3)
13 Fish with enlarged wing-like fins (3)
14 Affectation of being demure in a provocative way (7)
15 Body of salt water (3)
16 UN agency dealing with banking and finance (inits) (3)
18 Gave a military gesture (7)
20 Pompous fool (3)
21 Dissenting clique (4)
22 Oil reservoir in an engine (4)
23 Forest plants (5)
24 Shout out (4)

Down
1 Unemotional person (5)
2 Basic monetary unit of Mexico (4)
3 Consciously perceiving (8)
4 Neighbourhood of a watercourse (9)
5 Plant from which opium is obtained (5)
8 Dish of stewed meat served in a thick white sauce (9)
11 Small refracting telescope (8)
15 Tip at an angle (5)
17 Bringing death (5)
19 Catch sight of (4)

225

Across

1 Vehicle test (inits) (3)
3 South American republic (7)
6 Nudity (9)
8 Boat built by Noah (3)
10 Smaller (6)
13 Mild yellow Dutch cheese (4)
14 Cider fruit (5)
16 High in stature (4)
17 Small-seeded species of cereal crop (6)
20 Brother of George Gershwin (3)
21 Mutiny (9)
22 Receive a share of (7)
23 Earth's nearest star (3)

Down

1 Wall painting (5)
2 Military vehicles (5)
3 Maintenance (6)
4 Marked by refinement in taste and manners (7)
5 Aye (3)
7 Someone who skims across ice (6)
9 Provide with choice food or drink (6)

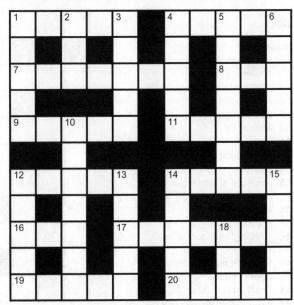

11 Most noticeable or important (7)
12 Number of turns in 60 seconds (inits) (3)
15 Intercede (6)
18 Actors' words (5)
19 Bird of prey's claw (5)
21 Style of music with a strong background beat (3)

226

Across

1 Chocolate powder (5)
4 Adjust a camera lens so as to get a sharp image (5)
7 Draw out (7)
8 Snare, trap (3)
9 Unspoken, implied (5)
11 Deplete (of resources) (5)
12 Walk noisily, heavily or angrily (5)
14 Roughly-built hut (5)
16 Abbreviation for the tenth month (3)
17 Teach (7)
19 Location, whereabouts (5)
20 Relating to punishment (5)

Down

1 Moved slowly and stealthily (5)
2 Feline mammal (3)
3 Expect (5)
4 Doomed (5)
5 Musical setting for a religious text (7)
6 Become established (3,2)
10 Country, capital Zagreb (7)
12 Swift descent through the air (5)
13 Separate part of a whole (5)
14 Part of a tree that remains after felling (5)
15 Rest on bended legs (5)
18 Miss Widdecombe, former MP (3)

227

Across

3 Toothed wheel engaged with a pawl (7)
6 Earthy metallic oxide (5)
7 Devoted to pleasure (7)
8 Form of musical entertainment (5)
10 Move sideways or in an unsteady way (6)
12 Salt of carbonic acid, used in soap powders (4)
14 Blow delivered with an open hand (4)
17 Grade or level (6)
19 Essential oil or perfume obtained from flowers (5)
20 Leonardo ___, Italian artist, engineer, scientist and architect (1452–1519) (2,5)
21 Digging implement (5)
22 Artist's paint-mixing board (7)

Down

1 Full of exultant happiness (6)
2 Showing keen practical judgment (6)
3 Amy Winehouse hit of 2007 (5)
4 Placed very near together (5-3)
5 Cipher used by Germany during World War II (6)
9 Edge of a highway (8)
11 Appropriate, seize (3)
13 Canadian capital (6)
15 Deadly (6)
16 Person employed to carry luggage (6)
18 Amount by which a salary is increased (5)

228

Across

1 Instrument for measuring a quantity (5)
4 Offering little or no hope (5)
8 Association of criminals (4)
9 National flag (6)
10 Melody (3)
11 Large and hurried swallow (4)
13 Arab sailing vessel (4)
14 Aficionado (7)
15 Measure of land equal to a quarter of an acre (4)
16 Stalk (4)
17 Pixie (3)
18 Gripping hand tool with two hinged arms (6)
19 Magnetic metallic element, symbol Fe (4)
21 Fearful expectation (5)
22 Exalt to the position of a god (5)

Down

2 Seventh letter of the Greek alphabet (3)
3 Affianced (7)
5 Descriptive word or phrase (7)
6 Female relative (9)
7 Guerilla (9)
8 Class of molluscs typically having a one-piece coiled shell (9)
12 Worship (7)
13 Abominate (7)
20 Cancelled (3)

229

Across

1 Parts of a river where the current is very fast (6)
4 Beat severely with a whip or rod (4)
6 Reproductive cells (3)
7 Attributes responsibility to (6)
9 Fine specks of detritus (4)
11 Past times (4)
13 Money risked on a gamble (5)
15 Mr Mosimann, famous chef (5)
16 Impudent or insolent rejoinder (3)
17 Surface burn (5)
19 Weapon that delivers a temporarily paralysing electric shock (5)
22 Germanic name (4)
24 Agitate (4)
25 Consecrate (6)
26 Sauce used in Chinese cookery (3)
27 Sagacious (4)
28 High-pitched cry (6)

Down

1 Garments (5)
2 Shopping centre (5)
3 Neither good nor bad (2-2)
4 Filled with a great quantity (5)
5 Conspicuous success (3)
8 Cord hole (6)
10 Took an oath (5)
12 Carnivorous bird, such as the eagle (6)
14 Contaminate (5)
18 Furze (5)
20 Dry white Italian wine from Verona (5)
21 Relating to the kidneys (5)
23 Plays with (4)
24 Adult female hog (3)

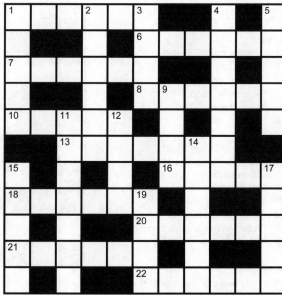

230

Across

1 Signboard, for example, bearing a shopkeeper's name (6)
6 Not outside a building (6)
7 Entertained (6)
8 Determines the direction of travel (6)
10 Bundle, of straw for example (5)
13 Tramp about (7)
16 Number (5)
18 Exposing to heat, so as to dry completely (6)
20 Oval-shaped nut (6)
21 Substance covering the crown of a tooth (6)
22 Food store (6)

Down

1 Dreads, worries (5)
2 One of two actors who are given the same status in a film (2-4)
3 Gives assistance (4)
4 Front limb (7)
5 Newly made (5)
9 Cassette (4)
11 Everlasting (7)
12 Mythical being, part man, part goat (4)
14 Boil slowly (6)
15 Afterwards (5)
17 Royal House (5)
19 Bold and impudent behaviour (4)

231

Across

1 Immodest (5)
4 Unlawful act (5)
7 Piece of embroidery demonstrating skill with various stitches (7)
8 Meaning (of a word or expression) (5)
10 Very thin candle (5)
12 Operatic airs (5)
14 Dined at home (3,2)
16 Rhythm in verse (5)
17 Shrimp-like crustacean (5)
19 Ore (7)
20 Manufacturer (5)
21 Romany (5)

Down

1 Ionised gas (6)
2 Blatant (4)
3 Unhealthy state of body or mind (7)
5 Journalist (8)
6 Breakfast food (6)
9 Wild headlong rush of frightened animals (8)
11 Sound excluder (7)
13 Light-sensitive membrane (6)
15 Four score and ten (6)
18 In the quickest time (inits) (4)

232

Across

1 Country, capital Bamako (4)
3 Device that attracts iron (6)
6 Decapod crustacean (4)
7 Expression used to frighten away animals (4)
8 Platform, dais (6)
9 Thing used instead of another (10)
14 Compound used as an antacid (6,4)
17 Body of water to the east of Eritrea (3,3)
19 Establishments where alcoholic drinks are served (4)
20 Woodworking tool (4)
21 Protect from damage or danger (6)
22 Water falling in drops (4)

Down

1 Apply badly or incorrectly (6)
2 Religious paintings (5)
3 Diagrammatic representation of an area (3)
4 With reference to (5)
5 Give out, as of a feeling of confidence, for example (5)
10 Fluffy scarf of feathers (3)
11 Charged particle (3)
12 Number in a brace (3)
13 Minister of religion (6)
14 Deciduous tree (5)
15 Paragon (5)
16 Not affected by alcohol (5)
18 Sum up (3)

233

Across

1 Pick out (6)
6 Not clear (6)
7 Person or scheme that comes to no good (coll) (3,3)
9 Fast-running African flightless bird (7)
10 Side sheltered from the wind (3)
12 Former republic in north central Europe (4,7)
17 Brazilian port, ___ de Janeiro (3)
18 Popular flavour of ice cream (7)
20 Quantity (6)
21 Shouts of approval (6)
22 Warning signals that wail (6)

Down

1 Barely noticeable (6)
2 Women (6)
3 Garments, clothes generally (4)
4 Aromatic liquid used in aftershave lotion (3,3)
5 Giacomo ___, composer of *Madame Butterfly* (7)
8 Instrument sounded to announce a meal (4)
11 Otalgia (7)
13 Lavatory (6)
14 Quantity of paper (4)
15 Stimulate (6)
16 Young people (6)
19 Young woman (4)

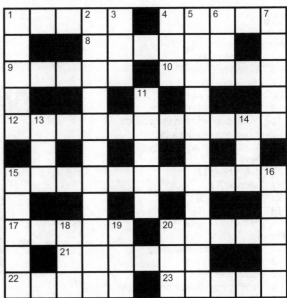

234

Across

1 Informal term for a drink of tea (5)
4 Biblical character (5)
8 African country, capital Kigali (6)
9 Water-spirit (5)
10 Having a healthy elasticity (5)
12 Device used to measure a vehicle's rate of travel (11)
15 Rich, buttery sponge with a close texture (7,4)
17 Drinking vessel (5)
20 Dwarf (5)
21 Decimal measurement system (6)
22 Slang for 'drunk' (5)
23 Tailed amphibians (5)

Down

1 Uncouth (5)
2 Dies earlier than (11)
3 Hand tool (3)
4 Little insect (3)
5 Period between childhood and maturity (11)
6 Dashed (3)
7 Point directly opposite the zenith (5)
11 Committee having supervisory powers (5)
13 Popular vegetable (3)
14 Large deer (3)
15 Strength or power (5)
16 Fencing swords (5)
18 Unit of electric current (abbr) (3)
19 Pigpen (3)
20 Alcoholic spirit (3)

235

Across

1 Distinctive odours (6)
6 Materialise (6)
7 Part of an animal (4)
8 Abominable (6)
10 Brook (5)
13 Confer dignity or honour upon (7)
16 Flavour (5)
18 Collection of townships to the south-west of Johannesburg in South Africa (6)
20 Computer modem data transmission rate (4)
21 Less light in colour (6)
22 Drool (6)

Down

1 Trick (5)
2 Reduced to liquid form (6)
3 Milk pudding ingredient (4)
4 Takes away (7)
5 Thin slice of potato fried in deep fat (5)
9 Financial obligation (4)
11 Nematode (7)
12 Entanglement (4)
14 Greek 'L' (6)
15 Digression (5)
17 Tree that produces berries in autumn (5)
19 Belonging to us (4)

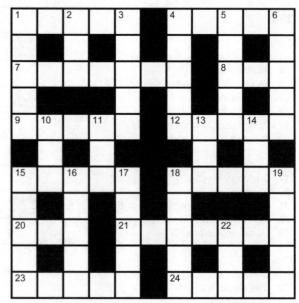

236

Across

1 Tying cords (5)
4 Writing material (5)
7 Inquisitive (7)
8 Division of a week (3)
9 Smallest amount (5)
12 Correspondence in the sounds of two or more lines (5)
15 Word used in an apology (5)
18 Devil (5)
20 Male sheep (3)
21 Offence (7)
23 Vegetables (5)
24 Designation (5)

Down

1 In the neighbourhood (5)
2 Motor vehicle (3)
3 Pathfinder (5)
4 Baffling question or problem (5)
5 Irrigated field where rice is grown (5)
6 Rolls-___, motor manufacturing company (5)
10 Former name of the Japanese capital Tokyo (3)
11 Form of address (3)
13 Gradation of a colour (3)
14 Chinese communist leader (1893–1976) (3)
15 Wash vigorously (5)
16 Dance of Cuban origin (5)
17 ___ sincerely, letter ending (5)
18 Accounting entry (5)
19 Female relative (5)
22 Pertinent (3)

237

Across

1 Garden tool for cutting grass on lawns (5)
3 Urticaria (5)
6 Change shape as via computer animation (5)
7 Post at the top or bottom of a flight of stairs (5)
10 Appropriate to grand and formal occasions (11)
13 Occupied by private houses (11)
15 Defamatory writing (5)
18 Employees' representative body (5)
19 Large box with a lid (5)
20 Location at which an event is held (5)

Down

1 Impersonate (5)
2 Swear-word (9)
3 Egg-laying fowl (3)
4 Solemn pledge (3)
5 Goes into a huff (5)
8 Being (9)
9 Photographer's subject (5)

11 Earlier in time than, poetically (3)
12 Country, capital Washington DC (inits) (3)

13 Remnant of the past (5)
14 Long spear (5)
16 Cheerio (3)
17 Illuminated (3)

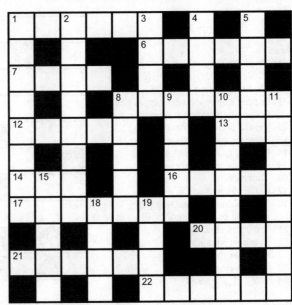

238

Across

1 Employees who keep records or accounts (6)
6 Band of fabric worn around the neck as a tie (6)
7 Weedy annual grass (4)
8 Cooking utensil (7)
12 Cool down (5)
13 Canton located in the centre of Switzerland, home to William Tell (3)
14 Girl's name, a diminutive form of Margaret (3)
16 Sugar frosting (5)
17 Put under a military blockade (7)
20 Lower part of an interior wall (4)
21 Travelling show (6)
22 Steal something (6)

Down

1 Underground cemetery (8)
2 Income (8)
3 Native of Glasgow, for example (4)
4 Region bordering Israel and Egypt (4)
5 Heavy wooden pole tossed as a test of strength (5)
8 Satisfy (thirst) (5)
9 Premium Bonds computer (5)

10 Alter so as to make unrecognisable (8)
11 Sound made by a mobile phone (8)
15 Suggestive of the supernatural (5)

18 Scratch (4)
19 Strong current of air (4)

239

Across

1 Indian prince of high rank (9)
8 Secretive or illicit relationship (5)
9 Conscious, aware (5)
10 Of a thing (3)
11 Praise, glorify (5)
13 Careless speed (5)
15 Stretch of grassy turf (5)
18 Paid out money (5)
20 Top card (3)
21 Bedroom on a ship (5)
22 Evident (5)
23 Make more attractive by adding ornament, colour, etc (9)

Down

2 At great height (5)
3 Month with 30 days (5)
4 Inundated (5)
5 John Quincy ___, sixth president of the USA (5)
6 Bag carried by a strap on one's back or shoulder (9)
7 Hating intensely (9)
12 Paddle used to move a boat (3)
14 Snow-capped mountain (3)
16 Book for collecting stamps (5)
17 Move to music (5)
18 Part of a flower's calyx (5)
19 Exercises evaluating skill or knowledge (abbr) (5)

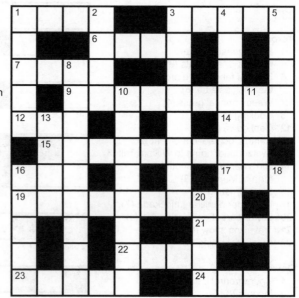

240

Across

1 Close by, near (4)
3 Municipal swimming pool (5)
6 White-tailed sea eagle (4)
7 Former communist country in eastern Europe and northern Asia (inits) (4)
9 Violent impact, crash (9)
12 Word expressing disgust (3)
14 Directly or exactly, straight (3)
15 Postpones a punishment (9)
16 That man (3)
17 Soften by soaking in water (3)
19 Political theory favouring the abolition of governments (9)
21 Religious song (4)
22 Dress worn primarily by Hindu women (4)
23 Racing vessel (5)
24 Tori ___, singer (4)

Down

1 Island republic in the South Pacific (5)
2 Brave man (4)
3 Disease caused by lack of thiamine (4-4)
4 Art of mounting the skins of animals so they have a lifelike appearance (9)
5 Pig, hog (5)
8 Represented in symbolic form (9)
10 One who writes the words for songs (8)
11 River that flows through York (4)
13 Broad smile (4)
16 Hirsute (5)
18 North African port (5)
20 Branch of Islam (4)

241

Across

1 Defeat some challenge or person (3,3)
6 Haphazard (6)
7 Countermand (6)
9 Repeat (7)
10 Present (5)
12 Given entirely to a specific person, activity or cause (7)
17 Derive, evoke (5)
18 Full-scale working models for study or testing (4-3)
20 Clothing (6)
21 Game associated with Wimbledon (6)
22 Instructed (6)

Down

1 Several parallel layers of material (6)
2 Begrudged (6)
3 Worry excessively (4)
4 Not yet proved (7)
5 Compass point at 180 degrees (5)
8 Capital of Ukraine (4)

11 Stinking (7)
13 Examination (4)
14 Throughout the time of (6)

15 Authoritative command (6)
16 Intestine (5)
19 Former (4)

242

Across

2 Elaborate and remarkable display on a lavish scale (9)
6 Alcoholic drink (coll) (5)
7 Flip to a vertical position (2-3)
9 Fetch (3)
10 Pass on (5)
12 Living quarters for female relatives in a Muslim household (5)
14 Small spiked wheel at the end of a spur (5)
17 Plant life (5)
19 Bladed chopping tool (3)
20 Very penetrating and clear (5)
21 Mexican comrade (5)
22 Not quite in the middle (3-6)

Down

1 Waxy animal substance used in perfume (9)
2 Destroy or ruin (5)
3 Lament for the dead (5)
4 Honesty (5)
5 Shout of approval (5)

8 Conduct (9)
11 (They) exist (3)
13 Completely (3)
15 Dock (5)

16 Become invalid through time (5)
17 Banquet (5)
18 Cocktail fruit (5)

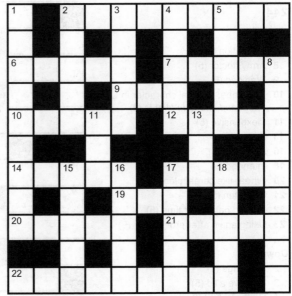

243

Across

2 Bearing (9)
6 Memorise (5)
8 Sound off (5)
11 Occurring at fixed intervals (7)
12 Structures built by birds (5)
13 Quickly (5)
14 Strongboxes for valuables (5)
17 Large wild ox with shaggy hair (5)
19 Scottish bread (7)
20 As a consequence of (3,2)
21 Maritime (5)
22 People who persistently (and annoyingly) follow along (7-2)

Down

1 Inhabited by settlers (9)
2 Brings up (5)
3 Yearns (5)
4 Alto violin (5)
5 Nigerian monetary unit (5)
7 Draw back (7)
9 Capsicum spice (7)
10 For a limitless time (9)
15 Warm dry wind that blows in the Alps (5)
16 Rock (5)
17 Stripes (5)
18 Number considered by some to be lucky (5)

244

Across

1 Habitation (9)
8 Army doctor (5)
9 Wrinkled (5)
10 ___ Baba, fictional character in *One Thousand and One Nights* (3)
11 Inexpensive (5)
13 Sword (5)
15 Accolade (5)
18 Intended (5)
20 Wheat-like cereal plant (3)
21 Enlighten (5)
22 Limited periods of time (5)
23 Using again after processing (9)

Down

2 Scrounge (5)
3 Remove a lid (5)
4 Off the cuff (2-3)
5 Dance involving a long line of people (5)
6 Cadaverous, wasted (9)
7 Promote, publicise (9)
12 Atmosphere (3)
14 Bruce ___, expert kung fu actor who died in 1973 (3)
16 Girl who features in Lewis Carroll's famous stories (5)
17 In a laconic manner (5)
18 Substance such as iron or aluminium, for example (5)
19 Protective garment (5)

245

Across
1 Imperial (5)
3 ___ del Sol, popular Spanish resort region (5)
7 Root vegetable from which sugar is derived (4)
9 Take away (6)
11 Provide again with weapons (2-3)
13 Celestial bodies (5)
14 Glorify (5)
15 Occupied a chair (3)
16 Instant (5)
17 Fluid product of inflammation (5)
20 Iridescent internal layer of a mollusc shell (5)
22 Brags (6)
23 Painting, sculpture, music, etc (4)
24 Minor parish official (5)
25 Commence (5)

Down
1 Picture puzzle (5)
2 Behind (5)
4 16th century V-shaped panel of stiff material worn over the chest (9)
5 Deflect, fend off (5)
6 Wander from a direct course (3)
8 Destroy completely, as if down to the roots (9)
10 Medicine that induces vomiting (6)
12 Express agreement (6)
16 Small percussion instrument (5)
18 Fad (5)
19 Returned from the dead (5)
21 Venomous snake (3)

246

Across
1 Colour of ripe cherries (6)
6 Boulevard (6)
7 Number of players in a baseball team (4)
8 Analysed (7)
10 Took in solid food (3)
12 Showing poise and confidence in one's own worth (4-7)
15 ___ Maria, prayer to the Virgin Mary (3)
16 Dissent (7)
19 Hollow metal device which rings when struck (4)
20 Native of Kathmandu, for example (6)
21 Person authorised to give legal advice (6)

Down
1 Fabric for a painting (6)
2 Rivulet (6)
3 Direction of the rising sun (4)
4 Part of a necklace (4)
5 Rudolf ___, Russian-born ballet dancer and choreographer (1938–93) (7)
8 Asp, for example (5)
9 Not fixed or appointed (5)
11 Type of hunting dog (7)
13 Seldom (6)
14 Distributor of playing cards (6)
17 Strap with a crosspiece on the upper of a shoe (1-3)
18 Loose earth (4)

247

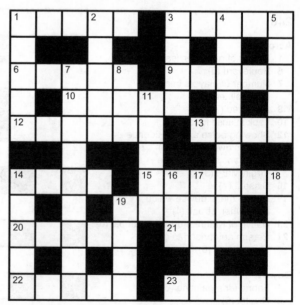

Across

1 In Greek mythology, the underworld (5)
3 Transfer to another track, of trains (5)
6 Initial (5)
8 Cheapskate (5)
9 Uncouth ill-bred person (4)
10 Positive answer (3)
12 Fish eggs (3)
13 Buying or selling securities or commodities (7)
14 Former US airline (1930–2001) (inits) (3)
15 Clairvoyance (inits) (3)
17 French word for Christmas (4)
19 Powerful herbivore with a horned snout (abbr) (5)
20 Canonised person (5)
21 Debentures issued by a government when borrowing money (5)
22 Cartoon duck often associated with Bugs Bunny (5)

Down

1 Of considerable weight and size (5)
2 Orient (4)
3 Occasionally (9)
4 Rapid rise (7)
5 Cardinal number (5)
7 Oppressive, despotic (9)
11 Railway building (7)
14 Pound, pulse (5)
16 Minor or small-minded (5)
18 Tibetan or Mongolian priest (4)

248

Across

1 Irish word for a lake (5)
3 Prospect (5)
6 Earthenware beer mug (5)
9 Loop formed in a cord (5)
10 Rental contract (5)
12 Covered with poorly groomed hair (6)
13 Gambling stake (4)
14 Crucifix (4)
15 Form of a word used to denote more than one (6)
19 Point in the time of a cycle (5)
20 Effigy (5)
21 Scene of the Allied conference between Churchill, Stalin and Roosevelt in 1945 (5)
22 Wet falling snow (5)
23 Of great weight (5)

Down

1 Fails to win (5)
2 Norwegian composer (1843–1907) (5)
3 Plant that produces grapes (4)
4 Villain (9)
5 Sharp, narrow ridge found in rugged mountains (5)
7 Complex and detailed (9)
8 Henpeck (3)
11 Slender, graceful young woman (5)
14 Harnesses (5)
16 Not of the clergy (3)
17 Accepted practice (5)
18 Having much foliage (5)
19 Closely confined (4)

126

249

Across

1 Chess piece (6)
6 Medicinal tincture used for bruises (6)
7 Equal portions into which the capital stock of a corporation is divided (6)
8 Walked with long steps (6)
10 Paramour (5)
13 Set apart from others (7)
16 Significance of a story (5)
18 Dry gully (6)
20 Make up one's mind (6)
21 Solid part of the Earth's surface (6)
22 Sordid (6)

Down

1 Sybil Fawlty's husband in *Fawlty Towers* (5)
2 Greek messenger and herald of the gods (6)
3 Authorisation to go somewhere (4)
4 Man who has lost his wife by death and has not married again (7)
5 Belly button (5)
9 Streetcar (4)
11 Expression of hatred (7)
12 Pink-tinged (4)
14 Acknowledgement of a hit in fencing (6)
15 Canine teeth of a carnivorous animal (5)
17 Suspicious, untrusting (5)
19 ___ and ends (4)

250

Across

1 Closed political meeting (6)
6 Size of a book (6)
7 Peruse (4)
9 Spring-flowering plant with bright yellow flowers (9)
13 Same again (5)
15 Call forth (5)
19 Taken out of code (9)
22 Boundary (4)
23 Trousers for casual wear (6)
24 Without effort (6)

Down

1 Felt concern or interest (5)
2 Military trainee (5)
3 Couch (4)
4 Wise Men who brought gifts to Jesus (4)
5 Unemployment benefit (4)
8 Behave (3)
10 Dotty, mentally irregular (slang) (5)
11 Piece of music for nine instruments (5)
12 Body part between the head and shoulders (4)
14 ___ of Man or Wight, for example (4)
16 Changes course abruptly (5)
17 Not divisible by two (3)
18 Foe (5)
19 Hyphen (4)
20 Cajole (4)
21 Posture assumed by models (4)

251

Across

1 Physician who specialises in the ear and its diseases (9)
8 Cause to lose one's nerve (5)
9 Egyptian capital (5)
10 Large northern deer (3)
11 Inventories (5)
13 Edible organs of an animal (5)
15 Form of speech with a meaning that cannot be derived from its words (5)
18 American raccoon (5)
20 Artificial language, a simplification of Esperanto (3)
21 Santa ___, Father Christmas (5)
22 Esteem (5)
23 Guerilla (9)

Down

2 Multiplication (5)
3 Actors' words (5)
4 Harmless tropical house-lizard (5)
5 Rigidly formal (5)
6 Common bird with a red throat and breast (9)
7 One who extracts fuel from a pit (4,5)
12 Likewise (3)
14 To and ___ (3)
16 Complacently foolish (5)
17 Scrooge, for instance (5)
18 Blanket (5)
19 Titan forced by Zeus to bear the sky on his shoulders (5)

252

Across

1 Droopy (5)
3 Consignment (5)
7 Niche (6)
10 Large, edible marine fish (4)
11 Fête (4)
12 Frugal (10)
15 Mass of calcium carbonate projecting upwards from the floor of a cave (10)
20 Gelling agent (4)
21 Lowest female singing voice (4)
22 Put into cipher (6)
23 Photocopier ink (5)
24 Informal term for a British policeman (5)

Down

1 Deliberately arranged for effect (6)
2 Utterance expressing disapproval (5)
4 Upstairs storage space (5)
5 All right (4)
6 Fellow members of a group working together (9)
8 Resin-like substance secreted by certain insects (3)
9 Hit hard (5)
13 Mexican comrade (5)
14 Only, just (6)
16 Roused from slumber (5)
17 Computer instruction that results in a series of instructions (5)
18 Small amount (3)
19 Actors in a play (4)

253

Across

1 Institution providing labour and shelter for the poor (9)
8 Chemically inactive (5)
9 Mixture of rain and snow (5)
10 Billiards stick (3)
11 Educate (5)
13 Savour (5)
15 Prices (5)
18 Rebuke (5)
20 Male 12 Down (3)
21 Covered with thin horny plates (5)
22 Exotic (5)
23 Getting the better of (9)

Down

2 Last Greek letter (5)
3 Sailing vessel (5)
4 Beginning of an offensive (5)
5 Appears to be (5)
6 Clever joke (9)
7 One who waits on another (9)
12 Animal kept as a domestic pet (3)
14 Joan of ___, French heroine (3)
16 Remove unwanted hair (5)
17 Fashion (5)
18 Astute (5)
19 Aromatic, edible bulb (5)

254

Across

1 Strangle (5)
4 Muscular spasm (5)
7 Form of address to a man (3)
8 Accumulate (5)
10 Dashed (3)
11 Feline animals (4)
12 Very frightening (5)
14 Time of life between the ages of 13 and 19 (5)
17 Sun-dried brick (5)
20 Coast (5)
22 Scottish hillside (4)
23 Expression of disapproval (3)
24 Theatrical entertainment (5)
26 Nought (3)
27 Convey (5)
28 Mountain call (5)

Down

1 Pandemonium (5)
2 Egg cells (3)
3 Literary composition (5)
4 Peak (5)
5 Acquiesce (5)
6 Gasps for breath (5)
9 Scour vigorously (5)
13 Morally reprehensible person (3)
15 Surrey town (5)
16 Not either (3)
17 Ancient Mexican civilisation (5)
18 Located externally (5)
19 Hard, dark wood (5)
20 In an unfortunate or deplorable manner (5)
21 Electronic message (5)
25 Put in (3)

255

Across
1 Lofty proud gait (5)
5 Branch (3)
7 Consumer (5)
8 City in western Germany (5)
9 Ellipses (5)
12 The 'fight or flight' hormone (10)
16 Undulate (4)
17 Moulding, in the form of the letter 'S' (4)
19 Possessing no natural aptitude or skill (10)
22 Scapegoat, fall guy (US slang) (5)
23 Biting tools (5)
24 Characteristic of a sheep (5)
25 Holy sister (3)
26 Indian lute (5)

Down
1 Children's outdoor toy (6)
2 Booking (11)
3 Projection at the end of a piece of wood (5)
4 Backless chair (5)
5 Orderly grouping (11)
6 Rugs (4)
10 Bowed stringed instrument (4)
11 Sediment in wine (4)
13 Collection of facts (4)
14 Slippery fishes (4)
15 Girl's name (3)
18 Book of the Old Testament (6)
20 Eagle's nest (5)
21 Carries with difficulty (5)
22 Sensation of acute discomfort (4)

256

Across
1 Commemorative award (5)
5 Biblical first woman (3)
7 Sources of illumination (6)
8 Natives of Kuwait or Qatar, for example (5)
10 The ___, tragi-comic play by Shakespeare (7)
12 Slice of bacon (6)
13 Novel, fresh (3)
16 Gambling establishment (6)
17 Desirous of a drink (7)
19 Bush with fragrant flowers (5)
21 Material used for surfacing roads or other outdoor areas (6)
22 Directly or exactly, straight (3)
23 Desire strongly or persistently (5)

Down
1 Deficient in amount or quality (6)
2 Liturgical vestment worn by priests (3)
3 Pay close attention to what is being said (6)
4 Impulse (4)
5 Crucial (9)
6 Direction of the rising sun (4)
9 Relate (9)
11 Vertical (5)
14 Ambush (6)
15 Brilliantly-coloured arboreal fruit-eating bird (6)
17 Semi-aquatic creature (4)
18 Agile (4)
20 Coat a cake with sugar (3)

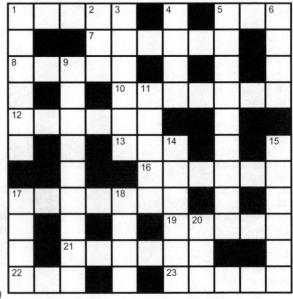

257

Across

1 Emphasise (6)
6 Small recess opening off a larger room (6)
7 Something done (6)
8 Charge falsely or with malicious intent (6)
10 Candle light (5)
13 Physical discomfort or illness (7)
16 Soup-serving spoon (5)
18 Borne on the water (6)
20 Give a prompt (6)
21 Rough shelter at the side of a house (4-2)
22 Performer who moves to music (6)

Down

1 Outerwear garment (5)
2 Brain-teaser (6)
3 Grains on the beach (4)
4 Situated (7)
5 Native American tent (5)
9 Extremely wicked (4)
11 Dental filler (7)

12 Island associated with Napoleon (4)
14 Fish that travels up a river to spawn (6)
15 Leaf that adorns the Canadian flag (5)
17 Tree that produces berries in autumn (5)
19 Stepped (4)

258

Across

1 Spine-bearing, succulent plant (6)
6 Making an attempt (6)
7 Wide street or thoroughfare (6)
8 Get by (6)
10 Agitates (5)
13 Marsh gas (7)
16 Tore down, levelled (5)
18 Heart condition marked by chest pain (6)
20 Hang about (6)
21 Bracelet (6)
22 Fabric for a painting (6)

Down

1 Packs to capacity (5)
2 Incumbency (6)
3 Stalk (4)
4 Buccaneers (7)
5 Correspond (5)
9 A long way off (4)

11 Form a mental picture (7)
12 Knock senseless (4)
14 Country, state (6)
15 Perhaps (5)
17 Acts presumptuously (5)
19 ___ Guinness, actor (1914–2000) (4)

259

Across

1 Flower, the source of saffron (6)
6 Overseas (6)
7 Upon (4)
8 Three score and ten (7)
9 Adult insect (5)
11 Man who has lost his wife by death and has not married again (7)
16 Pale (5)
17 Objectives (7)
19 Small area of water-surrounded land (4)
20 Foot-operated levers (6)
21 Believes in the honesty and reliability of others (6)

Down

1 Short line of text put onto a computer by a web site (6)
2 Person deprived of the protection of the legal system (6)
3 Satisfy completely (4)
4 Turns to ice (7)
5 Political organisation (5)
8 Turf (3)
10 Fabric in a plaid weave (7)
12 Had existence (3)
13 Type of monkey, macaque (6)
14 Not if (6)
15 Biblical tower intended to reach to heaven (5)
18 Examination (4)

260

Across

1 Heavenly body (5)
4 Drink of bourbon, sugar and mint over crushed ice (5)
7 Unfinished business (5,4)
10 Ultimate client for which a thing is intended (3,4)
11 Give or restore confidence in (8)
13 Fabled women, half human and half fish (8)
18 Large ape (7)
20 Bring to an end (9)
21 Machine tool (5)
22 Ballroom dance (5)

Down

1 Heavy wooden pole tossed as a test of strength (5)
2 Clement (4)
3 Plural of that (5)
4 Scoffs (5)
5 Form a queue (4,2)
6 Ski run densely packed with snow (5)
8 Belonging to us (3)
9 Large, ocean-dwelling mammal (3,4)
12 Fungus causing timber to crumble (3,3)
13 Drivers' stopover (5)
14 Nimble (5)
15 Compulsory military service (5)
16 Pose (3)
17 Relative magnitudes of two quantities (5)
19 Incline (4)

261

Across

1 Compress with violence (5)
4 Tall perennial grasses (5)
7 Barrier constructed to keep out the sea (4)
8 Look up to (6)
9 Crippled (4)
10 Go by boat (4)
12 Dribble (4)
13 Unit of energy equal to 4.2 joules (7)
14 Large container for liquids (4)
15 Behind schedule (4)
16 Digestive juice secreted by the liver (4)
17 Imaginary place considered perfect (6)
18 Fourth planet from the Sun (4)
20 Brought to a conclusion (5)
21 Mediterranean island, capital Valletta (5)

Down

2 Beam of light (3)
3 Emanating from stars (7)
4 Went on horseback (4)
5 Former province of northern Ethiopia (7)
6 Always watchful and alert (9)
7 State of being held in low esteem (9)
8 Pungent gas compounded of nitrogen and hydrogen (7)
11 Freezing (3-4)
12 Quandary (7)
16 Avian creature (4)
19 Furrow (3)

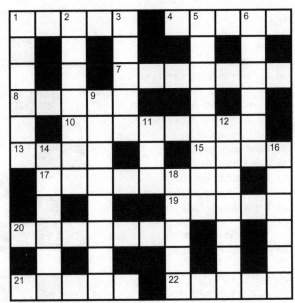

262

Across

1 Magnate (5)
4 Division of the year (5)
7 Meeting for an exchange of ideas (7)
8 Mattress cover (5)
10 Example (8)
13 Mentally healthy (4)
15 Beginner (4)
17 Agricultural (8)
19 Sightless (5)
20 Bundles, especially of corn (7)
21 Leg joints (5)
22 Man-made fibre (5)

Down

1 Lumps together (6)
2 Pasting (7)
3 Inventories (5)
5 Eastern (8)
6 Dealer (6)
9 Weaken mentally or morally (8)
11 High rocky hill (3)
12 Believing the worst of human nature and motives (7)
14 German city known to the French as Aix-la-Chapelle (6)
16 Informal term for your father (3,3)
18 Norwegian dramatist (5)

263

Across

1 Successive (6)
5 Speck of soot (4)
7 Office note (abbr) (4)
8 Small hard fruit (4)
9 One of a pair (4)
11 Overweight (3)
14 White-flowered plant used medicinally (8)
16 Ovum (3)
18 Case for 8 Across (3)
19 Light teasing repartee (8)
20 Stitch together (3)
22 Type of fat (4)
24 Cylindrical store-tower (4)
25 Double-reed woodwind instrument (4)
26 Fine specks of detritus (4)
27 Nuptial (6)

Down

1 Sea foam (4)
2 Relaxation (4)
3 Open to persuasion (8)
4 Went in advance of others (3)
5 Chronic drinker (3)
6 Canned (6)
10 Flog (4)
12 Primitive organism (4)
13 Monarch's companion or adviser (8)
15 Traditional knowledge (4)
16 Wiped out (6)
17 Taunt (4)
20 Exchanged for money (4)
21 Cry in despair (4)
23 Brandy measure (3)
24 Weep (3)

264

Across

1 Brings up (6)
6 Number denoting a score (6)
8 Drink given to people who are ill (4,3)
9 Aluminium silicate mineral (4)
10 Reddish-brown colour (5)
13 Delivery vehicle (3)
14 Pass from the body (7)
16 Cacophony (3)
17 Historical object (5)
19 Swinging or sliding barrier (4)
21 Fall to a lower level (7)
22 Point in the sky directly above the observer (6)
23 Spherical in shape (6)

Down

1 Picture puzzle (5)
2 Linguistic element added at the end of the word (6)
3 Tube of a tobacco pipe (4)
4 Disentangle (7)
5 English romantic poet (1788–1824) (5)
7 Person who serves at table (6)
11 Awaiting conclusion or confirmation (7)
12 Confront, solicit (6)
15 Service of china or silverware, used at table (3,3)
16 Giddy (5)
18 Religious doctrine (5)
20 Major industrial and coal mining region in north-west Germany (4)

265

Across
1 Happen to (6)
4 Not many (3)
6 Independent ruler or chieftain (4)
8 Contrition (7)
11 Unit of length equal to 45 inches (3)
12 Nautical term meaning to hold firm or stop (5)
13 Closer to the centre (5)
14 Dog ___, tattered (5)
15 Self-esteem (3)
16 Anew (5)
17 Wash off soap (5)
19 Augmenting (5)
21 Shortened forename of US president Lincoln (3)
22 Receptacles for electric plugs (7)
23 Girdle (4)
24 Poem with complex stanza forms (3)
25 Stayed temporarily (6)

Down
1 Country, capital Ouagadougou (7,4)
2 In a higher position (5)
3 Minus (4)
4 Permitted to graze or forage rather than being confined (4-5)
5 Having tasteful clothing and being neat (4-7)
7 Remarkably rapid (8)
9 Brittle greyish-white metallic element (9)
10 Noteworthy scarcity (8)
18 Marked with printing fluid (5)
20 Cosmetic preparation used on the eyelids (4)

266

Across
1 Fish with a hook (5)
4 Goes into a huff (5)
7 Search unsystematically (7)
8 Chaps (3)
9 Fine trap of gossamer threads (3)
11 Male bee (5)
14 Plain dough cake, often griddled (5)
16 Massage (5)
19 Army unit of two or more divisions (5)
21 Greek letter (3)
22 Not in good health (3)
23 State of lawlessness and disorder (7)
25 Item in a list (5)
26 Air cavity in the skull (5)

Down
1 Harsh or corrosive in tone (5)
2 Tissue that surrounds a tooth (3)
3 Circumvent (5)
4 Turns or places at a slant (5)
5 State of being disregarded or forgotten (5)
6 Feel (5)
10 Reverberation (4)
12 Manage (3)
13 Biblical ark-builder (4)
15 Small drink (3)
16 Cutting instrument (5)
17 Ceremonial elegance and splendour (5)
18 Daily written record of events (5)
19 Uncouth (5)
20 Painful eyelid swellings (5)
24 Metal container (3)

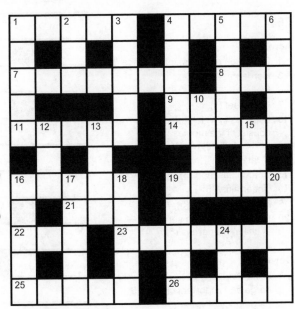

135

267

Across
1 Drinking vessel (5)
4 Group of one or more species (5)
7 Sound made by a dove (3)
8 Au revoir (5)
9 Far beyond the norm (5)
10 One of the supports for a table (3)
11 Reside (5)
14 Give qualities or abilities to (5)
17 Durable (5)
20 Commenced (5)
23 Alcoholic beverage (3)
24 Asian water lily (5)
25 Donor (5)
26 A couple (3)
27 Shrub with prickly leaves (5)
28 Fine net used for tutus (5)

Down
1 Sentry (5)
2 Burning (5)
3 Long oar mounted at the stern of a boat (5)
4 Scoop out (5)
5 Observed (5)
6 Limbless reptile (5)
12 Romance (3)

13 Cut part of a tree trunk (3)
15 So-named before marriage (3)
16 Large nation (inits) (3)
17 Cultivated land (5)
18 Up to a time that (5)
19 Excessively quick (5)
20 Biblical term meaning 'fathered' (5)
21 Judge's hammer (5)
22 Cheek! (5)

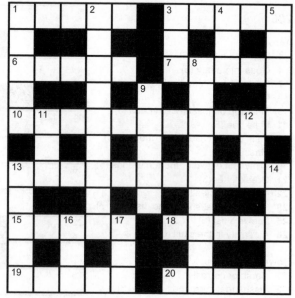

268

Across
1 Collection of cakes, for instance (5)
3 Horde (5)
6 Malicious (5)
7 Coral reef (5)
10 Lotteries in which the prizes consist of the monies paid by the participants (11)
13 Ill-fated (4-7)
15 Church passage (5)
18 Uncertainty (5)
19 Musical half-note (5)
20 Cold dessert often served at children's parties (5)

Down
1 Fillip, incentive (5)
2 Large and important church (9)
3 Large body of water (3)
4 Fuss (3)
5 Boys, men (5)
8 Change the order or arrangement of (9)

9 Seize and take control without authority (5)
11 Drenched with water (3)
12 Stretch (3)
13 Cramp (5)
14 Short simple song (5)
16 Offence (3)
17 Deciduous tree (3)

269

Across

1 Rod that forms the body of an arrow (5)
4 ___ Piaf, French cabaret singer (1915–63) (5)
7 Area for skating (3,4)
9 Fats ___, rhythm and blues pianist, singer and composer (6)
10 Feel sorrow (6)
12 Wound (4)
15 Small narrow pointed missile that is thrown (4)
17 Body orbiting a star (6)
19 Third sign of the zodiac (6)
20 Evergreen tree or shrub (7)
21 Church building (5)
22 Raise to a higher rank or position (5)

Down

1 Infrequently (6)
2 Letters and packages transported by plane (7)
3 Object (5)
5 Mended by sewing, as with socks, for example (6)
6 Frail (6)
8 Funeral procession (7)
11 Popular flavour of ice cream (7)
13 Great coolness and composure (6)
14 Spite (6)
16 Saucepan stand (6)
18 Curt, brusque (5)

270

Across

1 Physical or moral ruin (11)
7 Hoaxes (5)
9 Small and delicate (5)
11 Exclusive circle of people with a common purpose (7)
12 Signs from heaven (5)
13 Destiny, fate (5)
14 Adjust again after an initial failure (5)
17 Thing of value (5)
19 Arch of facial hair (7)
20 Large web-footed bird (5)
21 Biting flies (5)
22 Shop assistant (11)

Down

1 Deprives of confidence, hope, or the will to proceed (11)
2 Empty area (5)
3 Relaxes (5)
4 Employee who keeps records or accounts (5)
5 Conclude by reasoning (5)
6 Not affiliated with any one group (3-8)
8 Long-tailed primates (7)
10 Involvement (7)
15 Capital of South Korea (5)
16 Moves in large numbers, swarms (5)
17 Take part in a row (5)
18 Exchanges (5)

271

Across

1 Adult male deer (4)
3 Presents (5)
6 Dense growth located on the head, for example (4)
7 Fully developed (4)
9 Join back together (9)
11 Inflated pride (3)
12 Make a sucking sound, as when walking through mud (7)
14 Flow back (3)
16 Expectation, prospect (9)
18 Regrettably (4)
19 Spreads seeds (4)
20 Requires (5)
21 Eager (4)

Down

1 Tennis stroke that puts the ball into play (5)
2 Clarified butter used in Indian cookery (4)
3 Tiny grains (8)
4 Ride a bicycle with the pedals at rest, especially downhill (9)
5 Three score (5)
8 Stretched out and lying at full length . along the ground (9)
10 Wife of an earl (8)
13 In many cases or instances (5)
15 Bowl-shaped vessel (5)
17 Undertaking (4)

272

Across

1 Minor or small-minded (5)
4 Distinctive period of time (5)
9 Rounded thickly-curled hairdo (4)
10 Made by intertwining threads in a series of connected loops (7)
11 Joint in the leg (5)
12 Reduces in rank or position (6)
15 Land measure (4)
18 Marsh plant (4)
20 Become bone-like (6)
22 Small pendant fleshy lobe at the back of the soft palate (5)
23 Word opposite in meaning to another (7)
25 Approach (4)
26 Italian poet (1265–1321) (5)
27 Country of the Arabian Peninsula (5)

Down

1 Central American canal (6)
2 Cargo ships for carrying crude oil in bulk (7)
3 Country bumpkin (5)
5 Plausible glib talk (6)
6 Frequently, poetically (3)
7 Crumple (6)
8 Brick carrier (3)
13 Goon (3)
14 Mass celebrated for the dead (7)
16 Part of the eye (6)
17 Accompany (6)
19 Mythical fire-breather (6)
21 Childish word for scrumptious (5)
23 Added to (3)
24 Bronze (3)

273

Across
1 Ancient Mexican civilisation (5)
4 Boy's name (4)
7 Mortal (5)
8 Extremely cold (3)
10 Animal's den (4)
11 Arrangement (6)
13 Period of occupancy (7)
16 Occasions for buying at lower prices (5)
17 Not one nor the other (7)
18 Develop (6)
21 Type of food shop (abbr) (4)
23 Slippery fish (3)
24 Farewell (5)
25 Feeling of intense anger (4)
26 Took an oath (5)

Down
1 Bloc (4)
2 Plays with (4)
3 World's swiftest mammal (7)
4 Maria ___, opera singer (1923–77) (6)
5 Mother of the ancient Irish gods (3)
6 Haulage vehicle (5)
9 Bike (5)
12 Noisy riotous fight (5)
14 Jittery (7)
15 Arch (5)
16 Walk with long steps (6)
17 Lowest point (5)
19 Manufacturer of toy bricks (4)
20 Additional (4)
22 Cover with insulation to prevent heat loss (3)

274

Across
1 Lashes (5)
4 *The Mill on the ___*, George Eliot novel (5)
7 Money demanded by a kidnapper (6)
9 Arrived (4)
10 Close one eye quickly as a signal (4)
12 Plant family that includes the maple (4)
13 Endures (5)
15 Outer space as viewed from Earth (3)
17 Notions (5)
19 Bends the body as a sign of reverence (4)
21 Conspire (4)
23 Four-wheeled motor vehicle (4)
24 Law force (6)
25 Correct (5)
26 Item of bed linen (5)

Down
1 Interment (6)
2 Oil extracted from the flax plant (7)
3 Display (4)
5 Passes the tongue over (5)
6 Cook slowly in liquid (4)
8 Spiritless man or youth (7)
11 Word indicating a negative answer (3)
14 Carry on a romantic relationship with more than one person (3-4)
15 ___ volatile, smelling salts (3)
16 Express agreement (6)
18 Distinctive period of time (5)
20 Couple (4)
22 Weight units of 2240 lbs (4)

275

Across

1 Pathfinder (5)
4 Earnings (5)
7 Sloping kind of typeface (6)
9 Gumbo (4)
10 Front part of the human leg below the knee (4)
12 Corrosive compound (4)
13 Primitive plant forms (5)
15 Seek an answer to (3)
17 Most important or necessary part of something (5)
19 Impulse (4)
21 Waterless (4)
23 Opaque gem (4)
24 Hunting expedition (6)
25 Imperial units of length (5)
26 Rotund, extremely chubby (5)

Down

1 Relating to the backbone (6)
2 Egg-shaped and flutey-toned musical instrument (7)
3 Word denoting a person or thing (4)
5 In the middle of (5)
6 Thin strip of wood (4)
8 Vehicle framework (7)
11 Type, kind (3)
14 Price of a plane ticket (7)
15 Broadcast (3)
16 Directions for cooking something (6)
18 Cold vegetable dish (5)
20 Nosegay (4)
22 Panel forming the lower part of a wall (4)

276

Across

1 Sheen (5)
4 Moved slowly and stealthily (5)
7 Ask earnestly (7)
8 Foot digit (3)
9 Extended area of land (5)
11 Course (5)
12 Catapult (5)
14 Board game (5)
16 Yes (3)
17 Land area, especially of a farm (7)
19 Gentle poke (5)
20 Act of stealing (5)

Down

1 Give a sign of welcome (5)
2 Cereal grass (3)
3 Drained of energy or effectiveness (5)
4 Supply food ready to eat (5)
5 Cause to feel excited (7)
6 In that place (5)
10 Liquorice-flavoured herb (7)
12 Discolour (5)
13 Coating for ceramics, metal, etc (5)
14 Printer's mark, indicating an insertion (5)
15 Aroma (5)
18 Chopper (3)

277

Across

1 Deep and harsh sounding (5)
4 Mr Manilow, singer (5)
7 Daphne du Maurier novel (7)
8 Brief written records (5)
9 Humiliated, shamed (6)
12 Very small spot (5)
15 Urge or force to an action (5)
17 Wind off from a spool (6)
18 In a softened tone (5)
19 Two-wheeled vehicle (7)
20 Deceptive move (5)
21 Hinged lifting tool (5)

Down

1 Secretory organs (6)
2 Innumerable but many (7)
3 Abandon (7)
5 Discrimination against a person in the latter part of life (6)
6 Ebb (6)
10 Bodily disorder or disease (7)
11 British sculptor, Sir Jacob ___ (1880–1959) (7)
13 Light glass formed on the surface of some lavas (6)
14 Wax drawing implement (6)
16 Women (6)

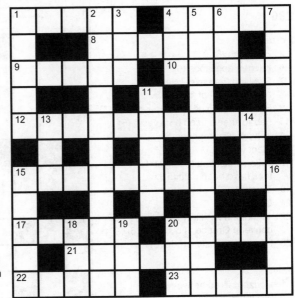

278

Across

1 Church council (5)
4 Available for immediate use (2,3)
8 Racing bird (6)
9 Pried (5)
10 Customary practices (5)
12 State of being suitable or opportune (11)
15 Decorated with needlework (11)
17 Framework of a railway carriage (5)
20 Religious song (5)
21 Real (6)
22 River mouth (5)
23 Man-made fibre (5)

Down

1 Of sound (5)
2 Decision of a coroner's jury affirming the occurrence of a suspicious death but not specifying the cause (4,7)
3 Carried out (3)
4 Throughout a period of time, poetically (3)
5 Without a sound (11)
6 Yellow-coloured explosive compound (inits) (3)
7 Temporary police force (5)
11 Below the required standards for a purpose (5)
13 Electrical resistance unit (3)
14 Billiards stick (3)
15 Flowed back (5)
16 Evil spirit (5)
18 Young woman (coll) (3)
19 Seventh Greek letter (3)
20 Cooking vessel (3)

279

Across

1 Interfered with in a troublesome or hostile way (8)
7 Underground worker (5)
8 Gives way or sinks under pressure (8)
9 Distinctive spirit of a culture (5)
10 Believer in a major religion (5)
11 Hindu woman's garment (4)
13 Charter (4)
15 Retire from military service (5)
18 Metal rod used to stir a fire (5)
20 Beat through cleverness and wit (8)
21 Take in with the tongue (3,2)
22 Adult male horse (8)

Down

1 Fails to catch (6)
2 Delicate, woven and decorative fabric (4)
3 Of an Arabic royal family (5)
4 Fix securely (5)
5 Destroy the peace of (7)
6 Morphine derivative (6)
10 So ugly as to be terrifying (7)
12 Hooded waterproof jacket (6)
14 Plaid associated with Scotland (6)
16 Spew forth lava and rocks (5)
17 Blackbird (5)
19 Hackney carriage (4)

280

Across

1 Emulates (6)
6 Kitchen appliance (6)
7 Swelling from excessive accumulation of fluid (6)
9 State of being behind in payments (7)
13 Fabric sheets used on a yacht (5)
14 In a peculiar manner (5)
15 Slant (5)
18 Token indicating that postal fees have been paid (5)
19 Earmark (7)
21 Coming (6)
22 Arm of the Mediterranean between Greece and Turkey (6)
23 Hearty and lusty, crude (6)

Down

1 Horizontal rod between two vertical posts (8)
2 Dessert courses (8)
3 Disfigurement (4)
4 Dragged (5)
5 Milky-white gem made by an oyster (5)
8 Artist of consummate skill (6)
10 Stirred up, excited (6)
11 Having a common boundary or edge (8)
12 Fellow feeling (8)
16 Post at the top or bottom of a flight of stairs (5)
17 Mechanical bar (5)
20 Weathercock (4)

281

Across
4 Love affair (5)
7 Capacious bag (7)
8 Flightless Australian bird (3)
10 Tertiary (5)
12 Hindu social class (5)
13 Country, capital Bamako (4)
15 A movement upward (9)
19 Male sovereign (4)
21 Pale (5)
24 Courage (5)
25 Consumed (3)
26 Christian holiday that follows Easter (7)
27 Undersides of shoes (5)

Down
1 Waterfall slide (5)
2 Makes an assertion of a right (6)
3 Lag behind (6)
4 Actor, ___ Baldwin, former husband of Kim Basinger (4)
5 Burden of responsibility (4)
6 Black bird (5)
9 Of the sea (6)
11 Loud and disturbing noise (6)
14 Protective fluid ejected into the water by cuttlefish, etc (3)
16 Be absorbed or understood (4,2)
17 Female monster (6)
18 Areas of grass found in gardens (5)
20 Implied (5)
22 Cry of greeting (4)
23 Information reported in the papers (4)

282

Across
1 Economises (5)
4 Chest for the Covenant (3)
6 Grinds with the teeth (5)
7 Consumer (5)
9 Distinguished (7)
11 Just right (7)
13 Prisoner held as a form of insurance (7)
15 Cheerio (7)
16 Pools (5)
17 Lively ballroom dance from Brazil (5)
18 Colouring agent (3)
19 Connecting parts of a chain (5)

Down
1 Drowsy (6)
2 Sloping mass of loose rocks at the base of a cliff (5)
3 Send (payment) (5)
4 Find out (9)
5 Held back (4)
8 Blue-green colour (9)
10 *Star Trek*'s original Doctor (5)
12 Against (6)
13 Atomic exploding device (1-4)
14 Floral leaf (5)
15 Framework (4)

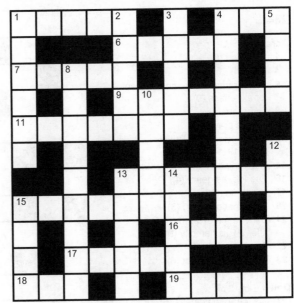

283

Across

3 Location of a series of pages on the internet (7)
6 Retch (5)
7 Irritable as if suffering from indigestion (7)
8 Extended area of land (5)
10 Cause to become widely known (9)
14 Side sheltered from the wind (3)
15 Armed struggle (3)
16 Unwavering (9)
18 Harnesses (5)
19 Sir Peter ___, British actor and playwright (1921–2004) (7)
20 Sing the praises of (5)
21 Winged two-legged dragons with barbed tails (7)

Down

1 Slum areas (7)
2 Short moral story, allegory (7)
3 Having the foot digits connected by a thin fold of skin (3-4)
4 Portable travelling bag for carrying clothes (8)
5 Violent young criminals (5)
9 Having the ability or power to construct (8)
11 Legendary creatures resembling tiny old men (7)
12 Professional entertainer (7)
13 Lymph glands located in the pharynx (7)
17 Nettlesome (5)

284

Across

1 Putrefied (6)
4 Prod (4)
6 Sum granted as reimbursement for expenses (9)
8 Large deer (3)
10 Artist's crayon (6)
13 Sir ___ Bogarde, British actor (1921–99) (4)
14 Matching set of furniture (5)
16 Engage, as gears (4)
17 Loophole (6)
20 Large nation (inits) (3)
21 Dark fleece of lambs, named after a Russian city (9)
22 Becomes older (4)
23 Upward movement (6)

Down

1 Cleaner of chimneys (5)
2 Crests (5)
3 As an alternative to (2,4)
4 Spanish nobleman (7)
5 Female deer (3)
7 Dental decay (6)
9 Identification tags (6)
11 Casual tops (1-6)
12 Be prostrate (3)
15 Disease transmitted by body lice (6)
18 Make a thrusting forward movement (5)
19 Contaminate (5)
21 ___ Khan (3)

285

Across
1 Makes reference to (5)
4 Coat with fat during cooking (5)
7 Protective metal outfit (6)
9 Basic unit of money in South Africa (4)
10 Small rodents (4)
11 Elastic straps that hold up trousers (6)
13 Grew older (4)
15 Flat floating platform for swimmers (4)
17 Comic book superhero (6)
20 Musical composition for one instrument (4)
21 Presidential assistant (4)
22 Inferior substitute or imitation (6)
23 Native American tent (5)
24 Incendiarism (5)

Down
1 Climb awkwardly (7)
2 Port and resort on the west coast of Florida (5)
3 Foam or froth on the sea (5)
5 Alongside each other (7)
6 Subdued colour (5)
8 Arousing or provoking laughter (7)
12 Reflective road stud (4-3)
14 Inhabitant (7)
16 Similar (5)
18 Largest artery of the body (5)
19 How a result is obtained or an end achieved (5)

286

Across
1 Filter (4)
3 Inferior substitute or imitation (6)
6 Alleviate (4)
7 Mythical Greek hero who fought against Troy in the Iliad (4)
8 Preserve in vinegar (6)
9 Company that hires only union members (6,4)
14 Suitable to or usual for the time of year (10)
17 Coated with fat during cooking (6)
19 Banking system (4)
20 Open river valley (in a hilly area) (4)
21 Pleaded (6)
22 Contest of speed (4)

Down
1 Look for (6)
2 Lone Star State of the USA (5)
3 Clairvoyance (inits) (3)
4 Harnesses (5)
5 Bulb, traditionally from Holland (5)
10 Poem intended or adapted to be sung (3)
11 Musical composition for two performers (3)
12 Globe (3)
13 Previously (6)
14 Roofing material (5)
15 Root vegetable (5)
16 Annoyance (5)
18 Informal term for a father (3)

287

Across

1 Makes a noise like a lion (5)
3 Marked by aggressive ambition (5)
6 Believer in a major religion (5)
8 Give a speech (5)
9 Pigswill (4)
11 At a lower place (7)
13 Saucepan cover (3)
15 Poker stakes (5)
17 Little rascal (3)
19 Gambling (7)
21 Elaborate song for a solo voice (4)
22 Transfer to another track, of trains (5)
23 Unlawful act (5)
24 Fleshy root (5)
25 Broom made of twigs (5)

Down

1 Amy Winehouse hit of 2007 (5)
2 Arm of the Indian Ocean between Africa and Arabia (3,3)
3 Foretelling events as if by supernatural intervention (9)
4 Cloak, often knitted (5)
5 Bear fruit (5)
7 Capital of Mongolia (4,5)
10 Aquatic creature (5)
12 Deciduous tree (3)
14 Boy's name (3)
16 Deprive of food (6)
17 Gusset (5)
18 Measure the depth of something (5)
20 Shine brightly, like a star (5)

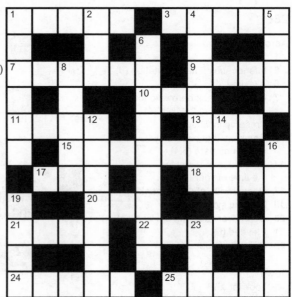

288

Across

1 Person who is in charge (5)
3 Simultaneous discharge of firearms (5)
7 Point in orbit (6)
9 American feline (4)
10 Mr Reed who had a *Perfect Day* (3)
11 Hoodlum (4)
13 Archaic form of the word 'your' (3)
15 Primitive freshwater creature with a round sucking mouth and a rasping tongue (7)
17 Felt cap of Morocco (3)
18 Fencing sword (4)
20 Former name of Tokyo, Japan (3)
21 Underground part of a plant (4)
22 Intelligence-gathering aircraft, used by the RAF (6)
24 Small mouselike mammal (5)
25 Appearing earlier in the same text (5)

Down

1 Talkative (6)
2 Hen's produce (3)
4 One who has had a limb removed (7)
5 Give sanction to (4)
6 Device used for communication (9)
8 Reproductive structure (5)
12 Newspaper or official journal (7)
14 More active than normal (coll) (5)
16 Offer for sale from place to place (6)
19 Painting, sculpture, music, etc (4)
23 Association of criminals (3)

146

289

Across
1 Caused to feel uneasy and self-conscious (11)
7 Burdensome (7)
9 Fowl's perch (5)
11 Choose or show a preference (3)
12 Longitudinal beam of the hull of a ship (4)
14 Plaything (3)
16 Angler's basket (5)
19 Type of lettuce (3)
21 Academic test (abbr) (4)
24 Imaginary monster or ogre (3)
26 Make sore by rubbing (5)
27 Quantity (7)
28 Detailed record of the background of a person under study (4,7)

Down
1 Mineral used as an abrasive (5)
2 Natural stream of water (5)
3 Member of a crowd causing a violent disturbance of the peace (6)
4 Pinnacle (4)
5 Fire a gun (5)
6 Powdery (5)
8 Atop (4)
10 Dry (wine) (3)
13 Unisex name (3)
15 Diameter of a tube (4)
17 Overabundance (6)
18 Sixth note in the tonic sol-fa scale (3)
19 Professional performer who tells jokes (5)
20 Glances over (5)
22 West Indian dance (5)
23 Of great weight (5)
25 Shrub (4)

290

Across
1 Oscar ___, Irish writer and wit (1854–1900) (5)
4 Form, category (5)
8 Head of the chapter of a cathedral (4)
9 Undulate (6)
10 Prod (3)
11 Official literary language of Pakistan (4)
13 Niggle (4)
14 Acorn-producing plant (3,4)
15 ___ Brittan, former Home Secretary (1983–85) (4)
16 Blackthorn fruit (4)
17 Behave (3)
18 Player who delivers the ball to the batsman (6)
19 Goddess of the rainbow (4)
21 Senior member of a group (5)
22 Sufferer from Hansen's disease (5)

Down
2 Frozen water (3)
3 Legendary Spanish nobleman and philanderer (3,4)
5 Attire (7)
6 Climbing plants that produce fragrant flowers (5,4)
7 Subject to individual discretion or preference (9)
8 Sleeping place for two people (6,3)
12 Entrance to a room (7)
13 ___ season, Christmas (7)
20 Extreme anger (3)

291

Across
1 Second letter of the Greek alphabet (4)
3 Frankfurter served in a bun (3,3)
5 Hoot with derision (3)
6 Murder (4)
7 Document showing that a fare has been paid (6)
9 Form into a solid mass or whole (11)
14 Not needing to be demonstrated or explained, obvious (4-7)
18 Cloth (6)
20 Fourth wife of Henry VIII, ___ of Cleves (4)
21 Be unwell (3)
22 Climb up (6)
23 Diplomacy (4)

Down
1 Cuts in half (7)
2 Bottomless gulf or pit (5)
3 Peppery (3)
4 Open and observable (5)
8 Important North Atlantic food fish (3)
10 Nothing (3)
11 Bulgarian monetary unit (3)
12 (They) exist (3)
13 Ask earnestly (7)
15 Exercises evaluating skill or knowledge (abbr) (5)
16 Hairy coat of a mammal (3)
17 Addressed, covered (5)
19 Bounder (3)

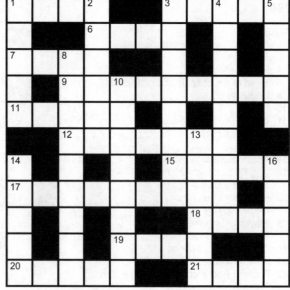

292

Across
1 Young of a cow (4)
3 Make parallel (5)
6 Singer who had a hit with *To Sir, with Love* (4)
7 Country road (4)
9 Not divided or shared with others (9)
11 Bedtime beverage (5)
12 Typographical error (7)
15 Involving a single component or element (5)
17 Chemist (9)
18 Indian nursemaid (4)
19 Hostelries (4)
20 River that runs through Glasgow (5)
21 Child's stringed toy (2-2)

Down
1 Acute abdominal pain (5)
2 Muscle that bends a joint (6)
3 Roman statesman who became emperor in 27 BC (8)
4 Health facility where patients receive treatment (9)
5 Devoid of clothing (5)
8 Essential (9)
10 Andrew ___, Scottish-born US industrialist and philanthropist (8)
13 Lacking a sense of security (6)
14 Concerned with one specific purpose (2,3)
16 Well-known internet search engine (5)

293

Across

1 Inflexible (5)
4 Fires from a job (5)
7 Pixie (3)
8 Russian rulers (5)
10 ___ Island, New York Bay area (5)
11 Possess (3)
12 Remoulded car tyre (7)
13 Kimono sash (3)
15 To the ___ degree (to the utmost) (3)
17 Rubbery (7)
20 Paddle used to move a boat (3)
21 Eddy (5)
22 Further (5)
23 Listening organ (3)
24 Drugged (5)
25 Mix up or confuse (5)

Down

1 Helicopter propeller (5)
2 Allowance (5)
3 Unkempt, disordered (11)
4 Roadside device triggered by fast-moving vehicles (5,6)
5 Large stringed instrument (5)
6 Japanese rice dish (5)
9 Sugary (5)
14 Wild rose (5)
15 Pried (5)
16 Bristles (5)
18 Carried with difficulty (5)
19 Fad (5)

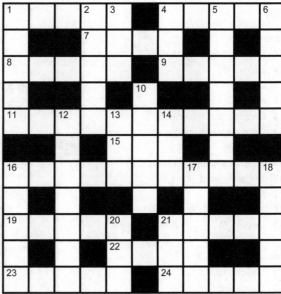

294

Across

1 Apartments (5)
4 Multiplication (5)
7 Gown (4)
8 German submarine in World War II (1-4)
9 Measures of land (5)
11 Feasible alternative (11)
15 At a great distance (3)
16 Done with careful diligence (11)
19 Board used with a planchette (5)
21 Small drum played with the hands (5)
22 Soft light (4)
23 Do without (5)
24 Joint of the leg (5)

Down

1 Dowdy woman (5)
2 Snares (5)
3 Chronic drinker (3)
4 Afternoon meal (3)
5 Cocktail of vermouth and gin (7)
6 Unassertive man or boy (5)
10 Slacken off (5)
12 More lustrous (7)
13 ___ and buts, objections (3)
14 Brother of George Gershwin (3)
16 Evidence (5)
17 Understood (5)
18 Fumble (5)
20 In the past (3)
21 Fluffy scarf of feathers (3)

295

Across

1 Constitutional capital of Bolivia (5)
4 Lady Nancy ___, first woman MP (5)
7 Small pampered canine (6)
10 Measure (out) (4)
12 Get back (8)
13 Peninsula of Ukraine, on the Black Sea (6)
14 Armoured combat vehicle (4)
16 Bittersweet (4)
19 Coincidence, accord (6)
22 Leading caption of a newspaper article (8)
23 Sleeping places (4)
24 Motor (6)
25 Cow's milk-gland (5)
26 Very poor, impoverished (5)

Down

1 Make amorous advances towards (7)
2 Island in the Bay of Naples (5)
3 Give expression to feelings (5)
5 Unspecified item (9)
6 In many cases or instances (5)
8 Small coffee cup (9)
9 Tiny grain, of sugar for instance (7)
11 Ms Herzigova, supermodel (3)
15 John F ___, former US president (7)
17 Having the leading position (5)
18 Crimson (3)
20 Fine strong silky fabric (5)
21 Grab roughly (5)

296

Across

1 Mountain ash tree (5)
4 Expect (5)
7 Dog of mixed breed (7)
8 Bladed chopping tool (3)
9 Become less intense (5)
11 Groom's partner (5)
12 Lads (5)
14 Woolly ruminant mammal (5)
16 Negative word (3)
17 Ricochet (7)
19 Travel rapidly (5)
20 Vassal (5)

Down

1 Dance of Cuban origin (5)
2 Came first (3)
3 Care for sick people (5)
4 Remark made spontaneously (2,3)
5 Greed (7)
6 Particular items (5)
10 Device for connecting non-matching plugs and sockets (7)
12 Brightly coloured seashell (5)
13 Atomiser (5)
14 Roman prophetess (5)
15 Military chaplain (5)
18 Application (3)

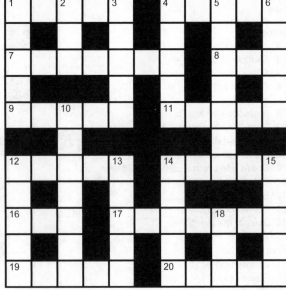

297

Across

1 ____-Herzegovina, European country (6)
6 Four-wheel covered carriage (6)
7 Slight stinging sensation (6)
9 One who imputes guilt or blame (7)
10 Japanese poem (5)
12 Child learning to walk (7)
17 Scene of action (5)
18 Pulpit (7)
20 Unstintingly extravagant (6)
21 Calculate (6)
22 Admission (6)

Down

1 Catty, malicious (6)
2 Brightly shining (6)
3 Boy's name (4)
4 Underwriter (7)
5 Tall tower referred to in the Bible (5)
8 Praise or glorify (4)
11 Thor Heyerdahl's famous raft (3-4)
13 Tibetan or Mongolian priest (4)
14 Formula (6)
15 Cleanses with soap and water (6)
16 One stroke over par in golf (5)
19 Arm bone (4)

298

Across

4 Having a sharp inclination (5)
8 Extended by pulling and stretching (9)
9 A person in general (3)
10 Framework of a military unit (5)
13 Large-flowered garden plant (5)
14 Succulent plant (4)
15 Disguised (9)
19 Pitch of the voice (4)
21 Become broader (5)
24 Tower supporting high-tension wires (5)
25 ____ de Cologne, perfumed liquid (3)
26 Cancellation of civil rights (9)
27 Heaps, stacks (5)

Down

1 Birthplace of Muhammad (5)
2 City in Ontario, Canada (6)
3 Man-eating giant (4)
4 Cease (4)
5 Persistent determination (8)
6 Biblical garden (4)
7 Samuel ____, English diarist (1633–1703) (5)
11 Muhammad ____, former boxer (3)
12 Make again (8)
16 Spanish city famous for steel and swords (6)
17 Yoko ____, artist (3)
18 Swift descent through the air (5)
20 Act of going in (5)
22 Distribute playing-cards (4)
23 Hard fruits (4)
24 Cleared a debt (4)

299

Across

3 Person given to excessive complaints and whining (3,4)
6 Find repugnant (5)
8 Servilely or fulsomely flattering (9)
9 Slender ropes (5)
10 Beat the seeds out of grain (6)
13 Uproar, disturbance of the peace (4)
16 Estimate the value (4)
18 Brief period of light rain (6)
20 Farewell remark (5)
22 Ancient region between the Mediterranean and the Jordan River (9)
23 Childminder (5)
24 In a perfect way (7)

Down

1 Malignant growth or tumour (6)
2 Ancient Egyptian king (7)
3 Outer layer on bread (5)
4 Strike against forcefully (6)
5 Beetroot soup (6)
7 Not divisible by two (3)
11 Quality of a colour (3)
12 Most noticeable or important (7)
14 Ground surrounded by water (6)
15 Capital of the US state of Kansas (6)
17 Written stories (6)
19 Wet (weather) (5)
21 Chemical that carries genetic information (inits) (3)

300

Across

1 Scene (5)
3 Tartan (5)
7 Prevents from speaking out (4)
9 Honourable or admirable (6)
11 Express in speech (5)
13 Ocean-going vessel (5)
14 Contributor (5)
15 Grow old (3)
16 Bounded, as if by an oath (5)
17 At a distance (5)
20 Punctuation mark (5)
22 Steering mechanism at the stern of a vessel (6)
23 Pack (4)
24 Furze (5)
25 Deadbeat (5)

Down

1 Devotional watch (5)
2 Appreciation (5)
4 One who waits on another (9)
5 Appliance that removes moisture (5)
6 Be in debt (3)
8 Explosive associated with Guy Fawkes (9)
10 Severe or trying experience (6)
12 Dreamlike state (6)
16 Branchlet (5)
18 Sat for a portrait (5)
19 Structure taller than its diameter (5)
21 Sphere (3)

301

Across

1 Capital of Russia (6)
6 Retaliate (6)
8 Actual, if not rightful or legally recognised (2,5)
9 Metal ring for lining a small hole (6)
10 Stoppage (7)
14 Witchcraft (7)
18 Follower of the Islamic religion (6)
19 Screen that separates a room into two parts (7)
20 Service of china or silverware, used at table (3,3)
21 Trousers that end above the knee (6)

Down

1 Doctor in the armed forces (5)
2 Bedlam (5)
3 Commonest liquid (5)
4 Bring into servitude (7)
5 Triangular area where a river divides (5)
7 Peeping Tom (6)
11 Rower (7)
12 Positive or favourable aspect (6)
13 Void of content (5)
15 Leaves out (5)
16 Capital of Egypt (5)
17 Imperial units of length (5)

302

Across

1 Urban centre (4)
3 Greek muse of love poetry (5)
6 Compass point (4)
7 Flat tableland with steep edges (4)
9 Very steep cliff (9)
12 One of four playing cards in a deck (3)
14 Angry (3)
15 Brightly coloured capsicum (3,6)
16 Partially opened flower (3)
17 Number indicated by the Roman X (3)
19 Release from entanglement or difficulty (9)
21 Goddess of the rainbow (4)
22 Image or representation of a god (4)
23 Storehouse (5)
24 Noblewoman (4)

Down

1 Punctuation mark (5)
2 Period of 52 weeks (4)
3 Country, capital Addis Ababa (8)
4 Instrument that measures the height above ground (9)
5 Possessed (5)
8 Way of catching motorists who drive too fast (5,4)
10 Precisely and clearly expressed (8)
11 Attention (4)
13 Most important point (4)
16 Facial hair (5)
18 Thoroughly unpleasant (5)
20 Make land ready for cultivation (4)

303

Across

3 Flower associated with alpine regions (7)
6 Angler's basket (5)
7 Crush (7)
8 Moves in a spiral course (5)
10 Pale (of colour) (6)
12 Chief port of Yemen (4)
14 Placed in position (4)
17 Official order (6)
19 ___ Rice Burroughs, creator of the character Tarzan (5)
20 Diacritical mark sometimes placed below the letter c (7)
21 Go after with the intent to catch (5)
22 Elongate, pull out (7)

Down

1 Tree and shrub species (6)
2 Formula for cooking (6)
3 Sheen (5)
4 Delighted (8)
5 Italian town, birthplace of St Francis (6)
9 Explosive device hidden in the ground (8)
11 Twitch (3)
13 Desert in order to join the opposition (6)
15 Arm of the Mediterranean between Greece and Turkey (6)
16 English county (6)
18 Achieve (5)

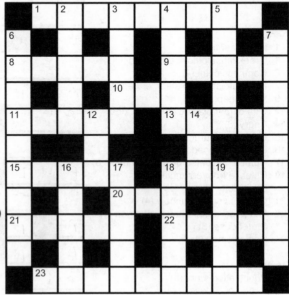

304

Across

1 Institute legal proceedings against (9)
8 Native New Zealander (5)
9 Bouquet (5)
10 Ornamental garland (3)
11 Be similar in end sound, eg dove and love (5)
13 Cut into small pieces (5)
15 Marsh (5)
18 Polish monetary unit (5)
20 Strong washing solution (3)
21 Dry red Spanish wine (5)
22 Fabric used to cover gaming tables (5)
23 Usually, as a rule (9)

Down

2 Having ample space (5)
3 Gateway in a fence (5)
4 Assertion of a right (5)
5 Prickle (5)
6 Opening (in a wall, ship or armoured vehicle) for firing through (9)
7 Means of protection from injury, hardship, etc (6,3)
12 Mother (3)
14 Not in good health (3)
16 Dwelling house (5)
17 Woodworking tool (5)
18 Striped African equine (5)
19 Projecting bay window (5)

305

Across

1 Number signified by the Roman VIII (5)
3 Water vapour (5)
7 Universe (6)
9 Collection of rules imposed by authority (4)
10 Death personified as a skeleton with a large scythe (4,6)
14 Mr Geller, psychic (3)
16 Be unconvinced (10)
19 Highly-strung, nervous (4)
20 Perplexing riddle (6)
22 Fling (5)
23 Star Trek's original Doctor (5)

Down

1 Coop up (6)
2 Sing with closed lips (3)
4 Bulb, traditionally from Holland (5)
5 Mixture of ground animal feeds (4)
6 Female cinema attendant (9)
8 Popular literary genre (abbr) (3-2)
11 Massage (3)
12 Sicken (3)
13 Fencing swords (5)
15 Per annum (6)
17 Authoritative declaration (3-2)
18 Tidy (4)
21 Joan of ___, French heroine (3)

306

Across

1 Space for movement (4)
3 Theatrical entertainment (5)
6 Not in action (4)
7 Flat round object (4)
9 By way of (3)
10 Corridor (7)
12 Ram's mate (3)
13 Fish eggs (3)
14 Renders capable for some task (7)
15 Not good (3)
16 Diving bird of northern seas (3)
18 Person who mates and sells the offspring of animals (7)
20 Inflated pride (3)
21 *Auld Lang* ___, song by Robert Burns (1788) (4)
22 Wire hairpin (4)
23 Unit of length (5)
24 Ship's small boat (4)

Down

1 Narrow raised strip (5)
2 Aluminium silicate mineral (4)
3 Elaborate (8)
4 Opponent (9)
5 Dumbfound (5)
8 Fast vehicle for travelling on water (9)
11 Forage (8)
15 Freshwater fish of the carp family (5)
17 Go down on bended legs (5)
19 Detect (4)

307

Across

1 Very fast (5)
3 Cinema attendant (5)
7 Mass of baked bread (4)
9 Item of dried fruit (6)
10 In this place (4)
11 Change direction abruptly (4)
12 Square root of 64 (5)
15 Common viper (5)
17 Settee (4)
19 Apiece (4)
20 Ludicrous acts done for fun (6)
21 Expletive (4)
22 Metalworker (5)
23 Potatoes (coll) (5)

Down

1 Experience again, often
   in the imagination (6)
2 Establish by deduction (5)
4 Painful wound caused by a wasp (5)
5 Travels on foot at a fast pace (4)
6 Uncensored or unrestricted
   print media (4,5)
8 In advance (5)

13 Disorderly outburst
   (coll) (3-2)
14 Feeling of sympathy
   and sorrow for
   the misfortunes
   of others (6)
16 Freewheel (5)
17 Large ladle (5)
18 Succeed in an
   examination (4)

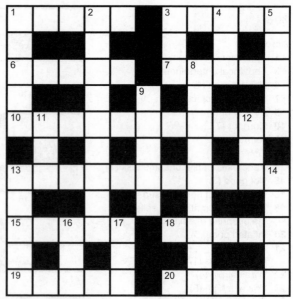

308

Across

1 Instrument for measuring time (5)
3 Annoying insects (5)
6 Complacently foolish (5)
7 Showing deterioration from age,
   as with bread for example (5)
10 Imperial units of capacity (5,6)
13 Biblical entrance to heaven (6,5)
15 Boy's name (5)
18 Country, capital Tripoli (5)
19 One of the Seven Dwarfs (5)
20 Stomach (5)

Down

1 Main (5)
2 Caretaker of apartments or a hotel (9)
3 Had existence (3)
4 Health resort (3)
5 Prophets (5)
8 Cautious (9)
9 Capital of Japan (5)
11 False statement (3)

12 To stretch out (3)
13 Trimmed (5)
14 Sheltered from
   light or heat (5)
16 Empty space
   between things (3)
17 Column of light (3)

309

Across

1 Deliberately causes a delay (6)
6 In a single direction (3-3)
7 Estimate the value (4)
8 Having a sharp tip (7)
9 Long fluffy scarf (3)
10 Anarchical (7)
16 Monkey (3)
17 Christening (7)
19 Enthusiastic devotees (4)
20 Want strongly (6)
21 In a cautious and suspicious way (6)

Down

1 One employed to make written copies of documents (6)
2 Real (6)
3 Alone (4)
4 Game played on a court (6)
5 Ring-shaped bread roll (5)
8 Animal's foot (3)

11 Reach (6)
12 Forest tree (3)
13 Highly seasoned fatty sausage (6)
14 Channel Island (6)
15 Judge's mallet (5)
18 Cook slowly in liquid (4)

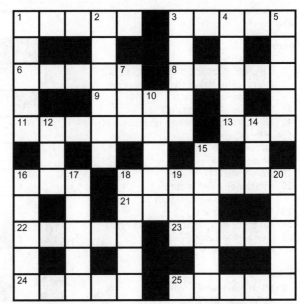

310

Across

1 Comical in a whimsical way (5)
3 Types, varieties (5)
6 Parts of a plant typically found under the ground (5)
8 Fowl's perch (5)
9 Cylinder (4)
11 Prehistoric human male (7)
13 Early form of modern jazz (3)
16 Buddy (3)
18 Formerly, mounted troops (7)
21 Stew (4)
22 Ballroom dance (5)
23 Shopping mall (5)
24 Drainage channel (5)
25 Without illumination (5)

Down

1 Order of Greek architecture (5)
2 Rubbish (6)
3 Enchantress (5)
4 Parallelogram with four equal sides (5)
5 Establish (3,2)
7 Quantity obtained by addition (3)

10 Hackneyed (5)
12 ___ Khan (3)
14 Rowing pole (3)
15 Fine white clay (6)
16 Studied closely (5)

17 Confine (5)
18 Long-distance bus (5)
19 Dignitary (inits) (3)
20 Bread-raising agent (5)

311

Across

1 Intimidate (5)
3 Mental picture (5)
7 Paws, trotters, etc (4)
9 Make certain of (6)
10 Deviates erratically from a set course (4)
11 Twist into coils or ringlets (4)
12 ___ Wilde, dramatist (5)
15 Distance downwards (5)
17 Bridge (4)
19 Advance slowly (4)
20 Mastermind (6)
21 Central Hawaiian island (between Molokai and Kauai) (4)
22 Religious building (5)
23 Landing stage (5)

Down

1 Flaw (6)
2 Region of South Africa, KwaZulu-___ (5)
4 Melodious sounds (5)
5 Sight organs (4)
6 Pleasure obtained from receiving punishment (9)
8 Lofty nest of a bird of prey (5)
13 Greek letter (5)
14 Boisterous and disobedient (6)
16 Integer that cannot be factored into other integers (5)
17 Plain dough cake, often griddled (5)
18 City, site of the Taj Mahal (4)

312

Across

1 Commence (5)
7 Official published verbatim report of the proceedings of Parliament (7)
9 Elaborate spectacle (7)
11 Opposite of 1 Across (6)
13 Musical notation written on a stave (4)
15 Jetty (4)
17 All people (9)
18 Be anxious (4)
19 Marsh plant (4)
20 Substance used to curdle milk in cheese-making (6)
23 Synthetic fabric (7)
24 Guarantees against loss or injury (7)
25 Gene Pitney song, *Twenty-four Hours from* ___ (5)

Down

2 Short preview of a film or TV programme (7)
3 Native of Bangkok, for example (4)
4 Against (4)
5 Untanned leather (7)
6 Person who does no work (5)
8 Chagrin (9)
10 Marked by excessive self-indulgence (6)
12 Athletic (6)
14 Famous mountain (7)
16 Folds of skin on the face (7)
18 Ripened reproductive body of a plant (5)
21 Irritate, nettle (slang) (4)
22 At a previous time (4)

313

Across

1 Blood vessel (4)
3 Line of contrasting colour (6)
5 Social insect (3)
6 Stylish (4)
7 Beefeater (6)
9 Not capable of being done (10)
14 Impair (3)
15 Before, poetically (3)
17 Sadness resulting from being forsaken or abandoned (10)
20 Capital of Austria (6)
22 Genuine (4)
23 Her (3)
24 Maintain a required pace or level (4,2)
25 Percussion instrument (4)

Down

1 Person who is tricked or swindled (6)
2 Topped tortilla chip (5)
3 Pigs' home (3)
4 Participants in a game (7)
8 Globe (3)
10 Physical discomfort or illness (7)
11 For (3)
12 ___ volatile, smelling salts (3)
13 Bruce ___, expert kung fu actor who died in 1973 (3)
16 Hold in high regard (6)
18 Holy sister (3)
19 Made a written record of (5)
21 Snake (3)

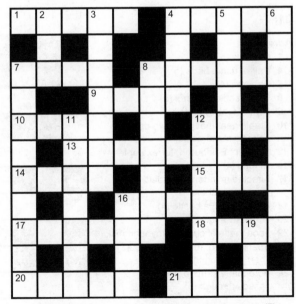

314

Across

1 Poisonous (5)
4 Make less visible, obscure (5)
7 Annoy, irritate (4)
8 "Open ___", magic words used by Ali Baba (6)
9 Curve (4)
10 Basic monetary unit of Uruguay (4)
12 Mark left by a wound (4)
13 Supermodel with the surname Bourret (7)
14 Jog (4)
15 Mend (4)
16 Short note (4)
17 Interment (6)
18 Molten rock (4)
20 Mournful poem for the dead (5)
21 Give a sign of welcome (5)

Down

2 Kimono sash (3)
3 Ship used to keep channels open for navigation (7)
4 Caused to procreate (animals) (4)
5 Bride-to-be (7)
6 Member of an irregular armed resistance force (9)
7 Honoured, respectable (9)
8 Underwater breathing device (7)
11 Whip used to inflict punishment (7)
12 Learned person (7)
16 Numerous (4)
19 Contend (3)

159

315

Across

1 Group of sheep (5)
4 Motor coaches (5)
8 Yield (4)
9 Capital of Turkey (6)
10 One of the two symbols used in Morse code (3)
11 Sudden attack (4)
13 Cylindrical store-tower (4)
14 Tell a story (7)
15 Former communist country (inits) (4)
16 Succulent plant (4)
17 Electrical resistance unit (3)
18 Marked by the appetites and passions of the body (6)
19 Thought (4)
21 Before due time (5)
22 Young sheep (5)

Down

2 Be in a horizontal position (3)
3 Popular British cheese (7)
5 Sporting dog (7)
6 Serialised TV programme (4,5)
7 Aquatic game played by swimmers (5,4)
8 An infection larger than a boil (9)
12 Underwriter (7)
13 Staying power (7)
20 Outward flow of the tide (3)

316

Across

1 Copious (5)
4 Pair of game birds (5)
7 Spheres (4)
8 Illegal setting of fires (5)
9 Item of footwear (4)
10 Stable gear that joins two draft animals at the neck (4)
12 Native of Edinburgh, for example (4)
15 Ripped (4)
17 Affected manners intended to impress others (4)
19 Ditch around a castle (4)
20 Furiously angry (5)
22 Food made of curdled soybean milk (4)
23 Spanish town, the centre of the sherry-making industry (5)
24 Hole that an anchor rope passes through (5)

Down

1 Chronological records (6)
2 Pastry dishes (4)
3 Hard, black wood used in cabinetwork (5)
5 Brown with a reddish tinge (6)
6 Hue (6)
11 Belonging to us (3)
13 Select (6)
14 Chatter (6)
16 Put up with (6)
18 Half-melted snow (5)
21 Eyeshot (4)

317

Across

1 Scented lozenge used to sweeten the breath (6)
6 Scandinavian kingdom (6)
7 Scratch repeatedly (6)
9 Umpire (7)
10 Board game (5)
13 Plague, annoy continually (5)
16 Decorative undersheet on a bed (7)
18 Not mature (of fruit) (6)
19 Light tanker for supplying water or fuel (6)
20 Exposed to the wind (6)

Down

1 Characteristic of the universe (6)
2 Dead body (6)
3 Exploiter (4)
4 Next to (6)
5 Erase (6)
8 Stuffs with soft material (4)
11 In direct opposition (4-2)
12 Thin, scanty (6)
13 Was present, is now gone (4)
14 Salty (6)
15 At an opportune moment (6)
17 Control or limit (4)

318

Across

1 Atomiser (5)
3 Formal proclamation (5)
7 Having decayed or disintegrated (6)
9 Body of the church (4)
10 Knotted item of clothing (3)
12 Come to earth (4)
13 Hinge joint in the arm (5)
15 Fluid used for writing (3)
17 Writing tables (5)
19 Salty Greek cheese (4)
21 Garland of flowers (3)
22 Follower of Hitler (4)
23 Admirable quality or attribute (6)
25 Walked through water (5)
26 Make understand (5)

Down

1 Leisurely walk (6)
2 Section of a play (3)
4 Brightest star in the constellation Cygnus (5)
5 Row or layer (4)
6 Concentrated (9)
8 Colour slightly (5)
11 Kind (3)
14 Open and observable (5)
15 Nickname of US president Eisenhower (3)
16 Bread shop (6)
18 Cut into pieces (5)
20 Chew on with the teeth (4)
24 Fishing implement (3)

161

319

Across

1 On someone's part (6)
5 Person's manner of walking, pace (4)
7 The smallest quantity (4)
8 Short-tailed wild cat (4)
9 Receptacle for a coin (4)
11 Suitable (3)
14 Certainty based on trust (8)
16 Male offspring (3)
18 Turf (3)
19 Type of cosmetic (8)
20 ___ Francisco, US city (3)
22 Mixer drink (4)
24 Unit of type, used in printing (4)
25 Fibs (4)
26 Piece of cotton used to apply medication (4)
27 Break between classes (6)

Down

1 Ali ___, fictional character who uttered "Open Sesame" (4)
2 Handle of a sword (4)
3 Women's underwear (8)
4 Controversially hunted animal (3)
5 Carbon dioxide, for example (3)
6 Belonging to the peerage (6)
10 Optical device (4)
12 Cunning tactic (4)
13 Similarly (8)
15 Musical finale (4)
16 Invasion by pathogenic bacteria (6)
17 Necessity (4)
20 Fill to satisfaction (4)
21 Tidings (4)
23 Priest's garment (3)
24 For each (3)

320

Across

1 Planetary satellites (5)
3 U-shaped curve in a stream (5)
6 Rose to one's feet (5)
8 Runs at a moderately swift pace (5)
9 Soap froth (4)
11 Cogwheel (4)
12 Refuse of processed grapes, etc (4)
13 Cover with insulation to prevent heat loss (3)
15 Tightly drawn (4)
16 Jumble (4)
18 Mentally healthy (4)
19 Signified (5)
20 Upright (5)
21 Pale (5)
22 Suggest indirectly (5)

Down

1 Ancient region between the Rivers Tigris and Euphrates (11)
2 Lasso (5)
3 Chooses (4)
4 Organic matter used as fuel (7)
5 Part of England that includes Devon, Cornwall and Somerset (4,7)
7 Twofold (4)
10 Play (5)
11 Rich stew (7)
14 Unit of heredity (4)
17 Watery fluid of the blood (5)
18 Knock senseless (4)

321

Across

1 Spare-time activity (5)
3 Impudence (5)
6 Asian country (5)
9 Stir up (a fire) (5)
10 Slant (5)
12 As an alternative to (2,4)
13 Noisy (4)
14 Skinny (4)
15 Gaudy, flash (6)
19 Jelly based on fish or meat stock (5)
20 Semi-transparent gemstones (5)
21 Mike ___, former heavyweight champion boxer (5)
22 Meat juices (5)
23 Roman senator who wrote a detailed description of the eruption of Vesuvius (5)

Down

1 Island in the West Indies (5)
2 Russian pancake (5)
3 Proceedings in a court of law (4)
4 Branch of social science dealing with finance (9)
5 Work dough (5)
7 Buddhist leader (5,4)
8 Time period (3)
11 Respiratory organs (5)
14 Flexible part of a whip (5)
16 Liable (3)
17 Basic unit of money in Saudi Arabia (5)
18 Name of eight kings of England (5)
19 Pale grey (4)

322

Across

1 Dye or other colouring material (5)
3 Light-beam amplifier (5)
7 Profound (4)
8 Wood-turning tool (5)
9 Australian 'bear' (5)
11 Disgrace, reproach or imputation of shameful conduct (11)
14 Holding back, limiting (11)
16 Turn over (2-3)
19 Black and white mammal (5)
20 Bitter (4)
21 Made a mistake (5)
22 Foam or froth on the sea (5)

Down

1 Simultaneous discharge of firearms (5)
2 Estate that passes to the heir on the death of the owner (11)
3 Basic unit of money in Albania (3)
4 Instrument played by the wind (7,4)
5 Health resort near a spring (3)
6 Interprets written words (5)
10 German submarine in World War II (1-4)
12 Pastry dish (3)
13 Pot, vase (3)
14 Line of travel (5)
15 Solemn (5)
17 Fruiting spike of a cereal plant (3)
18 Carried out (3)

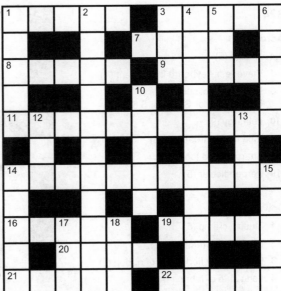

323

Across

1 Alloy of copper and zinc (5)
4 Fence made of shrubs (5)
7 In the past (3)
8 Horrify (5)
10 Holy ___, papal court (3)
11 US city at the foot of the Sierra Nevada Mountains (4)
12 Check marks (5)
14 Column, of light for example (5)
15 Humble (5)
16 Control board (5)
19 Drizzle (4)
20 Piece of metal with a hole used to secure a bolt (3)
21 Tedium (5)
23 Possess (3)
24 Dead language (5)
25 Small branch (5)

Down

1 Animal (5)
2 Unit of electric current (abbr) (3)
3 Shop assistant (11)
4 Primate species to which modern humans belong (4,7)
5 Contempt (7)
6 Vote in (5)
9 Chest for the Covenant (3)
13 Small, dark-coloured British bird (4,3)
15 Invalidate (5)
17 Girl's name (3)
18 Resting in a horizontal position (5)
22 Neither (3)

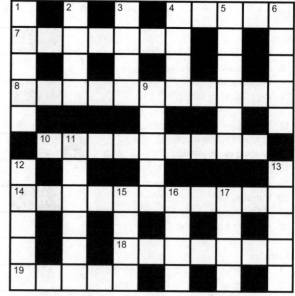

324

Across

4 Nozzle (5)
7 Playerless keyboard instrument (7)
8 Dairy product such as Emmentaler or Gruyère (5,6)
10 Lethargy (9)
14 Pale kind of treacle (6,5)
18 Sharp-edged tooth (7)
19 Perpendicular (5)

Down

1 Muscle cramp (5)
2 Hackney carriage (4)
3 Decoratively tied strips of ribbon (4)
4 Long strip of fabric (4)
5 Female monster (6)
6 Structure taller than its diameter (5)
9 Small rough-haired terrier (5)
11 Spin, wind or twist together (6)
12 Wide open (5)
13 Reproductive body produced a fern (5)
15 Way out (4)
16 Bag made of hessian or plastic (4)
17 Red eruption of the skin (4)

325

Across

1 Exhales forcibly (5)
4 Temporary stay of action (5)
7 Newspaper column giving opinions (9)
9 Transgression (3)
10 Oval fruit with a very large seed (5)
11 Hill of sand (4)
13 Abnormal protuberance (4)
15 Show mercy or leniency (5)
16 Slide fastener (3)
17 Large dog (5,4)
19 At no time (5)
20 Resin used in laminates (5)

Down

1 Prejudiced (6)
2 Stove (4)
3 Travel across snow (3)
5 Circle of light around the head of a saint (7)
6 Jewish salutation used at meeting or parting (6)
8 Large drinking vessel (7)
10 Communiqué (7)
12 False (6)
14 Tenure of office of a pope (6)
16 Nil (4)
18 Imitate (3)

326

Across

3 Trash (7)
6 Nimble, spry (5)
7 Factory where food is put into metal containers (7)
9 Stringed instrument (6)
10 Command, control (7)
13 Leave without permission (7)
17 Contraption (6)
18 Make wider (7)
19 Small pieces of stiff paper on which greetings are printed (5)
20 Prickly plant (7)

Down

1 Prehistoric supercontinent (7)
2 Irritable as if suffering from indigestion (7)
3 Summarise briefly (5)
4 Certificates of debt (usually interest-bearing or discounted) issued by a government (5)
5 Grate (5)
8 Organise (7)
11 Mental pictures collectively (7)
12 Self-importance (7)
14 Mooring (5)
15 Talons (5)
16 Series of rhythmical steps in time to music (5)

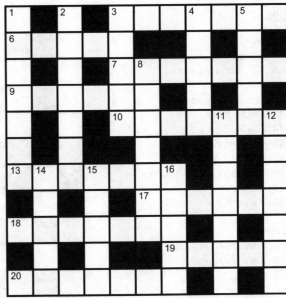

327

Across

1 Field on which a university's buildings are situated (6)
6 Connected to a computer network (6)
7 Money demanded by a kidnapper (6)
8 Cut or impressed into a surface (6)
10 Minor actor in crowd scenes (5)
13 Adopt or support (7)
16 Latin American dance (5)
18 Superior in quality (6)
20 Association of sports teams (6)
21 Billy ___, US evangelical preacher born in 1918 (6)
22 Position of a person in society (6)

Down

1 Arch (5)
2 Particularly difficult or baffling problems (6)
3 A few (4)
4 Lessen a load (7)
5 Prepared for action (5)
9 Tipster (4)

11 Rhyming slang word for a thief (3,4)
12 Pinnacle (4)
14 World's largest hot desert (6)
15 Maxim (5)
17 Baking appliances (5)
19 Common trees (4)

328

Across

1 Exceptional creative ability (6)
6 No particular person (6)
7 Friendly nation (4)
9 Evening prayers (7)
12 Military blockade (5)
14 Pen tip (3)
15 Let down (5)
18 Place out of sight (7)
21 Immaterial part of a person (4)
22 Repugnant (6)
23 Merely (6)

Down

1 Plant grown as a lawn (5)
2 Extremely cold (3)
3 Secure (4)
4 No longer here (4)
5 Female birds (4)
8 Caustic washing solution (3)
9 Concert place (5)
10 Animal prized for its fur (5)
11 Contest of speed (4)

13 Lazy (4)
16 Romance (3)
17 Pass along (5)
18 Native of Aberdeen, for example (4)
19 Abel's brother (4)
20 Fling (4)
21 Total (3)

329

Across

1 Coherent (5)
4 Capital raised by a corporation through the issue of shares (5)
7 Deeply sad (6)
9 Turns brown in the sun (4)
10 Cougar (4)
11 The act of coming out (6)
13 Not diluted (4)
15 Identical (4)
17 Edible shellfish (6)
20 Make new (4)
21 Put one's name to (4)
22 Young upwardly mobile professional individual (coll) (6)
23 Hands out playing cards (5)
24 Inclined to anger, with overtones of menace (5)

Down

1 Rubs soap all over (7)
2 Preside over (a meeting) (5)
3 Oozes slowly (5)
5 Lockjaw (7)
6 Lily-like tropical plant with bright flowers and strap-like leaves (5)
8 Protective care or guardianship (7)
12 Seemingly without end (7)
14 In a short and concise manner (7)
16 Get up (5)
18 ___ truly, letter ending (5)
19 Narrow towards a point (5)

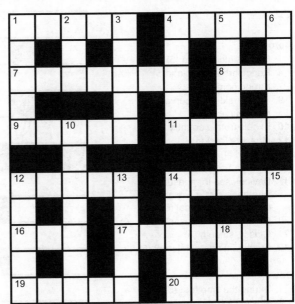

330

Across

1 Thread for cleaning between the teeth (5)
4 Unadorned (5)
7 Not devious (7)
8 Morsel left at a meal, crumb (3)
9 Spectacle (5)
11 Act of going in (5)
12 Three-dimensional (5)
14 Pay out (5)
16 ___ Lanka, country (3)
17 Stool to rest the feet of a seated person (7)
19 Find the answer to (5)
20 Examine thoroughly and closely (5)

Down

1 Young horses (5)
2 Cereal grass (3)
3 Cleaned with a broom (5)
4 Edible spread (5)
5 Original disciple (7)
6 Slang term for mentally irregular (5)
10 Name linking singer Peter and actor Byrne (7)
12 Barrels (5)
13 Struggle for breath (5)
14 Act that incriminates someone on a false charge (3-2)
15 Classroom fool (5)
18 Chinese communist leader (1893–1976) (3)

331

Across

1 Spiny-finned freshwater fish (5)
4 Artificial gems (5)
7 Free from external control (11)
8 Sense organs for hearing and equilibrium (4)
11 Deliver to an enemy by treachery (6)
14 Expression (6)
17 Calls for (4)
21 Very close in resemblance (11)
22 Sorts, types (5)
23 Produces musical tones with the voice (5)

Down

1 Cost (5)
2 Nickname of Corporal O'Reilly in *M*A*S*H* (5)
3 What remained in Pandora's box after she let out all the evils (4)
4 Divisions of a pound sterling (5)
5 Guide a vessel (5)
6 Item in a written record (5)
9 Burnt remains (3)
10 Expanse of salt water (3)
11 Stinging insect (3)
12 Afternoon meal (3)
13 Invite (3)
14 Length of sawn timber (5)
15 Develop fully (5)
16 Items of footwear (5)
18 European country (5)
19 Grows from, originates (5)
20 Objectives (4)

332

Across

1 Furious indignation (5)
4 Reddish-brown colour (5)
7 Strong cord (4)
9 Shorter side of a curved racecourse (6,5)
10 Expels from a country (6)
12 Measure (out) (4)
13 Expired (4)
14 Free-and-easy (6)
17 Device used to measure whether a surface is perfectly horizontal or vertical (6,5)
20 Offensively unpleasant odour (4)
21 Glossy, smooth (5)
22 Exorbitant rate of interest (5)

Down

1 During the time that (5)
2 Musical warble (5)
3 Brick carrier (3)
4 Rigid (3)
5 Flat upland area (7)
6 Joint just above the foot (5)
8 Oppress, cause to suffer (9)
11 Suppose (7)
13 Measures of medicine (5)
15 Looks for (5)
16 Water ice on a small wooden stick (5)
18 Vex (3)
19 Romanian monetary unit (3)

333

Across
1 Assorted (6)
4 Refuse heap (4)
6 Constricted (6)
8 Middle Eastern country (4)
10 Marsh plant (5)
12 Armoured fighting vehicle (4)
13 Long pointed rod used as a weapon (5)
14 One of the strands twisted together to make yarn (3)
16 Secretion of bodily membranes (5)
18 Metal food containers (4)
20 Brand name (5)
22 Distinctive and stylish elegance (4)
23 Language (6)
24 Head of the chapter of a cathedral (4)
25 Ant or beetle, for example (6)

Down
1 Infinitesimal (6)
2 Large hairy tropical spider (9)
3 Greek god of love (4)
4 Condescend (5)
5 Pool (4)
7 Strongly built, sturdy (4-3)
9 Parallelogram (9)
11 Time between sunrise and sunset (3)
14 Tavern (3)
15 Facet (6)
17 Cathedral priest (5)
19 Small ball with a hole through the middle (4)
21 Lend out (4)

334

Across
1 Holy person (5)
5 Breed of dog (3)
7 Incensed, enraged (5)
8 Russian river that flows into the Caspian Sea (5)
9 Parasitic insect (5)
10 Rapture (7)
13 Trace of something (7)
15 Drum held between the knees (5)
16 Famous American battle, Davy Crockett's last (5)
17 Dish of cold vegetables (5)
18 Headgear (3)
19 Agent that assists colonic irrigation (5)

Down
1 Characteristic of the former USSR (6)
2 Conjuror, prestidigitator (11)
3 Jewelled headdress (5)
4 Automobile race run over public roads (5)
5 Next-to-last (11)
6 Sticky paste (4)
11 Means of returning something by post (inits) (3)
12 Spanish married woman's title (6)
13 Light semi-transparent fabric (5)
14 Garden tool (5)
15 German composer (1685–1750) (4)

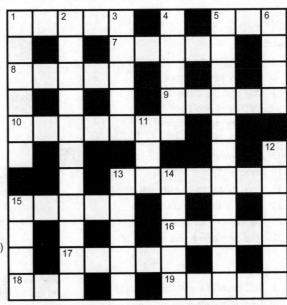

335

Across

1 Infrequently (6)
6 Agree (6)
7 Musical records (6)
8 Interlace yarn in a series of loops (4)
10 Fix securely (5)
13 Feed (3)
14 Female reproductive cells (3)
15 Shack (3)
16 Correct (5)
19 Muslim of the former Ottoman empire (4)
21 Person who finds and kills game (6)
22 Country, capital Belgrade (6)
23 Country, capital Oslo (6)

Down

1 Tool used for digging (5)
2 Extinguish (5)
3 Face covering (4)
4 Money set by for the future (4,3)
5 Large and elaborate meal (5)
9 Approach (4)
11 Marsh bird of the heron family (7)

12 Swinging or sliding barrier (4)
15 Jarring (5)
17 Closer to the centre (5)
18 Late (5)
20 Genghis ____, founder of the Mongol empire (4)

336

Across

1 Make someone do something (6)
6 Entertains or diverts (6)
7 Officer in the Queen's ceremonial bodyguard (6)
8 Spoil the appearance of (6)
10 Distressed (5)
13 Beat severely (7)
16 Snooze (5)
18 Personification of a familiar idea (6)
20 Skilful or adept in action (6)
21 Substance that turns red in acid (6)
22 Medicinal or magical mixture (6)

Down

1 Soft fur, also known as nutria (5)
2 Treat with excessive indulgence (6)
3 Territory (4)
4 Someone who breaks free (7)
5 County that borders the Thames estuary and the North Sea (5)
9 Long periods of time (4)
11 Furtiveness (7)
12 Roman cloak (4)
14 Dark purplish-red wine (6)
15 Not well (5)
17 Communion plate (5)
19 Wood file (4)

337

Across

4 Will (5)
7 Continental country house (7)
8 Averse (5)
10 Lobby, vestibule (5)
12 Sauce used in Chinese cookery (3)
13 Star divination (9)
17 Whatsoever (3)
19 Kingdom (5)
22 Combine (5)
23 Without taking a break (3-4)
24 One of the two main branches of orthodox Islam (5)

Down

1 Covered with thin horny plates (5)
2 Annoy continually (6)
3 Greek god of the west wind (6)
4 Waves breaking on the shore (4)
5 Nautical term used in hailing (4)
6 Measure equal to approximately 1.76 pints (5)
9 Entire (5)
11 Toxic form of oxygen (5)
14 Express grief verbally (6)
15 Spin around (6)
16 X mark (5)
18 Piles (5)
20 British county dissolved in 1996 (4)
21 Very short skirt (4)

338

Across

1 Rich soil (4)
3 Employee who keeps records or accounts (5)
6 ___ Karenina, Tolstoy novel (4)
7 Thomas ___, German writer (1875–1955) (4)
9 Make plain and comprehensible (9)
11 Nervous twitch (3)
12 Violent agitation (7)
14 Not well (3)
16 Lacking in usefulness or value (9)
18 Sound made to indicate a bad smell (4)
19 Hindu garment (4)
20 Daughter of one's brother (5)
21 Monetary rewards for good service (4)

Down

1 Restrict (5)
2 Tailless breed of cat (4)
3 Underbodice (8)
4 Set up (9)
5 Stringed toys flown in the wind (5)
8 Variety of peach (9)
10 Buy (8)
13 US novelist, creator of Tom Sawyer (5)
15 Lennox ___, retired heavyweight boxing champion (5)
17 Expectorate (4)

339

Across

3 Bag that fills with air or liquid (7)
6 Steam bath (5)
7 Listlessness (7)
8 Mythical Greek giant with 100 eyes (5)
9 Recess in a church (4)
11 In case (4)
14 Action performed intentionally or consciously (4)
17 Catch sight of (4)
19 Open, observable (5)
20 Caretaker of a building (7)
21 Remove the fleece from (5)
22 Monetary unit equal to one-hundredth of a peso in Chile, Colombia, Cuba, Mexico, etc (7)

Down

1 Launch an attack on (6)
2 Raymond Briggs's Bogeyman (6)
3 Light wood (5)
4 Stubbornly unyielding (6)
5 Develop (6)
10 Prefix meaning 'in favour of' (3)
12 Make violently angry (6)
13 Short-sleeved simple garment for the upper body (1-5)
15 Traditional hour for morning snacks (6)
16 Puts off, discourages (6)
18 Upper body (5)

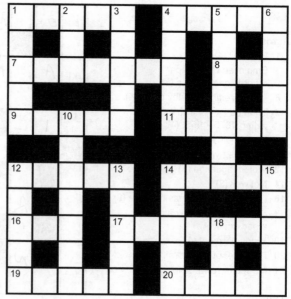

340

Across

1 Implement used to sharpen razors (5)
4 Determine the sum of (3,2)
7 Account for (7)
8 Primary colour (3)
9 Preceding all others (5)
11 Iciness (5)
12 Capital of Lombardy, Italy (5)
14 Explode (5)
16 Rubbish dump (3)
17 Foment (7)
19 Put on clothes (5)
20 Unlawful removal of property (5)

Down

1 Ledge (5)
2 Rend (3)
3 Living organism lacking the power of locomotion (5)
4 Loose-fitting garment (5)
5 Type of dog (7)
6 Treadle (5)
10 Regress (7)
12 In a softened tone (5)
13 Moves towards (5)
14 Constructed (5)
15 Behave towards (5)
18 Profound emotion inspired by a deity (3)

341

Across

1 Computer memory units (5)
4 Administrative capital of Bolivia (2,3)
7 Filled sack used to protect against floodwater (7)
8 The letter 'H' written as a word (5)
9 Exist as an essential, permanent, or characteristic attribute or quality of a thing (6)
12 Put in order (4)
15 Unable to hear (4)
17 One of four playing-card suits (6)
19 Vestige (5)
20 Picture made by sticking things together to form a montage (7)
21 Is aware of a fact (5)
22 Quiet (5)

Down

1 Distends (6)
2 Consistency (7)
3 Rice and raw fish wrapped in seaweed (5)
5 Woolly-headed (6)
6 Plant similar to the rhododendron (6)
10 Egg of a louse (3)
11 Meeting for boat races (7)
13 Native of Columbus, USA, for example (6)
14 Candle ingredient (6)
16 Violent and ferocious (6)
18 Marinate (5)

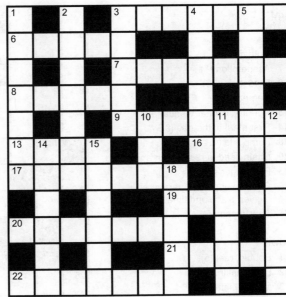

342

Across

3 Bright colour (7)
6 Make void (5)
7 Worry (7)
8 Fruit with sweet, juicy flesh (5)
9 Common, not specific (7)
13 Source of illumination (4)
16 Give a narcotic to (4)
17 Canvas shoe with a pliable rubber sole (7)
19 Enter (data or a program) into a computer (5)
20 Young of a sow (7)
21 Creepy (5)
22 Erle Stanley ____, writer of detective novels featuring Perry Mason (7)

Down

1 Warm-blooded vertebrates that suckle their young (7)
2 Arouse or excite feelings and passions (7)
3 Informal language (5)
4 Damaged irreparably (6)
5 Catch in a snare (6)
10 River that runs through Devon (3)
11 Children's playsuits (7)
12 Animal skin that has been tanned (7)
14 Heart condition marked by chest pain (6)
15 Abnormally deficient in colour (6)
18 Vertical pipe in a building (5)

343

Across

1 Manufactures (5)
4 Beat hard (3)
6 Japanese verse form (5)
7 State of being disregarded or forgotten (5)
9 Flashlight (5)
10 More than is needed (7)
13 Strong feeling or emotion (7)
15 Indian currency unit (5)
16 Scene of action (5)
17 Fathers (5)
18 Batch (3)
19 Cut in two (5)

Down

1 Annoy continually or chronically (6)
2 Large group of fish (5)
3 Raises up (5)
4 Profitable (9)
5 Network structure (4)
8 Review of troops (5,4)
11 Ms Thurman, Hollywood actress (3)
12 Breathe in (6)
13 Product of an oyster (5)
14 Secret store (5)
15 Bobbin (4)

344

Across

4 Nothing (5)
7 Assumption (7)
8 Detestation (5)
11 Remedy (5)
13 Country, capital Vientiane (4)
14 First meal of the day (9)
18 Bump into (4)
20 Chain used to restrain an animal (5)
23 Passenger ship (5)
24 Order to appear in person at a given place and time (7)
25 Apartments (5)

Down

1 Bobbin, reel (5)
2 High-ranking (6)
3 Motion picture (4)
4 Catherine ____ Jones, actress (4)
5 Entice (4)
6 Easy to reach (5)
9 Light touch or stroke (3)
10 Consumers (5)
12 Florida city (5)
15 Detection device (6)
16 Quoits target (3)
17 Pretend to be in a stronger position (5)
19 Garbage (5)
21 Region (4)
22 Noise made by a snake (4)
23 Allan ____, former test cricketer (4)

345

Across
1 Boys, men (5)
3 Circulatory organ (5)
6 Speeding (6)
9 Centre of an apple (4)
10 Desert of Mongolia and China (4)
11 Eager (4)
13 Single-digit number (3)
15 Body of water into which the River Jordan flows (4,3)
17 Bulgarian monetary unit (3)
18 Clock face (4)
20 Remove from office (4)
22 Mislaid (4)
23 Comfort, solace (6)
24 Leaves of a book (5)
25 Relating to Scandinavia (5)

Down
1 Robin Hood's beloved Maid (6)
2 Produce tones with the voice (4)
4 Stimulated (7)
5 Old-fashioned form of the word 'you' (4)
7 Censure severely (5)
8 Female deity (7)
12 Keen enthusiast (7)
14 Narrowing of the body between the ribs and hips (5)
16 Arm covering (6)
19 Pigswill (4)
21 Municipality smaller than a city (4)

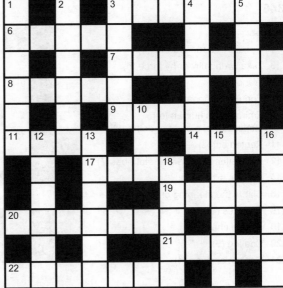

346

Across
3 Refuse, rubbish (7)
6 There (French) (5)
7 Cook rapidly over a high heat while mixing briskly (4,3)
8 Tribes (5)
9 Renowned lock-making company (4)
11 Woody plant (4)
14 Narrow thin strip of wood (4)
17 Rear (4)
19 Disgust (5)
20 German state famous for its beer (7)
21 Banter (5)
22 Eighth planet from the Sun (7)

Down
1 Shorebird with slender upward-curving bill (6)
2 Optical illusion often witnessed in deserts (6)
3 Aerated, effervescent (5)
4 Keg, cask (6)
5 Semi-precious gemstone (6)
10 Provide with weapons (3)
12 Lay waste to (6)
13 Capable of making a mistake (6)
15 Earnest or urgent request (6)
16 Astronomer who gave his name to a comet (6)
18 Speak (about unimportant matters) rapidly and incessantly (5)

347

Across

1 Message sent from one computer to another (5)
4 Specific points in history (5)
8 In the Roman calendar; the day that marked the middle of the month (4)
9 Non-professional person (6)
10 Popular drink (3)
11 Scottish hillside (4)
13 Shared on-line journal (4)
14 Female spirit of Irish folklore, whose wailing warns of death (7)
15 Fat used in cooking (4)
16 Steep rugged rock or cliff (4)
17 Egg cells (3)
18 Nicotinic acid (6)
19 Encourage (4)
21 Sing the praises of (5)
22 Country of the Arabian Peninsula (5)

Down

2 Mixture of earth and water (3)
3 Alternatively (7)
5 Heavy-bottomed glass (7)
6 Jewish place of worship (9)
7 Former British Prime Minister (9)
8 Lack of equilibrium between things (9)
12 Alongside each other (7)
13 Due to, on account of (7)
20 Unit of gravitational force (3)

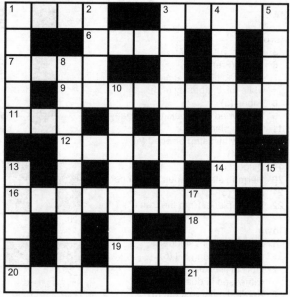

348

Across

1 Circuits of a racecourse (4)
3 Take wrongfully or by force (5)
6 Tranquil (4)
7 Popular carbonated drink (4)
9 Embodied in human form (especially of a spirit or deity) (9)
11 Rented out (3)
12 Fifth letter of the Greek alphabet (7)
14 Definite article (3)
16 Clarify the meaning of (9)
18 Chances (4)
19 Kind of cheese (4)
20 Coating (5)
21 Cook in an oven (4)

Down

1 In the vicinity (5)
2 Read quickly (4)
3 Portable defence against rain (8)
4 Resolutely courageous (9)
5 Physical strength (5)
8 Without exaggeration (9)
10 Client (8)
13 Milky-white gem made by an oyster (5)
15 Follow on from (5)
17 Grave (4)

349

Across

1 Open by force of leverage (5)
3 More recent (5)
6 Company badge (4)
8 Prickly desert plant (6)
9 Depleted (3)
11 Relative magnitude (5)
12 Wed (5)
13 Muhammad ___, former champion boxer (3)
14 Walk stealthily (5)
15 Covered with small pieces of rock (5)
18 Cut wood (3)
19 Opening that permits escape or release (6)
20 Disparaging remark (4)
21 Wheel coverings (5)
22 Equals in rank (5)

Down

1 Tablets (5)
2 Footrest (5)
3 Accidental collision that is narrowly avoided (4,4)
4 Aquatic birds (9)
5 Out of practice (5)
7 Fighter in ancient Rome (9)
10 Liability to failure under pressure or stress (8)
14 Fire a gun (5)
16 Appreciation (5)
17 Tall tales (5)

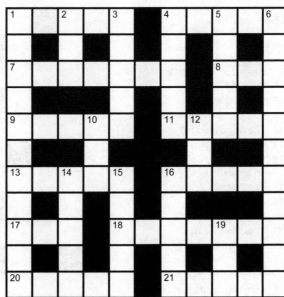

350

Across

1 Appear for the first time (5)
4 Bereaved wife (5)
7 Go back over (7)
8 Gossip (3)
9 Matching set of furniture (5)
11 Of the pope (5)
13 Modify (5)
16 Pulse (5)
17 Farmhouse cooker (3)
18 Memory loss (7)
20 Contest between opposing teams (5)
21 System of principles or beliefs (5)

Down

1 Chief port of Tanzania (3,2,6)
2 Nocturnal mammal (3)
3 Make fun of (5)
4 Give birth to puppies (5)
5 Excavate (3,2)
6 Australian musical instrument, played by holding in both hands and flexing (6,5)
10 Plumbing fixture (3)
12 Anti-tobacco organisation (inits) (3)
14 Separated (5)
15 Instruct (5)
16 Mixer drink (5)
19 Observe (3)

351

Across
1 Giraffe-like creature (5)
3 Uncertainty (5)
6 Hoot with derision (3)
7 Welsh breed of dog (5)
9 Young wolf (3)
10 Partial darkness (5)
12 Oven for firing pottery (4)
14 Prickly shrub with yellow flowers (5)
16 Looks at lecherously (5)
18 Varlet (5)
20 Crack (4)
21 Cattle farm (5)
23 Tease (3)
24 Trembling poplar (5)
26 Scottish port (3)
27 Puff up (5)
28 Register (5)

Down
1 Imaginary monster or ogre (3)
2 Wading bird (4)
3 Quantity of medication taken at any one time (6)
4 Superior (5)
5 Conical tent (5)
8 Pungent vegetable (5)
11 Sleep in a convenient place (4)
13 Star that ejects material (4)
15 Give form to (5)
17 Affable (6)
18 Pavement edges (5)
19 Bicker (5)
22 Long-eared creature, similar to rabbit (4)
25 Zero (3)

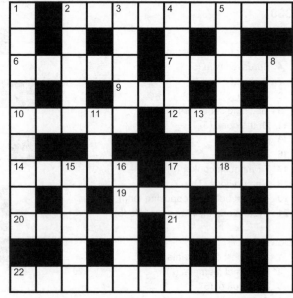

352

Across
2 Dependent upon or characterised by chance (9)
6 Ooze (5)
7 In the vicinity (5)
9 Low-breed dog (3)
10 The items here (5)
12 Subtraction sign (5)
14 Gas formerly used as an anaesthetic (5)
17 Scavenging carnivore (5)
19 Chopping tool (3)
20 Freeze off (5)
21 In existence (5)
22 Lacking flavour (9)

Down
1 Climbing plants that produce fragrant flowers (5,4)
2 Accommodate (5)
3 Bit (5)
4 Clock that wakes a sleeper at a preset time (5)
5 Fruit of the oak (5)
8 Profession of belief (9)
11 Institute legal proceedings against (3)
13 Frosty (3)
15 Divisions of a day (5)
16 Assortment (5)
17 Retch (5)
18 Prepares for printing (5)

353

Across

1 Protect (5)
4 Chafe at the bit, like a horse (5)
7 Utmost (7)
8 Plural of the word 'am' (3)
9 Device used to connect computers by a telephone line (5)
11 Liable (5)
12 Contending (5)
14 Desolate (5)
16 Web (3)
17 Outstanding musician (7)
19 Deserve (5)
20 Evil spirit (5)

Down

1 Glisten (5)
2 Towards the rear (3)
3 Fantasy (5)
4 Relatively low in price (5)
5 Edible shellfish, a source of mother-of-pearl (7)
6 Man in chess or draughts (5)
10 Wanderer (7)
12 Poison of snakes, etc (5)
13 Whole range (5)
14 Intermingle (5)
15 Understood (5)
18 Mr Selleck, who played the lead role in *Magnum PI* (3)

354

Across

1 Flower associated with Remembrance Sunday (5)
3 Measure the depth of something (5)
6 International alliance begun in 1949 (inits) (4)
7 Making an attempt (6)
9 Redeeming quality or characteristic (6,5)
12 Publicly calling attention to (11)
14 Thread used for sewing (6)
17 Religious painting (4)
18 Terminate (5)
19 Play truant from work or school (coll) (5)

Down

1 Takes short quick breaths (5)
2 Providing carefully for the future (9)
3 Standard strokes made for a hole in golf (3)
4 Israeli submachine-gun (3)
5 Framework of a railway carriage (5)
7 Make taut (7)
8 Measure or standard used for comparison (9)
10 Economic assistance (3)
11 Sealed metal storage container (3)
12 Capital of Ghana (5)
13 Class of artistic endeavour having a characteristic form (5)
15 Also (3)
16 Not in (3)

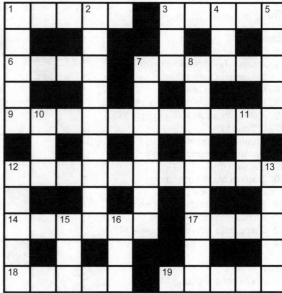

355

Across
2 Item for sharpening edged tools or knives (9)
6 Comes down to earth (5)
7 Packs, fills (5)
9 Slippery fish (3)
10 Brood (on) (5)
12 Panache (5)
14 Small bone in the middle ear (5)
17 Cause to drop or sink (5)
19 Lyricist, ___ Gershwin (3)
20 Map collection (5)
21 Water flow resulting from sudden rain or melting snow (5)
22 Employment paid for by the amount produced (9)

Down
1 Emotional theatrical piece (9)
2 Cringe (5)
3 Painting stand (5)
4 Exchanges for money (5)
5 Organ of a flower (5)
8 Be the leader of (9)
11 Hawaiian floral garland (3)
13 Likewise (3)
15 Worth (5)
16 Strong, tightly twisted cotton thread (5)
17 Noosed rope (5)
18 Dried seaweed (5)

356

Across
1 Equine animal (3)
3 African river flowing into the Indian Ocean (7)
6 Make or pass laws (9)
8 Poem with complex stanza forms (3)
10 Treat with excessive indulgence (6)
13 Difficult (4)
14 Rotund, extremely chubby (5)
16 Barrier between rooms (4)
17 Solution (6)
20 Tropical black cuckoo of central America (3)
21 Substances that unite or bond surfaces together (9)
22 Compound with a minty taste (7)
23 Cambridgeshire city (3)

Down
1 Concerned with one specific purpose (2,3)
2 Cut-price events (5)
3 Capital of Croatia (6)
4 Pours forth, as smoke from a chimney, etc (7)
5 Decorate with frosting (3)
7 Deep serving bowl (6)
9 One whose age has impaired his intellect (6)
11 Capable of meeting financial obligations (7)
12 Beverage (3)
15 Whine tearfully (6)
18 Squander (5)
19 Dangerous (5)
21 Intention (3)

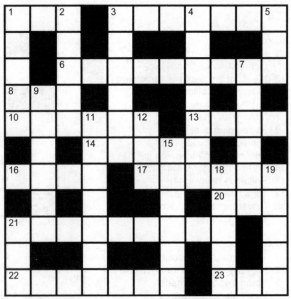

357

Across

1 Abandonment, decay (6)
6 Necktie (6)
7 Muslim learned in Islamic theology and law (6)
9 In accordance with reason (7)
13 Austere, bare (5)
14 Small, open pies (5)
15 Fall to a lower level (7)
19 Governing authority of a political unit (6)
20 Part of a dress above the waist (6)
21 Notified of danger (6)

Down

1 Capital of Syria (8)
2 Sweetened cream beaten with wine (8)
3 Sound reflection (4)
4 Public passenger vehicle (4)
5 Region bordering Israel and Egypt (4)
8 Compound capable of turning litmus blue (6)
10 Small chin beard trimmed to a point (6)
11 Government by force (8)
12 Unfinished business (5,3)
16 Vehicles from outer space (inits) (4)
17 Mix (4)
18 Sketched (4)

358

Across

1 Lengthwise crack in wood (5)
4 Burning (5)
9 Throb dully (4)
10 Innumerable but many (7)
11 Brief written records (5)
12 Disc used in slot machines as a substitute for coins (5)
16 Avian creature (4)
18 Back of the neck (4)
19 Contrite (5)
22 Constellation with a Great Nebula (5)
23 Situated (7)
25 Unforeseen obstacle (4)
26 Discourage (5)
27 Consisting or suggestive of earth (5)

Down

1 Substitute on hand (5-2)
2 Alphabetic characters (7)
3 Believe in (5)
5 Make plump (6)
6 Water in a solid state (3)
7 Flightless bird of South America (4)
8 To the full extent (poetically) (3)
13 Belonging to you and me (3)
14 Country, capital Windhoek (7)
15 Church house (7)
17 Senility (6)
20 Mountain call (5)
21 District (4)
23 Hallucinogenic drug (inits) (3)
24 Popular pet (3)

359

Across
1 Area where animals graze (5)
4 Unit of weight for precious stones (5)
7 Series of pictures representing a continuous scene (7)
8 Riotous crowd (3)
9 Ravioli, for example (5)
11 Covered with lather (5)
12 Braid of hair (5)
14 Sediment that has settled at the bottom of a liquid (5)
16 Penultimate Greek letter (3)
17 Word opposite in meaning to another (7)
19 Bent from a vertical position (5)
20 Quick evasive movement (5)

Down
1 Bored, having had enough (3,2)
2 Umberto ___, author of *Foucault's Pendulum* (3)
3 Roman goddess of the hunt (5)
4 Form, category (5)
5 Storm around (7)
6 Cat with a grey or tawny coat mottled with black (5)
10 Enduring strength and energy (7)
12 Aperture in the iris of the eye (5)
13 Characteristic (5)
14 Passé (5)
15 Battleground of World War I (5)
18 Diminutive of Edward (3)

360

Across
1 Forfeit (4,2)
4 Rounded thickly-curled hairdo (4)
6 Thus (9)
8 The night before (3)
10 Growing area (6)
13 Chancy (coll) (4)
14 Come into (5)
16 Foreman (4)
17 Bother (6)
20 All the same (3)
21 Lopsided (9)
22 Conical tent of skins used by Mongolian nomads (4)
23 Get away (6)

Down
1 Norwegian composer (1843–1907) (5)
2 Elector (5)
3 Inconsistent in quality (6)
4 Personal matters (7)
5 A single (3)
7 Lottery in which the prizes are goods (6)
9 Bravery (6)
11 Movement downward (7)
12 Unspecified member of a large series (3)
15 Sharp-eyed birds (6)
18 Country, capital Damascus (5)
19 Short composition for a solo instrument (5)
21 Clinging plant (3)

182

361

Across

1 Vigilant (5)
4 Money container (5)
7 Mexican liquor (7)
8 Not anti! (3)
9 Stop (5)
11 Lacking experience of life (5)
12 Gambling game using two dice (5)
14 Section of an orchestra (5)
16 Rechewed food (3)
17 Learned institution (7)
19 Scorch (5)
20 Euphoric (5)

Down

1 Member of a Mexican tribe overthrown by Cortes in 1519 (5)
2 Polite title appended to a man's name (abbr) (3)
3 Lining of the stomach of a ruminant used as food (5)
4 Edible crustacean (5)
5 Reproduction (7)
6 Run off to wed (5)
10 Forsake (7)
12 Adult male birds (5)
13 Declare (5)
14 Shore (5)
15 In a bashful way (5)
18 Clairvoyance (inits) (3)

362

Across

1 Garden bush (5)
4 Bathroom fixture (5)
7 ___ de Cologne, perfumed liquid (3)
8 Adult male person (3)
10 Unassailable (11)
11 Across or above, poetically (3)
13 Cubicle (5)
14 Be in the red (3)
18 Talk in a dogmatic and pompous manner (11)
19 Basque terrorists (inits) (3)
20 *The Catcher in the ___*, J D Salinger novel (3)
21 Suitably (5)
22 Limbless reptile (5)

Down

1 Leader of an Arab village (5)
2 Harvests (5)
3 Recipient of money, etc, from a will or insurance policy (11)
4 City served by Jorge Newbery airport (6,5)
5 Walt Disney film of 1941 (5)
6 Photocopier ink (5)
9 Beers (4)
12 Study intensively for an exam (4)
14 Musical entertainment (5)
15 Ordain (5)
16 Old name for the capital of Bangladesh (5)
17 Aladdin's spirit (5)

363

Across

1 Debacle (6)
6 Asian temple (6)
7 Take in liquids, drink (6)
10 Pronounce clearly (9)
12 Remains (5)
13 19th letter of the Greek alphabet (3)
15 Amusement (5)
18 In a difficult situation (2,3,4)
20 Also (2,4)
21 Unwell (6)
22 Surname of Roseanne Barr's ex-husband Tom (6)

Down

1 Travels by plane (5)
2 Gleaming (5)
3 Exposed (4)
4 Napoleon ___, French emperor (9)
5 Tall tower referred to in the Bible (5)
8 *Jack and the ___*, pantomime (9)
9 Commotion (6)
11 Compact masses (6)
14 Vociferous (5)
16 Native of Des Moines, for example (5)
17 Successfully potted (5)
19 Heroic tale (4)

364

Across

1 Is without (5)
5 Stitch together (3)
7 Prime minister of India from 1947 to 1964 (5)
8 Country, capital Naypyidaw (5)
9 Giddy (5)
12 Lacking zest or vivacity (8)
16 Roofed colonnade (4)
17 Respiratory organ (4)
20 Belief in (or acceptance of) something as true (8)
23 Have a cigarette (5)
25 Hospital rooms with more than one bed (5)
26 Depart, go (5)
27 For what reason? (3)
28 Person afflicted with Hansen's disease (5)

Down

1 Identification tags (6)
2 Italian operatic tenor (1873–1921) (6)
3 Garden pest (5)
4 Garden buildings used for storage (5)
5 Egyptian canal (4)
6 Keenly cautious (4)
10 Offshore area (4)
11 Metallic element (4)
13 Object (4)
14 Short, sharp nail (4)
15 Augment (3)
18 Remove packaging (6)
19 Hot spring (6)
21 Give in return or recompense (5)
22 Wooden pin (5)
23 Demonstrate (4)
24 Greasy (4)

184

365

Across

1 Smooth brown oval nut (5)
3 Squeeze (5)
6 Top cards (4)
8 Beauty treatment involving massage and cleansing (6)
10 Florida resort (5)
12 Tertiary (5)
14 Share, division (7)
15 Fumble (5)
16 Momentary flash of light (5)
18 Lessens in intensity (6)
19 Disciple of Jesus also known as Matthew (4)
20 Puts on an equal basis (5)
21 Musical composition that evokes rural life (5)

Down

1 Religious song (5)
2 Beast of burden (3)
3 Rehearse (8)
4 Do away with (9)
5 Firm and hearty (5)
7 Lose water due to heating (9)
9 Radio receiver (8)
11 Cleaning implement (3)
13 Plant with flowers used in brewing (3)
15 Look fiercely (5)
17 Shrimp-like planktonic crustaceans (5)
19 Cover (3)

366

Across

1 Carried, conveyed (5)
3 English explorer said to have been saved by Pocahontas (5)
6 Bird's home (4)
8 Ensign (6)
9 Historical period (3)
11 Wife of a rajah (5)
12 Parasitic arachnids (5)
14 Small fish (7)
15 As a consequence of (3,2)
16 Country, capital Nairobi (5)
18 Bow (3)
19 Joan Collins' role in *Dynasty*, ___ Carrington (6)
20 Pull apart (4)
21 Endures (5)
22 Split fifty-fifty (5)

Down

1 Radio set (5)
2 Implore (7)
3 Nazi emblem (8)
4 Freedom from guilt (9)
5 Hurts, damages (5)
7 Not marked by the use of reason (9)
10 Exercise that increases the need for oxygen (8)
13 Motionlessness (7)
15 Slow speech with prolonged vowels (5)
17 Correspond (5)

367

Across

1 Pulls along behind (5)
4 Successful attempts at scoring (5)
7 Mature (4)
8 Very tired (coll) (3,2)
9 Painting applied to a wall surface (5)
11 Plant grown for its pungent, edible root (11)
15 Set down (3)
16 Haughtily stubborn (5-6)
19 Distinctive period of time (5)
21 Metal currency units (5)
22 Burden (4)
23 Perfume (5)
24 Fruit (5)

Down

1 Decease (5)
2 Southern US breakfast dish (5)
3 Immoral act (3)
4 Precious stone (3)
5 Experiencing motion nausea (7)
6 Slight woman or girl (5)
10 Trick (5)
12 Horizontal plant stem with shoots above and roots below (7)
13 Mischievous gnome (3)
14 Affirmative word (3)
16 Stops the flow of a liquid (5)
17 Elected (5)
18 Covered with a layer of fine powder (5)
20 Peppery (3)
21 Young bear (3)

368

Across

2 Device used to open bottles (9)
6 Stalks of a plant (5)
7 Acknowledge (5)
9 Browning of the skin caused by the sun (3)
10 Analysis of a substance such as gold or silver, to determine its make-up (5)
12 Twilled cloth used especially for military uniforms (5)
14 Violent and needless disturbance (5)
17 Territory occupied by a nation (5)
19 Frequently, poetically (3)
20 Supernatural being in Muslim folklore (5)
21 Young bird of prey (5)
22 Breakthrough (9)

Down

1 Without suffering any injury or harm (9)
2 Masticates (5)
3 Impaired in skill by neglect (5)
4 Smack with an open hand (5)
5 Cuban dance (5)
8 Period of three months, or an academic term (9)
11 Bustle (3)
13 Strike (3)
15 Blood vessels (5)
16 Major African river (5)
17 Keep or accumulate for future use (5)
18 Narrow street with walls on both sides (5)

369

Across
1 Piece of fiction (5)
4 Thick sugary liquid (5)
8 Transported (4)
9 Ship's officer who keeps accounts (6)
10 Sharp knock (3)
11 Mantle (4)
13 Skin irritation (4)
14 Glowing (7)
15 Plunder (4)
16 Lone (4)
17 Pistachio or cashew, for example (3)
18 Nuclear (6)
19 Encourage to do wrong (4)
21 Discharge, throw out (5)
22 Noise made by a sheep (5)

Down
2 Golfing device (3)
3 Place affording peace and quiet (7)
5 Italian rice dish (7)
6 Superior paper resembling sheepskin (9)
7 Machine, contraption (9)
8 Absence from work, due to illness (4,5)
12 Ask to marry (7)
13 Place or fix in position ready for use (7)
20 Ms Herzigova, supermodel (3)

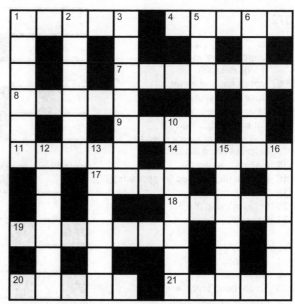

370

Across
1 Loft (5)
4 Bottle that holds oil or vinegar for the table (5)
7 Unforeseen difficulty (7)
8 Priory residents (5)
9 Offshore territory (4)
11 Capital of Liechtenstein (5)
14 Surplus to requirements (5)
17 Become soft or liquid, usually by heating (4)
18 Take exception to (5)
19 In an artificial environment outside the living organism (2,5)
20 Cud-chewing mammal of desert regions (5)
21 Period of darkness (5)

Down
1 Isaac ___, science fiction author (6)
2 Sealed in a can (6)
3 Overturn (a boat) accidentally (7)
5 Automatic response (6)
6 Long, thin cake filled with cream (6)
10 Disappointment (3-4)
12 List of items for discussion (6)
13 Referee (6)
15 Measuring the duration of (6)
16 Exceedingly sudden and unexpected (6)

371

Across
1 Lumps together (6)
6 Buccaneer (6)
8 Conflict following Iraq's invasion of Kuwait (4,3)
9 Up-to-date (6)
10 Beaten (5)
13 Opening, especially the mouth of a bodily organ (7)
16 Oddity (5)
18 Good look (coll) (6)
20 Spanish classical guitarist, Andrés ___ (1893–1987) (7)
21 Refrains from taking (6)
22 Large shrimps often coated in batter (6)

Down
1 Legerdemain (5)
2 Put up with something unpleasant (6)
3 Junk email (4)
4 Food provider (7)
5 Jules ___, author of *Around the World in Eighty Days* (5)
7 Humorously sarcastic (6)

11 Bunch of sweet-smelling flowers or herbs (7)
12 Neglect (6)
14 Roof in the form of a dome (6)
15 Cold dessert made of fruit juice (5)
17 Native of Muscat, for example (5)
19 Fewer (4)

372

Across
1 Church official in charge of a diocese (6)
6 Frozen spike of water (6)
7 Make a dull sound (4)
8 Badly behaved (7)
10 Not easily explained (3)
12 Fine screen of gauze used to keep out biting insects (8,3)
15 Make a mistake (3)
16 Kitchen utensil used for spreading (7)
19 Division of a hospital (4)
20 Looking glass (6)
21 Seem (6)

Down
1 Underside (6)
2 Noises (6)
3 Small round bread which can open into a pocket (4)
4 Male sovereign (4)
5 Praise unduly (7)
8 Small island in the central Pacific Ocean, also known as Pleasant Island (5)

9 Extreme (5)
11 Large, ocean-dwelling creature (7)
13 Invalidate (6)
14 Dealer, seller (6)
17 Covering for a wheel (4)
18 Former unit of money in Italy (4)

373

Across
1. Upright wooden post that is part of a wicket in a game of cricket (5)
3. Postpone (5)
7. Lubricates (4)
9. Appreciated (6)
11. Avid (5)
13. Delicate, fragile (5)
14. Plant exudation (5)
15. Alcoholic brew (3)
16. Enclose (3,2)
17. Lower oneself (5)
20. Provide food (5)
22. Maltreater (6)
23. Flesh (4)
24. Informal term for a father (5)
25. Group that tries actively to influence legislation (5)

Down
1. Jeer (5)
2. Ethnic group of Kenya and Tanzania (5)
4. Old-fashioned way of saying 'eighty' (9)
5. Noble gas (5)
6. Reverential salutation (3)
8. Soil composed mainly of decaying foliage (4,5)
10. Apprehend (6)
12. Brief look (6)
16. Squirrel away (5)
18. Speed at which music is to be played (5)
19. Concise and full of meaning (5)
21. Noah's boat (3)

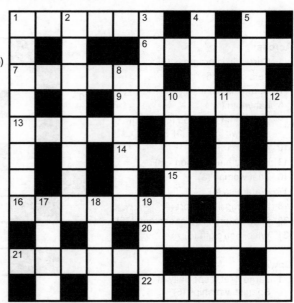

374

Across
1. ___ Mahler, composer, 1860–1911 (6)
6. Sickener (6)
7. Exacting (6)
9. Woman who invites guests to a social event (7)
13. Species of bacteria that can threaten food safety (1,4)
14. Thrash hard (3)
15. Evidence (5)
16. Public toilet in a military area (7)
20. Public speaker (6)
21. ___ butter, popular spread (6)
22. Dodger (6)

Down
1. Accelerator lever in a car (3,5)
2. Get on top of, deal with successfully (8)
3. Vote against (4)
4. Band to tie around the body (4)
5. Organs of locomotion and balance in fishes (4)
8. Very hot and finely tapering pepper (6)
10. Smile affectedly (6)
11. Accompanied (8)
12. Mariner (8)
17. Towards the side sheltered from the wind (4)
18. Units of scoring in cricket (4)
19. Brief written record (4)

375

Across

1 Small crude shelters used as dwellings (6)
6 Creature (6)
7 Semi-solid fat, used in cooking (4)
8 Make amorous advances towards (7)
12 French goodbye (5)
13 Undermine (3)
14 Order of Greek architecture (5)
15 Meeting devoted to a particular activity (7)
19 Is victorious (4)
20 Spanish word for 'tomorrow' (6)
21 At the bottom (6)

Down

1 Curriculum (8)
2 Commercial flight companies (8)
3 Palm starch used in puddings (4)
4 Equipment for the reproduction of sound (2-2)
5 Hindu woman's garment (4)
8 Japanese dish (5)
9 Plant with flowers on long spikes (5)
10 Happen simultaneously (8)
11 Stocky (8)
16 Round cheese with a red rind (4)
17 One who works during a strike (4)
18 Egg-shaped (4)

376

Across

1 Currently in progress (5)
3 Sets on fire (5)
7 Compass point (4)
8 Labyrinth (4)
9 Group that released the album *Meltdown* in 2004 (3)
10 Alienate (8)
13 Brief communications (8)
16 That woman (3)
17 Waterless (4)
18 Requiring little effort (4)
20 Facial expression of contempt (5)
21 Wise man's gift (5)

Down

1 Large fleet, especially of Spanish warships (6)
2 Number (3)
4 Cause to lose one's nerve (5)
5 Footprint (4)
6 Astronomer (9)
7 The place at which (5)
11 Extravagantly and emotionally demonstrative (5)
12 Cherry brandy (6)
14 Creep (5)
15 Celebration of the Eucharist (4)
19 Where the sun shines and the stars twinkle! (3)

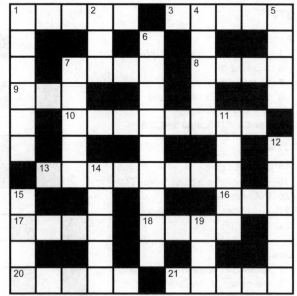

377

Across

1 Talents or skills (9)
8 Employing (5)
9 Floor consisting of open space at the top of a house (5)
10 Stitch back (3)
11 Hibernated (5)
13 Be overcome by a sudden fear (5)
15 Birds' homes (5)
18 Item worn on the hand (5)
20 Attempt (3)
21 Rub out (5)
22 Triangular glass shape used to deviate a beam of light (5)
23 Setting straight or right (9)

Down

2 Groom's partner (5)
3 Of comparatively little physical weight (5)
4 Hobo (5)
5 Consumed (5)
6 Irritations (9)
7 Refreshing treats served in cornets (3,6)
12 Hole in the ground, usually deep (3)
14 Entirely (3)
16 Dais (5)
17 Ancient upright stone slab bearing markings (5)
18 Member of a nomadic people (5)
19 Aromatic edible bulb (5)

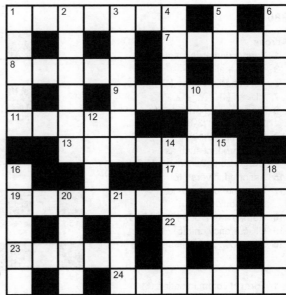

378

Across

1 Salary given to an employee who is ill (4,3)
7 Lagoon encircled by a coral reef (5)
8 Emaciated (5)
9 Scrap of fabric (7)
11 Jewish scholar (5)
13 Hang freely (7)
17 Hospital worker (5)
19 Futile (7)
22 More glacial (5)
23 Native of Baghdad, for example (5)
24 This evening (7)

Down

1 Sweetening agent (5)
2 Small pieces of bread, for example (6)
3 Regional dialect (6)
4 Measure of 36 inches (4)
5 O ___ All Ye Faithful, Christmas carol (4)
6 Piece of material used for cleaning (5)
10 List of options (4)
12 Male of domestic cattle (4)
14 Regimental flag (6)
15 Losing water (6)
16 Marie ___, chemist who discovered radium (5)
18 Type of heron (5)
20 Jacob's biblical twin (4)
21 Make changes in text (4)

379

Across

1 Examine so as to determine accuracy (5)
3 Holy apparition (5)
6 Ethical (5)
7 In an unpalatable state (3)
8 Playthings (4)
9 Country, capital Beijing (5)
12 Investigate judicially (3)
14 Lair (3)
15 Secret watcher (3)
17 Item (5)
20 Notion (4)
21 Organ of sight (3)
22 Gives one's support or approval to (5)
23 Periodic rises and falls of the sea (5)
24 Cricketing trophy (5)

Down

1 Professional performer who tells jokes (5)
2 Range of mountains (5)
3 Assign a duty to (7)
4 1990 Patrick Swayze film with a love-beyond-the-grave theme (5)
5 Of imposing height (5)
10 Jump lightly (3)
11 Words that modify something other than nouns (7)
13 Hasten (3)
15 Aroma (5)
16 Bear fruit (5)
18 Cures (5)
19 Oxygen and nitrogen, for example (5)

380

Across

1 Young, unmarried woman (4)
3 Cause fear in (5)
5 Very short distance (4)
7 Like so (4)
8 Tree-dwelling primate of Madagascar (3-3)
9 Assessment (10)
13 Dairy product such as Gorgonzola, Stilton, etc (4,6)
15 Assorted, diverse (6)
17 Sculpture of the head and shoulders (4)
18 Roman emperor 54–68 AD (4)
19 UK currency unit (5)
20 Pay received for employment (4)

Down

1 Form of communication (6)
2 Plant fibre used to make rope (5)
3 Coconut ___, popular fairground stall (3)
4 Synthetic silk-like fabric (5)
6 Procession of people travelling on horseback (9)
10 Pointed tool for punching small holes (3)
11 Material from which metal is extracted (3)
12 Stinging plant (6)
13 Well done! (5)
14 Sharp bend in a road or river (5)
16 Conclude (3)

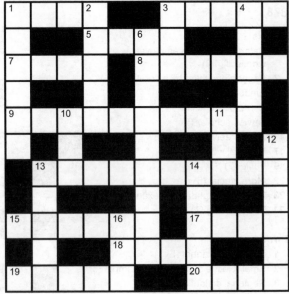

381

Across
1 Off-white colour (5)
4 Egg-shaped object (5)
7 Awkward, stupid person (3)
8 Computer instruction that results in a series of instructions (5)
9 Criminal (5)
10 Strong-scented perennial herb (3)
11 Plait of hair (5)
14 Passenger (5)
17 Correct program faults (5)
20 Very cross (5)
23 Quarrel (3)
24 Main artery of the body (5)
25 Public square in Ancient Greece (5)
26 21st letter of the Greek alphabet (3)
27 Copy on thin paper (5)
28 Melodies (5)

Down
1 Heavenly body (5)
2 Compere (coll) (5)
3 Berths, ties up (5)
4 Proposal (5)
5 Lubricated (5)
6 Basic unit of money in Jordan (5)
12 Cereal crop (3)
13 Small coin (3)
15 Electrically charged particle (3)
16 Organ of hearing (3)
17 Preliminary sketch (5)
18 Asian country (5)
19 Vine fruit (5)
20 Be in store for (5)
21 Utterance expressing disapproval (5)
22 William Butler ____, Irish poet (5)

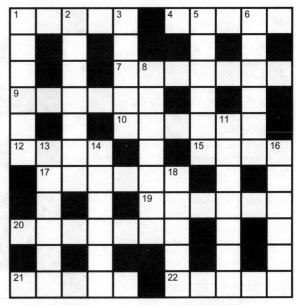

382

Across
1 Enchant (5)
4 Dandruff (5)
7 Unattractively thin and weedy (7)
9 Stan ____, film partner of Oliver Hardy (6)
10 Withdraw from an organisation (6)
12 Edith ____, French cabaret singer (1915–63) (4)
15 Have the courage (4)
17 Any leafy plants eaten as vegetables (6)
19 Engrave (6)
20 Associate who works with others (7)
21 Mr Manilow, singer (5)
22 King of England (944–975) (5)

Down
1 Conscript for military service (4,2)
2 Shaped like a ring (7)
3 Mulls over, ponders (5)
5 Maddened (6)
6 Official responsible for managing and protecting an area of forest (6)
8 Wash (7)
11 Sweetheart (7)
13 Large grey-green lizard of tropical America (6)
14 Shackle (6)
16 This or that (6)
18 Sloping mass of loose rocks at the base of a cliff (5)

383

Across
1 Small arachnids (5)
4 Inuit dwelling (5)
7 Powder applied to the cheeks (5)
8 Take place again (5)
9 Wood plant (4)
11 At a distance (4)
12 Take illegally, as of territory (5)
14 Be of service (3)
16 Cash registers (5)
18 Owl's cry (4)
20 Sign of something about to happen (4)
22 Carriageways (5)
23 Defence of some offensive behaviour or failure to keep a promise (5)
24 Devoid of clothing (5)
25 Landscaped area for playing golf (5)

Down
1 Masonry bond (6)
2 Huge destructive wave (7)
3 Type of fat (4)
5 Area surrounding the hole on a golf course (5)
6 Man-eating giant (4)
8 Tear violently (4)
10 Advance (5)
13 Strong feeling (7)
14 Voluntary contributions to aid the poor (4)
15 Moral principles (6)
17 Hotel for travellers (5)
19 Food prepared from the husks of cereal grains (4)
21 Carpentry pin (4)

384

Across
1 Had ownership (9)
8 Accuse of a wrong (7)
9 Honey-producing insect (3)
10 Short line at the end of the main strokes of a character (5)
12 Tartan (5)
13 Electronic device that generates a series of beeps (5)
15 Casing (5)
16 Had a meal (3)
17 Greek goddess of divine retribution and vengeance (7)
19 Stretch of open pavement for walking beside the seashore (9)

Down
2 Implement used to propel or steer a boat (3)
3 Not flexible or pliant (5)
4 The first light of day (3-2)
5 Clasp another person in the arms (7)
6 Pouched mammal (9)
7 Social system that developed in Europe in the eighth century (9)
11 Return to a former state (7)
14 Of the kidneys (5)
15 One of the twelve Apostles (5)
18 Sex Pistols' bassist, ___ Vicious (1957–79) (3)

385

Across

1 African country (5)
4 Drinking tube (5)
7 Sincere (7)
8 Variety of beet with broad edible leaf stalks (5)
9 Train carriage with berths for overnight passengers (7)
13 Thaw (4)
16 Simple, bare (4)
17 Capital of Kyrgyzstan (7)
19 Primitive plant forms (5)
20 Smokestack (7)
21 Temporary love of an adolescent (5)
22 Jack in a pack of cards (5)

Down

1 Be fatally overwhelmed (7)
2 Causes to run off the tracks (7)
3 Depends on (5)
5 Bicycle for two (6)
6 Reply (6)
10 Side sheltered from the wind (3)

11 Framework that supports climbing plants (7)
12 Government income due to taxation (7)

14 Alternative – this or that (6)
15 Thick, innermost digits of the hand (6)
18 Arctic canoe (5)

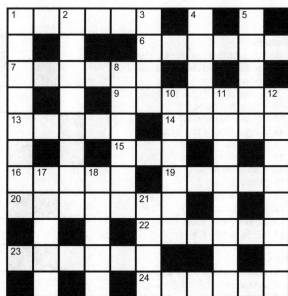

386

Across

1 Unnatural lack of colour in the skin (6)
6 Newspaper chief (6)
7 Sign of the zodiac (6)
9 Whole number (7)
13 Mimicking (5)
14 Agitate, waken (5)
15 Large African antelope (3)
16 Legitimate (5)
19 Lively ballroom dance from Brazil (5)
20 Defendant in a court of law (7)
22 Pearl-producing shellfish (6)
23 Lords (6)
24 Worked hard (6)

Down

1 Plaits of hair worn at the sides of the head (8)
2 Short-tailed furry-footed rodents of circumpolar distribution (8)
3 Harness strap (4)
4 TV programme recording device (5)
5 Ciphers (5)
8 Argue over petty things (6)
10 Faithful, dependable (6)

11 Grey corrosion-resistant form of bronze containing zinc (8)
12 Mended (8)

17 Monetary units of Spain, France, Germany, etc (5)
18 Put into service, practise (5)
21 Expense (4)

387

Across
1 Boasts (5)
4 Emblem (5)
7 Vocal pitch (3)
8 Got up (5)
10 Silvery metal (3)
11 City with a famous tower (4)
12 Closed litter for one passenger (5)
14 Composed (5)
17 Choral work (5)
20 Go stealthily (5)
22 Common rodents (4)
23 Vat (3)
24 Greek author of fables (5)
26 Garbage container (3)
27 Rigid part of a bicycle (5)
28 Took in liquid (5)

Down
1 Small vessels for travel on water (5)
2 Gone by (3)
3 Hank of knitting wool (5)
4 Rule made by a local authority (2-3)
5 Mark used to indicate the word above it should be repeated (5)
6 Mr Wise, former comedian (5)
9 Place at intervals (5)
13 Former name of Tokyo, Japan (3)
15 Wash off soap (5)
16 Light mid-afternoon meal (3)
17 Repeated theme (5)
18 Bone of the leg (5)
19 Clan (5)
20 Endure, put up with (5)
21 Coin, one hundredth of a rouble (5)
25 Large body of water (3)

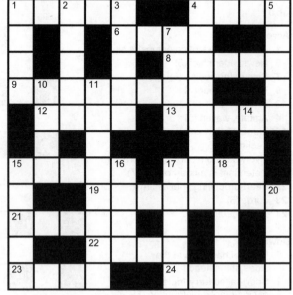

388

Across
1 Long narrow bands of material (5)
4 Mediocre and disdained writer (4)
6 Vagrant, tramp (4)
8 Spring month (5)
9 Crack in a bone (8)
12 Yours and mine (4)
13 Singer whose hits include *Jailhouse Rock* (5)
15 Great unhappiness (5)
17 Capital of Norway (4)
19 Enjoyable (8)
21 Embankment (5)
22 Hindu princess (4)
23 Belonging to that woman (4)
24 Glide across ice (5)

Down
1 Quarrel about petty points (4)
2 Seasoned, colourful rice (5)
3 Closes (5)
4 Desperate (8)
5 Puts to death (5)
7 Naked (4)
10 Bellow (4)
11 Spreading plants such as ivy or periwinkle (8)
14 Smoothing tool used on clothing (4)
15 Narrow gorge with a stream running through it (5)
16 Jumping insect (4)
17 Desert garden (5)
18 Insect in the stage between egg and pupa (5)
20 Wear out, exhaust (4)

196

389

Across
2 Cooked over an outdoor grill (9)
6 Popped (5)
8 Deserving of a scratch (5)
11 Moral (7)
13 Ballet dancer's skirt (4)
14 Large brown mushrooms (Boletus edulis) (4)
15 Make brown and crisp by heating (5)
16 Leave out (4)
18 Small area of water-surrounded land (4)
20 Use again after processing (7)
23 Gain a goal (5)
24 King of Judea who ordered the death of many children (5)
25 Group of prestigious US universities (3,6)

Down
1 Having a strong desire for success (9)
2 Cap with no brim or peak (5)
3 Book of the Old Testament (4)
4 Long narrative poem (4)
5 Husband of one's aunt (5)
7 Speak haltingly (7)
9 Producing a sensation of touch (7)
10 Twenty-four hours ago (9)
12 Republic in southern Europe (5)
17 Witty language used to convey scorn (5)
19 Wait on (5)
21 Give up (4)
22 Muffled explosive sound as of a slowly running internal-combustion engine (4)

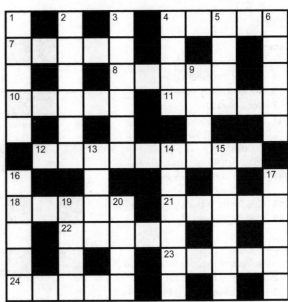

390

Across
4 Vigorous and enthusiastic enjoyment (5)
7 Woollen item worn about the neck (5)
8 Snares (5)
10 Not in a state of sleep (5)
11 North American elk (5)
12 Daily publication (9)
18 Arrangement or neatness (5)
21 Serpent (5)
22 Positively charged electrode (5)
23 Relating to the organ of smell (5)
24 Piece of cloth used to cover the head and shoulders (5)

Down
1 Muslim religion (5)
2 Appetiser usually of a thin slice of toast spread with a savoury paste (6)
3 Dessert (6)
4 Largest and most southerly island in the Marianas (4)
5 Tolerable, indifferent (2-2)
6 Proprietor (5)
9 Grandeur (4)
13 Small bird (4)
14 Missing (6)
15 Slip away (6)
16 Stretches of heathland (5)
17 Back parts of human feet (5)
19 Facts given (4)
20 Bread bun (4)

391

Across

1. Utter monotonously and repetitively (5)
4. Device used to stop a vehicle (5)
7. Skilled trades (6)
9. Excitedly eager (4)
11. Berkshire town, famous for its racecourse (5)
12. Small air-breathing arthropod (6)
14. Fling up (4)
16. Small biting fly (4)
19. Move rapidly (6)
21. Speak up (5)
22. William ____, former British prime minister (4)
23. Long noosed rope (6)
25. Native American tent (5)
26. Saltpetre (5)

Down

1. Using a bike (7)
2. Natives of Kuwait or Qatar, for example (5)
3. Small measure of drink (3)
5. Nuclear plant (7)
6. Entangles (5)
8. Schoolbag (7)
10. Gunge (3)
13. Give the right to (7)
15. Term of endearment (7)
17. Racket (5)
18. Fitting (3)
20. Wind round and round (5)
24. Beard found on a bract of grass (3)

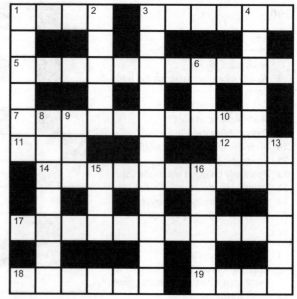

392

Across

1. Table condiment (4)
3. Roof of the mouth (6)
5. Not absolutely essential (11)
7. Not likely (10)
11. Means of returning something by post (inits) (3)
12. Peculiar (3)
14. Teacher (10)
17. Magic word used in a spell or in conjuring (11)
18. Gas found in the atmosphere (6)
19. Swirling current (4)

Down

1. Natives of Riyadh, for example (6)
2. Belonging to them (5)
3. In law, to agree to admit guilt in return for a lesser charge (4-7)
4. Underwater missile (7)
6. Weep (3)
8. Computer file in which incoming emails are stored (7)
9. Writing implement (3)
10. Destiny (3)
13. Lacking in liveliness or charm (6)
15. Watering place (3)
16. Rugged box used for shipping (5)

393

Across

1 Annoyed and irritable (6)
4 Discontinue (4)
6 Guerilla (9)
8 Flightless bird, now extinct (3)
10 Incapable of sustaining life (6)
13 Piece of leather forming the front upper of a shoe (4)
14 Talk pompously (5)
16 Coagulate (4)
17 Imperial capacity measure equal to four pecks (6)
20 Chopper (3)
21 Attack of violent mental agitation (9)
22 Makes a wager (4)
23 Upward slope (6)

Down

1 Move to a higher point (5)
2 Sacred table in a church (5)
3 Edge, rim (6)
4 Makes strenuous efforts (7)
5 Cooking vessel (3)
7 Malleable odourless plastic explosive (6)
9 Annie ____, famous US sharpshooter (6)
11 Spins on an axis (7)
12 Take into custody (3)
15 Bulbous plants associated with Amsterdam (6)
18 Rush (5)
19 Slightest (5)
21 Central part of a car wheel (3)

394

Across

1 Oven-cooked stew (9)
8 River that flows through Paris (5)
9 Loose garment worn by Muslim women (5)
10 Mr Reed who had a Perfect Day (3)
11 Pastorale (5)
13 Relating to them (5)
15 Penetrate gradually (5)
18 Organisation of employees (5)
20 Large vase (3)
21 Former statutory unit of gas supplied in the UK (5)
22 Oliver ____, Dickens character (5)
23 Cultural anthropology (9)

Down

2 Friendship (5)
3 Witch's incantation (5)
4 Prove to be false or incorrect (5)
5 Very slow in tempo (5)
6 Swing from side to side regularly (9)
7 Filberts (9)
12 Resinous substance used to make varnish, sealing wax, dyes, etc (3)
14 Adult female bird (3)
16 Representative (5)
17 Mortal (5)
18 Up to a time that (5)
19 Frosting (5)

395

Across

1 Pulse vegetables (5)
4 Pipes (5)
7 The day before (3)
8 Small creatures eaten by whales, etc (5)
9 Cereal plant yielding corn (5)
10 Impatient, especially under restriction or delay (7)
12 Last letter of the alphabet (3)
14 Most vital part of some idea (3)
16 Nationalist (7)
19 Blasts (5)
20 Wayside plant with daisy-like flowers (2-3)
21 Former French gold or silver coin (3)
22 Food made from a dough of flour or meal (5)
23 Firm (5)

Down

1 Motorcyclist (5)
2 Farewell remark (5)
3 Voluntarily assumed or endured (4-7)
4 Characterised by violent emotions (11)
5 Air attack (5)
6 Velocity (5)
11 World's second-largest living bird (3)
13 Consciousness of one's own identity (3)
14 Rich man (5)
15 Act of immoderate indulgence (5)
17 Perfect type (5)
18 Vogue (5)

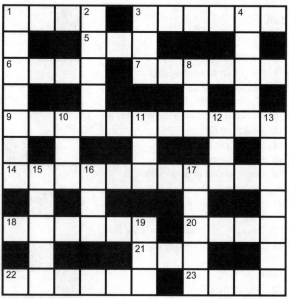

396

Across

1 Baseball bat (4)
3 Burrowing animal (6)
5 Unspecified (quantity) (3)
6 Weeps convulsively (4)
7 Extremely cold (6)
9 Motley assortment of things (4,3,4)
14 Placed on a reduced roll of names, especially of candidates for a job (11)
18 On time (6)
20 Extremely wicked (4)
21 Grow older (3)
22 The process of flowing in (6)
23 Water from the eye (4)

Down

1 Traditions (7)
2 Footing (5)
3 Scandinavian type of knotted pile rug (3)
4 Overgrown with a clinging plant (5)
8 Signal for action (3)
10 Two performers (3)
11 Nought (3)
12 Negative word (3)
13 Maker of equestrian equipment (7)
15 Wading bird (5)
16 Tool for driving or forcing something by impact (3)
17 Dish served as the last course of a meal (5)
19 Charge a contribution to state revenue (3)

200

397

Across

1 Makes a connection (5)
4 Basic units of electric current (abbr) (4)
6 Primates (4)
7 Tolerate (4)
8 Cord passed through eyelet-holes to fasten an item of footwear (8)
12 Speck of soot (4)
14 Cover with colouring matter (5)
15 Scottish lake (4)
16 Hired murderer (8)
20 River that flows through Darlington and Middlesborough (4)
21 US midwestern state (4)
22 Addition (4)
23 Rascal (5)

Down

1 Supports for a table (4)
2 'Fiddling' Roman emperor (4)
3 Cruise (4)
4 Fireproof material (8)
5 Stiff pompous gait (5)
9 Mythical lover of Leander (4)
10 Special and significant stress (8)
11 Sign of the zodiac (5)
13 Variety of citrus fruit (4)
15 Pause during which things are calm (3-2)
17 Slightly open (4)
18 Musical composition with words (4)
19 Appellation (4)

398

Across

1 Building for carrying on industrial labour (5)
4 Commerce (5)
7 One or other (6)
9 Not in good health (4)
10 Put together (4)
11 Wide road (6)
14 Cannabis plant (4)
15 *Old King* ___, nursery rhyme (4)
16 Lie in a comfortable resting position (6)
20 Long-necked bird (4)
21 Country, capital Lomé (4)
22 Tool used with a mortar (6)
23 Stitched (5)
24 Jerks violently (5)

Down

1 Removes the rind from (5)
2 Stage-player (5)
3 Subject (5)
5 Fruit of a flowering thorny shrub (7)
6 Runs off suddenly (7)
8 Difficult, entangling situation (3,4)
12 Couple (7)
13 Ugly object (7)
17 Adversary, foe (5)
18 Many times (5)
19 Jugs (5)

399

Across

1 Acid found in milk (6)
6 Nocturnal wild cat of Central and South America (6)
7 Return (2,4)
9 King who unknowingly killed his father and married his mother (7)
10 Part of milk containing the butterfat (5)
12 L-shaped support (7)
17 In snooker, to pocket the cue ball after hitting another (2-3)
18 Adrift (7)
20 Hitchcock film of 1960 (6)
21 Former Spanish monetary unit (6)
22 Refreshed as by sleeping or relaxing (6)

Down

1 Gift in a will (6)
2 Spider's snare (6)
3 Fuel produced by the distillation of coal (4)
4 Inhabitant (7)
5 Egyptian falcon-headed god (5)
8 State of deep unconsciousness (4)
11 Body of water between Kazakhstan and Uzbekistan (4,3)
13 Expression of love (4)
14 Male domestic feline (6)
15 Have the financial means to buy something (6)
16 Donated (5)
19 Stout rounded pole used to support rigging (4)

400

Across

1 Cock-a-leekie, for instance (4)
3 Severe or trying experience (6)
5 High mountain (3)
6 Landlocked republic in north-west Africa (4)
7 Conveying (6)
9 State of mild depression (3,7)
14 Enterprising or ambitious drive (coll) (3-2-3-2)
17 Muscle that flexes the forearm (6)
19 Young girl (4)
20 Rapid bustling commotion (3)
21 Decapitate (6)
22 Midday (4)

Down

1 Comparative figure of speech (6)
2 Causes emotional distress (5)
3 Decide, make a choice (3)
4 Female relatives (5)
8 Colourful, ornamental fish (3)
10 Very small (3)
11 One who is playfully mischievous (3)
12 *Father ___*, sitcom starring Dermot Morgan (3)
13 Deteriorate (6)
14 Filth (5)
15 Foot digit (3)
16 Synthetic fabric (5)
18 Mournful (3)

401

Across

1 Ms Sarandon, Oscar-winning Hollywood actress (5)
4 Popular pub game (5)
7 Person responsible for a collection of books (9)
9 Make up for past sins (5)
10 Scarf bandage (5)
12 Bird of New Zealand (4)
14 In addition (4)
16 Fine strong silky fabric (5)
18 Large body of water (5)
20 Being of the same dimensions as an original (4-5)
21 Playing card not allied to any suit in the pack (5)
22 Actions (5)

Down

1 Decreased in size (6)
2 Grain-storage tower (4)
3 Alfred ____, Swedish 'Prize' instigator (5)
5 Overbearing pride (9)
6 Expresses gratitude (6)
8 Disingenuous (9)
11 Hostel (3)
13 Dark blue colour (6)
15 Proprietors (6)
17 Seeped (5)
19 Boundary, rim (4)

402

Across

1 Diagnostic test of substance from the body (6)
6 On land (6)
7 Vegetable, emblem of Wales (4)
9 Enquiry into the finances of a person applying for monetary aid (5,4)
13 Gush (5)
15 Informal farewell remark (3)
16 Bus garage (5)
20 Child's toy (5,4)
23 Use a keyboard (4)
24 Knitting tool (6)
25 Desired (6)

Down

1 Solid projectiles shot by a musket (5)
2 Fire iron (5)
3 Gape (4)
4 Bird symbolising peace (4)
5 Converge (4)
8 Large flightless bird (3)
10 Held off, kept distant (2,3)
11 Leather with a napped surface (5)
12 Japanese form of wrestling (4)
14 Uncontaminated (4)
17 Having been consumed (5)
18 Enquire in a meddlesome way (3)
19 Horizontal part of a stair (5)
20 Weight units of 2240 lbs (4)
21 Judge, consider (4)
22 Exhaled with force (4)

403

Across

1 Royal House of William III of England (6)
4 Uttered aloud (4)
6 Make free from bacteria (9)
8 Diminutive of Henry (3)
10 Afternoon nap (6)
13 Bony outgrowth on an animal's head (4)
14 Gifted, competent (4)
15 Dock (6)
19 Novel, fresh (3)
20 Sum total of many miscellaneous things (9)
21 Stained with a colourant (4)
22 Joined together (6)

Down

1 Profane or obscene expressions (5)
2 Long, narrow passageway (5)
3 Relatively large in size (5)
4 Abundant element, atomic number 16 (7)
5 Female deer (3)
7 Place of worship associated with a sacred thing or person (6)
9 Safety device in a motor vehicle (3,3)
11 Soiled by smudging (7)
12 Intent (3)
16 Once more (5)
17 Clumsy (5)
18 Prize (5)
20 Append (3)

404

Across

1 Dog house (6)
6 Insusceptible (6)
7 Greek letter (4)
8 Glass vessel with a narrow neck (6)
10 Short-lived (5)
13 Reduce to ashes (7)
16 Deciduous conifer (5)
18 To the opposite side (6)
20 Advance (4)
21 Blanket-like cloak (6)
22 Mixture of blue and red (6)

Down

1 Cubes of meat cooked on a skewer (5)
2 Not so far off (6)
3 Jointed appendage (4)
4 Cattle thief (7)
5 Number indicated by the Roman VII (5)
9 Relating to speech (4)
11 Area for skating (3,4)
12 Professional charges (4)
14 Maker and alterer of garments (6)
15 Mr Richardson, knighted actor (1902–1983) (5)
17 Circumstance upon which subsequent events depend (5)
19 Retail establishment (4)

405

Across

1 Vanish (9)
7 Aroma (5)
8 Bring together (5)
9 Bathroom fixture (3)
10 Out of practice (5)
12 Sense of good style (5)
14 Adjust again after an initial failure (5)
17 Banquet (5)
19 *Much ___ about Nothing*, Shakespeare play (3)
20 Vehicles used to travel over snow (5)
21 Ball game (5)
22 In earnest (9)

Down

2 Grows from, originates (5)
3 Dough-like mixture used to secure panes of glass (5)
4 Release suddenly and often violently (5)
5 Harnesses (5)
6 In the near future (9)
7 Startled (9)
11 Definite article (3)
13 Grow old (3)
15 Goes in search of (5)
16 Weapon that delivers a temporarily paralysing electric shock (5)
17 Do without (5)
18 Mythical Greek giant with 100 eyes (5)

406

Across

1 Edible black marine bivalve (6)
6 Collection of beehives (6)
7 Magic spell or charm (4)
9 In another location (9)
12 Ancient Mexican civilisation (5)
13 17th letter of the Greek alphabet (3)
15 Fortune-teller's pack of cards (5)
18 Pointed tip of a dart-like weapon (9)
20 Stand up on the hind legs (4)
21 Crown or headband worn by a sovereign (6)
22 Ice cream served with a topping (6)

Down

1 African venomous snake (5)
2 Took without the owner's consent (5)
3 Body of water (4)
4 Island republic off the coast of Senegal (4,5)
5 Used a keyboard (5)
8 Fast narrow current in the atmosphere or ocean (3,6)
10 Spirally threaded cylindrical rod (5)
11 Put pen to paper (5)
14 Black and white, bamboo-eating mammal (5)
16 Elvis Presley's middle name (5)
17 Concise in manner (5)
19 Folds over and sews together (4)

205

407

Across

1 Put into a bank account (9)
8 Soup-serving spoon (5)
9 Electronic device that generates a series of beeps (5)
10 Affirmative word (3)
11 Flock of geese in flight (5)
13 Cavalry weapon (5)
15 Salad vegetable (5)
18 For this reason (5)
20 Popular hot beverage (3)
21 Inclined to drip (5)
22 Written publications (5)
23 Find out (9)

Down

2 Give qualities or abilities to (5)
3 Huge sea (5)
4 Cause to move forward with force (5)
5 Encourage, cause to act (3,2)
6 Something achieved by a narrow margin (5,4)
7 Poetry without rhyme or regular rhythm (4,5)

12 ___ and outs, details of a situation (3)
14 Time period (3)
16 Chris ___, ex-husband of Billie Piper (5)

17 Fashion (5)
18 Use (5)
19 Ms Campbell, model (5)

408

Across

1 Disperse from a central point to cover a wide area (3,3)
6 Rupture in smooth muscle tissue (6)
7 Reach a destination (6)
10 Business conducted over the internet (1-8)
12 Thick quilt (5)
14 Flower leaf (5)
17 Gut (9)
19 Official in charge of a prison (6)
20 Tiny Japanese tree (6)
21 Ditch worn by running water (6)

Down

1 Criminal deception (5)
2 Postponed for attention at a later date (2,3)
3 Those people (4)
4 Put into code (9)
5 Stratum (5)
8 Highly offensive (9)
9 Electors (6)
11 Short-sightedness (6)

13 Legs or arms (5)
15 Recruit into an army (5)
16 Haulage vehicle (5)

18 Slender shoot growing from a branch (4)

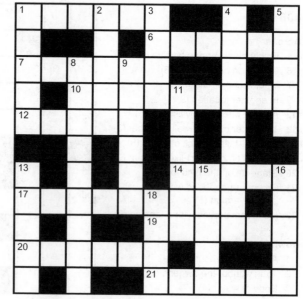

409

Across

1 Food used in a trap (4)
3 Small pouch for shampoo, etc (6)
6 Not in favour of (4)
7 Crust-like surface of a healing wound (4)
8 Distant but within sight (6)
9 Not responsive (to argument, feeling, etc) (10)
14 Showing sensitive insight (10)
17 Young cattle (6)
19 Overtake (4)
20 Strip the skin off (4)
21 Intense dislike (6)
22 Shafts of light (4)

Down

1 ____-Herzegovina, European country (6)
2 Item of furniture (5)
3 Enclosure for swine (3)
4 Garlic mayonnaise (5)
5 Level betting (5)
10 Food in a pastry shell (3)
11 Compete (3)
12 Mr Geller, psychic (3)
13 Population count (6)
14 Pedestrianised public square (5)
15 Thin pancake (5)
16 Narrow to a point (5)
18 Distressing (3)

410

Across

1 Happening quickly or promptly (5)
3 Committee having supervisory powers (5)
6 Muslim name for the one and only God (5)
7 Greek letter (5)
10 State or society governed by the wealthy (10)
13 2011 film produced, directed and starring Ralph Fiennes (10)
16 Deflect, fend off (5)
19 Happen (5)
20 Gentle poke (5)
21 Race run at Epsom (5)

Down

1 Token indicating that postal fees have been paid (5)
2 Person who uses insincere praise (9)
3 Plead (3)
4 Aspire (3)
5 Hollywood actress, Cameron ___ (4)
8 Slide of snow from a mountainside (9)
9 Rôle player (5)
11 Resin-like substance secreted by certain insects (3)
12 Second person pronoun (3)
14 Atomiser (5)
15 Farm outbuilding (4)
17 Conclude (3)
18 Golf peg (3)

411

Across

1 Ecstasy (5)
4 Founded (5)
7 Example, instance (4)
9 Magic word used in a spell or in conjuring (11)
10 Marked with spots (6)
12 Held back, retained (4)
13 Small island lying to the east of Guernsey (4)
14 At an angle (6)
17 Hate coupled with disgust (11)
20 Forcibly pulled apart (4)
21 Fourth letter of the Greek alphabet (5)
22 Ms Parton, songstress (5)

Down

1 Lacking taste or flavour (5)
2 Less than the correct or full amount (5)
3 Pouch (3)
4 Plot of ground in which plants grow (3)
5 Field of study (7)
6 Passed out playing cards (5)
8 Sedimentary rock (9)
11 Violent disturbance (7)
13 Burn with steam (5)
15 Bingo (5)
16 Fop (5)
18 Lyricist, ___ Gershwin (3)
19 Added to (3)

412

Across

1 Crucial (9)
8 In the centre of (5)
9 Bar of metal (5)
10 American ___, poisonous shrub (5)
11 Controlled a vehicle (5)
12 Head/body connectors (5)
15 Christ (5)
17 Exaggerated nasality in speech (5)
18 Man-made fibre (5)
19 Moving staircase (9)

Down

2 Rebuke (5)
3 Enthusiastic (5)
4 Chinese secret society (5)
5 Prefix denoting a partly British connection (5)
6 Motherhood (9)
7 Putting emphasis on (9)
13 Forms a layer over (5)
14 18th letter of the Greek alphabet (5)
15 Military dictators (5)
16 Volley (5)

413

Across

3 Feeling uneasy and self-conscious (7)
6 Consecrate (5)
7 Blood-red (7)
8 Deport from a country (5)
9 Large, edible marine fish (4)
11 Face (4)
14 Prescribed selection of foods (4)
17 As well (4)
19 Cow's milk-gland (5)
20 Abstaining from food (7)
21 Throw with great effort (5)
22 Looked after a small child in the absence of a parent (7)

Down

1 Mother superior (6)
2 In arrears (6)
3 Valuable quality (5)
4 Counterpane (6)
5 Come out (6)
10 Increases (3)
12 Island in the Ionian Sea, the legendary home of Odysseus (6)
13 Hearty and lusty, crude (6)
15 Native of Mumbai, for example (6)
16 Country, capital Ankara (6)
18 Had better (5)

414

Across

1 Impertinent (coll) (5)
4 Circle of rope used in a throwing game (5)
7 Characteristic of a clan (6)
10 Barrier constructed to keep out the sea (4)
12 Blithe (8)
13 Being moderately fond of (6)
14 Finishes (4)
16 Ramble aimlessly (4)
19 Disorderly fighting (6)
22 Component of blood, essential for clotting (8)
23 Scoff (4)
24 Salad herb (6)
25 Donkeys (5)
26 Irritable, peevish (coll) (5)

Down

1 Coloniser (7)
2 Film of oil floating on water (5)
3 Ache, long (5)
5 Without clothing (9)
6 Irritated (5)
8 Vessel in which pans and their contents are slowly heated (4-5)
9 Beneficiary of a will (7)
11 Japanese currency unit (3)
15 Appearance of a place (7)
17 Affords access to (5)
18 Alcoholic beverage (3)
20 Relating to the forearm (5)
21 Supply sparingly and with restricted quantities (5)

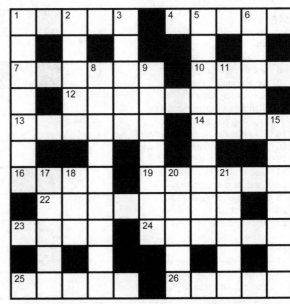

415

Across
1 Male bee (5)
4 Bath's river (4)
6 Press down tightly (4)
7 Vulgar (4)
8 Natural bright daylight (8)
12 Soap froth (4)
14 Rebuffs, refuses to acknowledge (5)
15 Utterance made by exhaling audibly (4)
16 Held captive (8)
20 Anise-flavoured Greek liqueur (4)
21 Contest of speed (4)
22 Sudden attack (4)
23 Garden tool (5)

Down
1 Excavates (4)
2 Domesticated bovine animals (4)
3 Corrode, as with acid (4)
4 Social activities and entertainment following a day on the piste (5-3)
5 Demands (5)
9 Fruit, a cross between a tangerine and a grapefruit (4)
10 Strong line connecting a weight to a sliding window (4,4)
11 Entomb, especially after cremation (5)
13 Bird symbolising peace (4)
15 Clean with hard rubbing (5)
17 Professional charges (4)
18 Star that ejects material (4)
19 British peer of the highest rank (4)

416

Across
4 Hate coupled with disgust (5)
8 Not decorated (9)
9 Consumption (3)
10 Vile, despicable (5)
13 Disfigures permanently by inflicting a wound (5)
14 Thin strip of wood or metal (4)
15 Tube to carry rainwater away (9)
19 Outlying farm building (4)
21 Machine for bundling hay (5)
24 Confused scuffle (5)
25 Large nation (inits) (3)
26 Respect (9)
27 Antarctic explorer (5)

Down
1 Adult male domestic cattle (5)
2 Large, spotted feline of tropical America (6)
3 Replicate (4)
4 Burden of responsibility (4)
5 Give an account of (8)
6 Estimation (4)
7 Residence of a clergyman (5)
11 Ancient (3)
12 Scenery of a dramatic production (5,3)
16 Losing colour or brightness (6)
17 On a former occasion, poetically (3)
18 Complies (5)
20 On no occasion (5)
22 Board game (4)
23 Vessel made of planks (4)
24 Female equine animal (4)

417

Across

1 Conceal (5)
3 Close-fitting trousers of heavy denim (5)
7 Remainder (4)
9 Emotional wound or shock (6)
10 Not any (4)
11 Opaque gem (4)
12 Narrow backstreet (5)
15 Remote in manner (5)
17 Professional cook (4)
19 Succulent plant (4)
20 Capital of Greece (6)
21 Slope or hillside in Scotland (4)
22 Fruit pulp (5)
23 Biblical shepherd who slew Goliath (5)

Down

1 Barrier (6)
2 Sing the praises of (5)
4 Electronic message (5)
5 Moved through water (4)
6 Unwavering (9)
8 Common gastropod (5)
13 Medium that was once supposed to fill all space (5)
14 Cause to feel resentment or indignation (6)
16 Abnormally fat (5)
17 Venomous hooded snake (5)
18 Moist (4)

418

Across

1 Contagious viral disease (5)
4 Type of bread used as a pocket for filling (5)
7 Memorisation by repetition (4)
8 Coupling (5)
9 Value (5)
11 Break-up, disintegration into parts (11)
13 Ill-fated (4-7)
16 Generally accepted truth (5)
18 Ms Radcliffe, British long-distance runner (5)
19 Assist in doing wrong (4)
20 Unit of currency (5)
21 Very poor, impoverished (5)

Down

1 Fungus which thrives in damp conditions (5)
2 Formal school or college balls held at the end of a year (5)
3 Boy child (3)
4 Church bench (3)
5 Popular root vegetables (7)
6 Anaemic-looking (5)
10 Consternation (5)
12 Large, ocean-dwelling mammal (3,4)
13 Skin covering the top of the head (5)
14 Flatfish (5)
15 Daily written record of events (5)
17 Month with 31 days (3)
18 Female swan (3)

419

Across

1 Holy city (5)
4 Quantity of twelve items (5)
7 Goggling, as in surprise (3-4)
8 Particular items (5)
10 Domesticated (5)
12 Former Nigerian capital (5)
14 Naming words (5)
16 Divisions of a dollar (5)
17 Reddish-brown hair dye (5)
19 Traveller (7)
20 Central pillar of a circular staircase (5)
21 Ocean-going vessel (5)

Down

1 Hilary ___, author of *Bring up the Bodies* (6)
2 Cipher (4)
3 Mollify (7)
5 Take too much medication (8)
6 Number indicated by the Roman XI (6)
9 Barrier formed from upright wooden posts or stakes (8)
11 Hold spellbound (7)
13 Nobody specifically (6)
15 Bracing atmosphere by the coast (3,3)
18 Indian bread, baked in a clay oven (4)

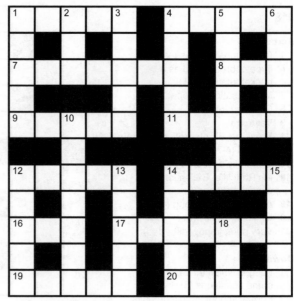

420

Across

1 Pointed projection on a fork (5)
4 Diversion requiring physical exertion (5)
7 Participant in some activity (7)
8 Metal container (3)
9 Arctic marten (5)
11 Fragment (5)
12 Popular board game (5)
14 Cut-price events (5)
16 Encountered (3)
17 Lodger (7)
19 Discontinue (5)
20 Rub out (5)

Down

1 Machine used for printing (5)
2 Select as an alternative (3)
3 Wine-making fruit (5)
4 Assemble (3,2)
5 Porridge ingredient (7)
6 Unit of weight equivalent to 1000 kilograms (5)
10 Drink given to people who are ill (4,3)
12 Child's magazine (5)
13 Cavalry sword (5)
14 Ordered series (5)
15 Bout, period of indulgence (5)
18 Chemical that carries genetic information (inits) (3)

421

Across
1 Holds fast (5)
4 Colour of bleached bones (5)
7 Rules as a monarch (6)
9 Cobbler's stand (4)
10 Garden building (4)
12 In one's sleeping place (4)
13 Far beyond the norm (5)
15 Unattended machine (outside some banks) that dispenses money (init) (3)
17 Conform (5)
19 Army's temporary living quarters (4)
21 Individual unit (4)
23 Gelling agent (4)
24 Elaborate (6)
25 Habitation (5)
26 Metal-shaping machine (5)

Down
1 Hard deposit on the teeth (6)
2 Liquorice-flavoured herb (7)
3 Performs an act of transgression (4)
5 Elevated open grassland in southern Africa (5)
6 Abominable snowman (4)
8 Mechanical device on a camera (7)
11 Common type of tree (3)
14 Person who accepts the world as it literally is (7)
15 Appropriate (3)
16 Each (6)
18 Broadcast (a programme) on radio or television (5)
20 Long detailed story (4)
22 Repast (4)

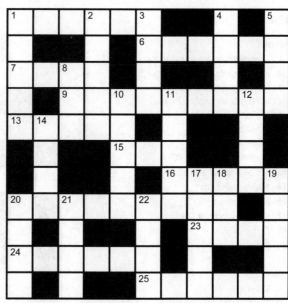

422

Across
1 Mars, ruins (6)
6 Domesticated South American mammal with long silky fleece (6)
7 Alike (4)
9 Preserve by removing all liquids from (9)
13 Diversion requiring physical exertion (5)
15 Atmosphere (3)
16 Secreting organ in animals (5)
20 Formal separation from an alliance or federation (9)
23 Greenish-blue (4)
24 Emergence (6)
25 Force or compel (6)

Down
1 Closes with a bang (5)
2 Closer to the centre (5)
3 Dress worn primarily by Hindu women (4)
4 Spanish sparkling white wine (4)
5 Female pantomime character (4)
8 Artificial language, a simplification of Esperanto (3)
10 Thrusting blows (5)
11 Welsh breed of dog (5)
12 Urban area (4)
14 Funeral pile (4)
17 In the area (5)
18 None in particular (3)
19 Closely packed (5)
20 Printing command to ignore a former deletion (4)
21 Stiff paper (4)
22 Neither good nor bad (2-2)

423

Across
- **1** Scorches (5)
- **4** Picture taken by a camera (abbr) (5)
- **9** Wide-mouthed jug (4)
- **10** Yearbook (7)
- **11** US novelist, creator of *Tom Sawyer* (5)
- **12** Mourn the loss of (6)
- **15** Diplomacy (4)
- **18** Type of food shop (abbr) (4)
- **20** Departs (6)
- **22** Edict with force of law in tsarist Russia (5)
- **23** Situated at or extending to the side (7)
- **25** Graphic symbol (4)
- **26** Shabby (5)
- **27** Twelvemonths (5)

Down
- **1** Group of six (6)
- **2** With a side or oblique glance (7)
- **3** Jargon (5)
- **5** Piled (6)
- **6** Have (3)
- **7** Wild plant with spiny bracts once used to comb wool (6)
- **8** Imaginary monster or ogre (3)
- **13** Hardy annual cereal grass (3)
- **14** Porch along the outside of a building (7)
- **16** Domesticated llama (6)
- **17** Flair (6)
- **19** Paragons (6)
- **21** Denigrate, defile (5)
- **23** Ignited (3)
- **24** Small child (3)

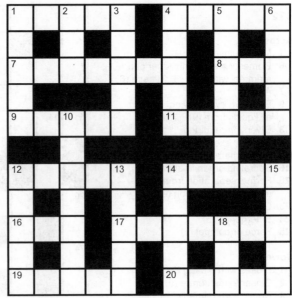

424

Across
- **1** Utensil used for serving ice cream (5)
- **4** Impart skills or knowledge (5)
- **7** One of the three superpowers in *Nineteen Eighty-Four* (7)
- **8** French vineyard or group of vineyards (3)
- **9** Male duck (5)
- **11** Cutting instrument (5)
- **12** Throws away as refuse (5)
- **14** Makes beer (5)
- **16** Armed struggle (3)
- **17** Father's mother (7)
- **19** Digress (5)
- **20** Privet boundary (5)

Down
- **1** Warhorse (5)
- **2** Device used to propel a boat (3)
- **3** No longer fashionable (5)
- **4** Show appreciation (5)
- **5** Depository containing historical records (7)
- **6** Typical dwelling-place (5)
- **10** Fan, supporter (7)
- **12** Rolling treeless highland (5)
- **13** Not fitting closely (5)
- **14** Offensively bold (5)
- **15** Stone writing tablet (5)
- **18** Informal term for a father (3)

425

Across

1 Travelling show (4)
3 A long way away (3,3)
5 Muhammad ___, former boxer (3)
6 Smut from a fire (4)
7 Eastern marketplace (6)
9 Free of external influence or control (10)
14 Wife of your father by a subsequent marriage (10)
17 Equipment for taking pictures (6)
19 Heavy ornamented staff carried as a mark of authority (4)
20 Tear apart (3)
21 Not often (6)
22 Take care of (4)

Down

1 Involving financial matters (6)
2 Proportion (5)
3 White lie (3)
4 Apartments (5)
8 Facility where wild animals are housed for exhibition (3)
10 Small insectivorous bird (3)
11 Electrical resistance unit (3)
12 Yuck (3)
13 Pal, chum (6)
14 Remove body hair (5)
15 Female sheep (3)
16 Entice (5)
18 Limb (3)

426

Across

1 Trudge (5)
4 Magic charm (5)
7 Broaden (6)
9 Section of glass (4)
10 Metropolis (4)
11 Impels (6)
13 Coarse file (4)
15 Cure (4)
17 Rogue (6)
20 Metallic element, symbol Pb (4)
21 Naked (4)
22 Exercise authority over (6)
23 Sore often found in the mouth (5)
24 Private instructor (5)

Down

1 One dozenth (7)
2 Rôle player (5)
3 One-hundredths of a pound (5)
5 Egyptian paper reed (7)
6 Golf course by the sea (5)
8 Cloth used when washing-up (7)
12 Educational institution (7)
14 Pale lager with a strong flavour of hops (7)
16 Evenly matched (5)
18 Take as one's own (5)
19 Deceive (5)

427

Across

1 Footrest (5)
3 Thin biscuit often eaten with ice cream (5)
7 Uncle's wife (6)
9 Ascend (4)
10 Rug (3)
12 Foundation (4)
13 Animal similar to the giraffe (5)
15 Acid present in all living cells (inits) (3)
17 Santa ___, Father Christmas (5)
19 Head honcho (4)
21 ___ Tolstoy, Russian writer (3)
22 Aware of (4)
23 Canine film star (6)
25 Tall stories (5)
26 Exposes to view (5)

Down

1 Tattered (6)
2 Frequently, poetically (3)
4 Main artery of the body (5)
5 Waterside plant (4)
6 Small European flatfish (5,4)
8 Belonging to the organ of smell (5)
11 Alias (inits) (3)
14 Devoutly religious (5)
15 Repent (3)
16 Appraise (6)
18 On your own (5)
20 Vessel for travel on water (4)
24 Bathing resort (3)

428

Across

1 Bullet casing (9)
8 Jolly ___, pirates' flag (5)
9 Rod which forms the body of an arrow (5)
10 Bird similar to an ostrich (3)
11 Discernment (5)
13 Follow as a result (5)
15 Prices (5)
18 Scatter about (5)
20 Bovine creature (3)
21 Empty area (5)
22 Principal river of Pakistan (5)
23 Contagion (9)

Down

2 Backing or support of a person or organisation (5)
3 Number in a trio (5)
4 Come forth (5)
5 Drinking vessel (5)
6 Disapproval expressed by pointing out faults or shortcomings (9)
7 Else (9)
12 Brandy measure (3)
14 Mesh (3)
16 Mass of eggs deposited by frogs (5)
17 Panorama (5)
18 Bird that resembles a swallow (5)
19 Medium for communication (5)

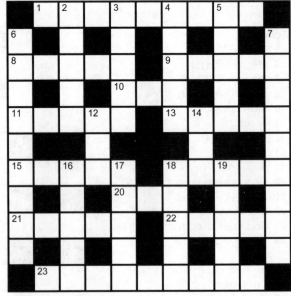

429

Across
1. Groups forming sides in a sport (5)
3. Fatigued (5)
6. Vicious angry growl (5)
8. Trades for money (5)
9. Mail (4)
11. Japanese dish of thinly sliced raw fish (7)
12. Engage in espionage (3)
13. Inhale audibly through the nose (5)
15. That girl (3)
17. Customers (7)
19. Sneering look (4)
20. Forbidden (5)
21. Sketched (5)
22. Compass point (5)
23. Restless, fidgety (5)

Down
1. Elephant 'horns' (5)
2. Changes shape as via computer animation (6)
3. Showed to be right, proven (9)
4. Toy figures (5)
5. Powdery (5)
7. Garment worn around the hips, usually by men (9)

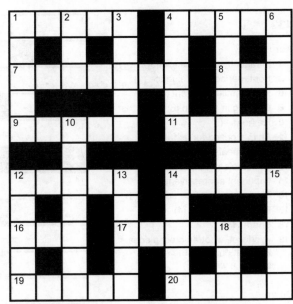

10. Grin (5)
14. Small vicious animal employed in unearthing rabbits (6)
15. Glossy fabric (5)
16. Glowing fragment of wood or coal left from a fire (5)
18. Bright and pleasant (5)

430

Across
1. Raise one's shoulders to indicate indifference (5)
4. Young leaf or bud signifying the coming of spring (5)
7. Fabric made of silk (7)
8. Prowess (3)
9. Small, open pies (5)
11. Place where milk, butter, cheese, etc is produced (5)
12. Assumed name (5)
14. Cloak, often knitted (5)
16. Sign of the zodiac (3)
17. Device for connecting non-matching plugs and sockets (7)
19. Squander (5)
20. Muggy (5)

Down
1. Search, reconnoitre (5)
2. Harass with persistent ridicule (3)
3. Group containing one or more species (5)
4. Pedestal (5)
5. Musical toy (7)
6. Moth-eaten (5)
10. Calamitous (7)
12. Permit (5)
13. Wobble (5)
14. Pulverise (5)
15. Glaringly vivid (5)
18. Woollen cap of Scottish origin (3)

431

Across

1 Vegetable used as a substitute for spinach (5)
4 Walt Disney's flying, cartoon elephant (5)
8 Eject in large quantities (4)
9 Study for an examination (6)
10 Singing couple (3)
11 Organ of smell (4)
13 At the summit of (4)
14 Engage in boisterous, drunken merrymaking (7)
15 Frozen rain (4)
16 Precipitation of ice crystals (4)
17 Wildebeest (3)
18 Upper house of the US Congress (6)
19 At a great distance (4)
21 Emit an odour (5)
22 Harmless tropical house-lizard (5)

Down

2 Fruit of a rose plant (3)
3 Harsh or unfair treatment (coll) (3,4)
5 Make damp (7)

6 Subdue (9)
7 Continuing for more time than usual (9)
8 Process of producing a chemical compound from others (9)
12 Study of the physical world (7)
13 Ease or lessen (7)
20 Enquire (3)

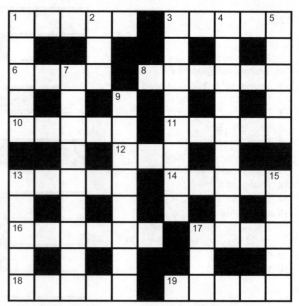

432

Across

1 Pleasantly cold and invigorating (5)
3 Bout, period of indulgence (5)
6 Presidential assistant (4)
8 Cooking in an oven (6)
10 Ice house (5)
11 Animal prized for its fur (5)
12 Prefix meaning recent or modern (3)
13 Censure severely (5)
14 Impudent aggressiveness (5)
16 Grim ___, death personified (6)
17 French for 'father' (4)
18 Snares (5)
19 In cricket, wooden crosspieces that rest on top of the stumps to form a wicket (5)

Down

1 American raccoon (5)
2 That girl (3)
3 Writer's or musician's last work (4,4)
4 Pay back (9)
5 Bird of prey (5)

7 Spiritual head of Tibetan Buddhism (5,4)
9 Filleted (8)
13 Printer's mark, indicating an insertion (5)
15 Fencing swords (5)
17 Pulse vegetable (3)

433

Across
1. Imbecile (5)
3. Fake, false (5)
6. Hand tool for boring holes (5)
9. General conscious awareness (5)
10. Of a thing (3)
12. Colour of the rainbow (6)
13. Small gentle horse (4)
14. Clarified butter used in Indian cookery (4)
15. Antiseptic used to treat wounds (6)
18. Curious (3)
19. Sternwards (5)
20. Home planet (5)
22. In an unfortunate manner (5)
23. Enclosures for pets (5)

Down
1. US state, capital Boise (5)
2. Cardinal number (3)
3. Low in pitch (4)
4. Venetian boatman (9)
5. Sleazy or shabby (5)
7. Cemetery (9)
8. Equip (3)
11. Lukewarm (5)
14. Substance from which window panes are made (5)
16. Lyric poem (3)
17. Distinctive spirit of a culture or an age (5)
18. All right (4)
21. ___ Khan, Islamic religious leader (3)

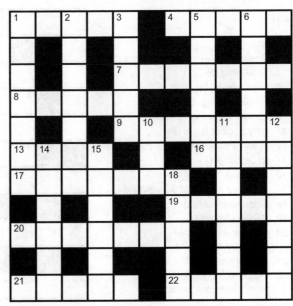

434

Across
1. Discontinue (5)
4. Covered entrance to a building (5)
7. In a murderous frenzy (7)
8. Territory occupied by a nation (5)
9. Free from tears (3-4)
13. Mosque official (4)
16. Level to the ground (4)
17. Low wall along the edge of a roof (7)
19. Pursue like a ghost (5)
20. Christen (7)
21. Stratum (5)
22. Lament for the dead (5)

Down
1. Spring flower (7)
2. Spanish fortress or palace built by the Moors (7)
3. Implant (5)
5. Edible shellfish (6)
6. Spanish conquistador who conquered Mexico (6)
10. *The Catcher in the ___*, J D Salinger novel (3)
11. Capital of Cameroon (7)
12. Fortune (7)
14. Spanish word for 'tomorrow' (6)
15. Cloak (6)
18. Motif (5)

435

Across

1 Table condiment (4)
3 Bearskin hat (5)
6 Small area of land (4)
7 Former communist country (inits) (4)
9 Chemical used to kill rodents or insects (9)
11 Playing card (3)
12 Disordered (7)
14 Sicken (3)
16 Consciousness (9)
18 Successor (4)
19 Reverberation (4)
20 Senior member of a group (5)
21 Remove (4)

Down

1 Aqualung (5)
2 Cause to be bored (4)
3 Denigrate (8)
4 Set of steps (9)
5 Country bumpkin (5)
8 In a particular way (9)
10 Astronauts (8)
13 Cold vegetable dish (5)
15 Above average in size (5)
17 Fired a bullet at (4)

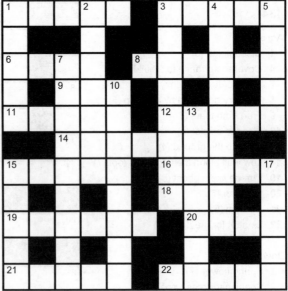

436

Across

1 Combined stakes of the betters (5)
3 Scallywag (5)
6 Lay slabs (4)
8 Gentle teasing (6)
9 Former French gold or silver coin (3)
11 Holy book of Islam (5)
12 Teatime sweet bread roll (5)
14 Exceptional (7)
15 Capital of Tibet (5)
16 Twist into a state of deformity (5)
18 Seize suddenly (3)
19 Underweight (6)
20 Consciousness of one's own identity (4)
21 Rate of travel (5)
22 Occurring at regular intervals, seven times per week (5)

Down

1 Material used for stuffing and insulation (5)
2 Protective shoe-coverings (7)
3 Planetary house, one of twelve (4,4)
4 Early form of sextant (9)
5 Rid of impurities (5)
7 Adaptable (9)
10 Not deserved (8)
13 Card game, a form of rummy using two decks of cards and four jokers (7)
15 Inventories (5)
17 Exalted (5)

437

Across

1 Dense woodland (6)
6 Compelling immediate action (6)
8 Capital of Kenya (7)
9 Acid found in vinegar (6)
10 Hitches (5)
13 In the interval (7)
16 Product derived from cane or beet (5)
18 Preposterous (6)
20 Old soldier (7)
21 Short, pointed beard (6)
22 Protestant layman who assists the minister (6)

Down

1 Hollow teeth of a venomous snake (5)
2 Infuriate (6)
3 Type of sousaphone (4)
4 Gambling (7)
5 Glued (5)
7 Wealth (6)
11 Atrocious (7)
12 Deprive of food (6)
14 Greek "I have found (it)" (6)
15 Mrs Simpson, Bart Simpson's mother (5)
17 Angry dispute (3-2)
19 Feat (4)

438

Across

1 Bludgeon (4)
3 Protection (6)
5 Israeli submachine-gun (3)
6 Inner surface of a hand (4)
7 Provider of money (6)
9 Thinking about (11)
14 Game in which players try to flip plastic disks into a cup (11)
18 Abduct, usually for a ransom (6)
20 ___ Strauss, jeans manufacturer (4)
21 Film starring Bette Davis, *All about ___* (3)
22 Major river of Brazil (6)
23 Savoury taste experience (4)

Down

1 One who imitates the behaviour of another (7)
2 Organic component of soil (5)
3 Small drink (3)
4 Sharp-pointed tip on a stem (5)
8 Thick flammable liquid distilled from wood or coal (3)
10 Move the head up and down (3)
11 Free from liquid (3)
12 Small hotel (3)
13 Young goose (7)
15 Mode of expression (5)
16 Hideout (3)
17 Arm off of a larger body of water (5)
19 Livestock enclosure (3)

439

Across

1 Screens from light or heat (6)
6 Counting frame (6)
7 Delicate, woven and decorative fabric (4)
8 Frame supporting the body of a car (7)
12 Experiment (5)
13 Difficult or unusual feat (5)
14 ___ and buts, objections (3)
15 Large body of salt water (5)
18 Communion table (5)
19 Small bunch of sweet-scented flowers (7)
21 Roast (4)
22 Eat greedily (6)
23 Be constantly talking or worrying about something (6)

Down

1 Answer (8)
2 Repositories for documents, etc (8)
3 Girdle (4)
4 Area of the body below the ribs (5)
5 Spice used in curry powder (5)
8 Hold on tightly (5)
9 Put to the test (5)
10 Portable travelling bag for carrying clothes (8)
11 First courses (8)
16 North Atlantic food fish of the cod family (5)
17 Fabulist of Ancient Greece (5)
20 Rounded thickly curled hairdo (4)

440

Across

2 Fictional character with special powers (9)
7 Regret (3)
8 Milk pudding ingredient (7)
10 Building where plays are performed (7)
12 Animal doctor (abbr) (3)
13 Involve as a necessary condition or consequence (9)
18 Solidify (3)
20 Brilliant solo passage near the end of a piece of music (7)
22 Currency used in Kabul, for example (7)
23 Cereal crop (3)
24 Gambit, ploy (9)

Down

1 Thin meat soup (5)
2 Withered (4)
3 Having indentations on the surface (6)
4 Fully developed (4)
5 Guided anti-ship missile (6)
6 Airport in Chicago (5)
9 Skilled craftsman (7)
11 Reverential salutation (3)
14 Forest fire fighter (6)
15 Relinquishing control over (6)
16 Consumed (3)
17 Informal conversations (5)
19 Tall tower referred to in the Bible (5)
20 Insincere talk about religion or morals (4)
21 Standard (4)

441

Across

1 One half of one third (5)
3 Cooks in an oven (5)
7 Recollect (6)
10 Digestive secretion stored in the gall bladder (4)
11 Declare openly (4)
12 One who torments (10)
15 Showing indifference or disregard (10)
20 Drudge (4)
21 Cable (4)
22 Relating to the backbone (6)
23 Saying: "He who pays the ___ calls the tune" (5)
24 Vigilant, awake (5)

Down

1 Angel of the highest order (6)
2 Melts, as of ice (5)
4 Chief monk (5)
5 Dance move (4)
6 Most courageous or daring (9)
8 Day before a festival (3)
9 Welsh breed of dog (5)
13 Pungent edible bulb (5)
14 Missile discharged from a firearm (6)
16 Blockade (5)
17 Apparatus used in the making of alcoholic spirits (5)
18 By means of (3)
19 Stage item (4)

442

Across

1 Small trout-like silvery fish (5)
3 Websites on which to record individual opinions (5)
7 Bedding material (6)
9 Elaborate song for a solo voice (4)
10 Cereal grass (3)
11 Young herring (4)
13 Brick carrier (3)
15 Body of water between Israel and Jordan (4,3)
17 Large edible mushroom (3)
18 Request on an invitation (inits) (4)
20 Grazing land (3)
21 Competent (4)
22 Time of year (6)
24 Drying cloth (5)
25 Use jointly or in common (5)

Down

1 Cause (a liquid) to spatter about (6)
2 Auction item (3)
4 Animal skin (7)
5 Kill intentionally (4)
6 Message transmitted by radio or television (9)
8 Mark (~) placed over the letter 'n' in Spanish (5)
12 Exhaust, use up (7)
14 Fertile tract in the desert (5)
16 Primitive multicellular marine animal (6)
19 Male red deer (4)
23 Fire residue (3)

443

Across
1 Agricultural dwelling, buildings and land (9)
7 Fossilised resin (5)
8 Person who does no work (5)
9 Hydrogen, for example (3)
10 Bring up (5)
12 Offering of a tenth part of some personal income (5)
14 Cause an engine to stop (5)
17 Giuseppe ___, composer of operas such as *Aida* (5)
19 ___ Baba (3)
20 Until now (2,3)
21 Injured by a bee or wasp (5)
22 Robinson Crusoe's helpful assistant (3,6)

Down
2 Jewish spiritual leader (5)
3 Twilled woollen fabric (5)
4 Have actual being (5)
5 Style of glazed pottery (5)
6 Exchanging goods without involving money (9)
7 Industry and technology concerned with aviation, satellites, etc (9)
11 Roman god of the sun (3)
13 Nickname of US president Eisenhower (3)
15 Bottomless gulf or pit (poetic) (5)
16 Language of ancient Rome (5)
17 Peak of a cap (5)
18 Circular (5)

444

Across
1 Obvious and dull (5)
3 Aromatic herb (5)
6 Locations (5)
8 Lowest point (5)
9 Hard-shelled fruit of a tree (3)
11 Female sibling (6)
13 Professional charges (4)
14 Small amount (3)
16 Fat used in cooking (4)
17 Forbid the public distribution of (6)
19 Golf peg (3)
20 Each (5)
22 Hazardous (5)
23 Tendon connecting muscle to bone (5)
24 Position of professor (5)

Down
1 Books that retail in very large numbers (11)
2 Broker (5)
3 Forbid (3)
4 Sorrow (7)
5 Supplication that begins "Our Father" (5,6)
7 Edible fat (4)
10 Extended area of land (5)
12 Physician who performs operations (7)
15 Antlered animal (4)
18 Characteristic sound made by a horse (5)
21 Coniferous tree (3)

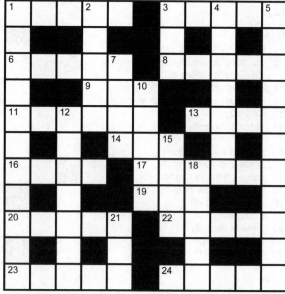

445

Across

1 Short intake of breath (4)
3 Muscle that flexes the forearm (6)
5 Side sheltered from the wind (3)
6 Primitive chlorophyll-containing, mainly aquatic organism (4)
7 Go on a journey (6)
9 Usual song or turn which someone performs when called on to entertain (5,5)
14 Alcoholic beverage (3)
15 Append (3)
17 Manage as a steward (10)
20 Glass vessel (6)
22 In one's sleeping place (4)
23 Joan of ___, French heroine (3)
24 Cup without a handle (6)
25 Hardy cabbage with curly leaves (4)

Down

1 Italian brandy made from the residue of grapes after pressing (6)
2 Living organism lacking the power of locomotion (5)
3 Wager (3)
4 Come before (7)
8 Bladed chopping tool (3)
10 In the current fashion or style (1,2,4)
11 Scarlet (3)
12 Cooking vessel (3)
13 Animal kept as a domestic pet (3)
16 Drag the bottom of a lake (6)
18 Encountered (3)
19 Light, informal meal (5)
21 Fruiting spike of a cereal plant (3)

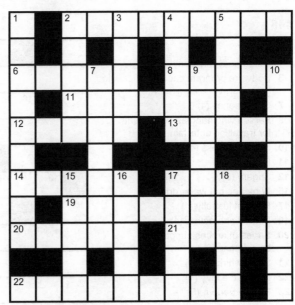

446

Across

2 Adding flavour to (9)
6 Reminiscent of the past (fashion) (5)
8 Plait hair (5)
11 Stress (7)
12 Run off to marry (5)
13 Time of life between childhood and adulthood (5)
14 Tall stories (5)
17 Right-hand page of a book (5)
19 Artist's workroom (7)
20 Stupefied by drugs (5)
21 Hanging cloth used as a blind (5)
22 First James Bond film in which Pierce Brosnan starred (9)

Down

1 Reaped (9)
2 Fight (3-2)
3 Make up for (5)
4 Celestial path (5)
5 Asinine, silly (5)
7 Full to satisfaction (7)
9 Graceful woodland animal (3,4)
10 Corruptible (9)
15 Facing of a jacket (5)
16 Grasslike marsh plant (5)
17 Long, narrow hill (5)
18 Lifting machine (5)

447

Across

1 Manufacturer of toy bricks (4)
3 Fully developed person (5)
6 Farm outbuilding (4)
7 Basic knitting stitch (4)
9 Undocumented feature in computer software included as a bonus (6,3)
11 Sauce typically served with pasta (5)
12 Informing by words (7)
15 Having a shape which tapers from a circular base to a point (5)
17 Deadlock (9)
18 In a lazy manner (4)
19 Elegant and stylish (4)
20 Have another go (5)
21 Alleviate (4)

Down

1 Take in with the tongue (3,2)
2 Of a sphere, flattened at opposite sides (6)
3 Candied plant stalks used to flavour cakes and trifles (8)
4 Genuine, sincere (9)
5 Piquant (5)
8 Discipline in personal and social activities (9)
10 Ability to meet financial obligations as they become due (8)
13 Intimation of dismissal (6)
14 On the move (5)
16 Bank robber, Bonnie's partner in crime (5)

448

Across

1 Tailed heavenly body (5)
3 Software program capable of causing great harm to a computer (5)
7 Chest bones (4)
9 Person who handles equipment for travelling entertainers (6)
10 Hindu princess (4)
11 Departed (4)
12 Sugary (5)
15 Wine and hot water drink (5)
17 Stare at lustfully (4)
19 Printed characters (4)
20 Series of arches supported by columns (6)
21 Small whirlpool (4)
22 Imposed a levy (5)
23 Beauty parlour (5)

Down

1 Enclosure for cattle or horses (6)
2 Literary composition (5)
4 Extremely angry (5)
5 Look for (4)
6 Dish of mutton, potatoes and onions (5,4)
8 Fearless (5)
13 Encouraged (5)
14 Put one's faith in (4,2)
16 Clear space in an area of woodland (5)
17 Drama set to music (5)
18 Stop (4)

449

Across

1 Mayhem (5)
4 Swim for pleasure (5)
7 Minor skirmish (7)
8 Poker stakes (5)
9 Antipathetic (6)
12 Russian city on the Vyatka River (5)
15 Haywire (5)
17 Fix up (6)
18 Downright (5)
19 Polish to a high sheen (7)
20 Look at intently (5)
21 Rich cake (5)

Down

1 Seize (a vehicle) in transit (6)
2 Speculative undertaking (7)
3 Plant which is the source of tapioca (7)
5 Corroborate (6)
6 Splits down the middle (6)
10 Hearing distance (7)
11 Conveyance attached to a motorcycle (7)
13 Break into suddenly (6)
14 Icebreaker (6)
16 Fairy (6)

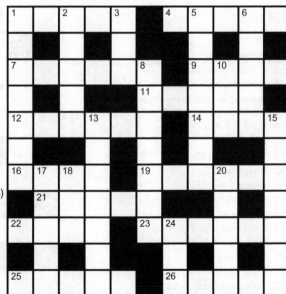

450

Across

1 Ability to see (5)
4 Collection of cakes, for instance (5)
7 Military personnel (6)
9 Land measure (4)
11 Light narrow boat (5)
12 Alter the dimensions of (6)
14 Crash out (4)
16 Additional (4)
19 Treeless Arctic plain (6)
21 Spooky (5)
22 Breathe noisily, as when exhausted (4)
23 Corrupt morally (6)
25 Commonly encountered (5)
26 Accumulate (5)

Down

1 Release (3,4)
2 Gets bigger (5)
3 Give money as a reward for a service (3)
5 Desert, leave (7)
6 Heals, makes better (5)
8 Perfumed (7)
10 Make the sound of a dove (3)
13 Disposition to remain inactive (7)
15 Ability to walk steadily on the deck of a pitching ship (3,4)
17 Bounds (5)
18 One-hundredth of a yen (3)
20 Excitement (5)
24 Ms Braun, Hitler's mistress (3)

451

Across

1 Begin a journey (3,3)
6 In or of the month preceding the present one (6)
7 Rectifies (6)
8 Copyist (6)
10 Has existence (5)
13 Usually (2,1,4)
16 Gasps for breath (5)
18 Pleasantly occupied (6)
20 Herbivorous lizard of tropical America (6)
21 Cream-filled pastry (6)
22 Country formerly known as Formosa (6)

Down

1 Tiny (5)
2 Units of weight (6)
3 Bother (4)
4 Inhabitant of a town or community (7)
5 Sweet substance produced by bees (5)
9 Strikingly successful move (4)
11 In an unfocused or imprecise way (7)
12 Reason for wanting something done (4)
14 Lapis ___, azure blue semi-precious stone (6)
15 Smooth surface (as of a cut gemstone) (5)
17 Murdered (5)
19 Grime (4)

452

Across

1 Frame of iron bars to hold a fire (5)
3 Caused to overflow (5)
6 Customary observance (4)
8 Surgical knife with a pointed double-edged blade (6)
9 Type of cobra (3)
11 Abrasive (5)
12 Commenced (5)
13 Be unwell (3)
14 Stylistic talent (5)
15 Authoritative proclamation (5)
18 Division of a tennis match (3)
19 Container with a long nozzle to apply lubricant to machinery (6)
20 Part of the ear (4)
21 Cher's former singing partner (5)
22 Colouring medium (5)

Down

1 Band around a horse's belly (5)
2 Lock of hair (5)
3 Condition of great disorder (8)
4 Disguised (9)
5 Largest satellite of Saturn (5)
7 Waterproofed canvas (9)
10 Apothecary's shop (8)
14 *The Mill on the ___*, George Eliot novel (5)
16 River mouth (5)
17 Provide with a gift (5)

453

Across

1 Hurled (5)
3 Franz ___, Hungarian composer (1811–1886) (5)
7 Device to interrupt the flow of electricity when overloaded (4)
9 Turn inside out (6)
11 Give expression to (5)
13 Disrobe (5)
14 Carapace (5)
15 Touch quickly and gently with the flat of the hand (3)
16 Ballroom dance of Latin American origin (5)
17 At liberty (5)
20 Smudge, daub (5)
22 Maker of beer (6)
23 Collapsible shelter (4)
24 Remains of buildings that have fallen down (5)
25 Daisy-like flower (5)

Down

1 Bunches of feathers or hair (5)
2 Fragrant resin used as incense (5)
4 Dock worker (9)
5 Full amount (5)
6 Cherry stone (3)
8 Vast plain and National Park in Tanzania (9)
10 Snuggle (6)
12 Be against (6)
16 Fleshy root (5)
18 Obscene expressions (5)
19 Come in (5)
21 Form of address for a married woman (abbr) (3)

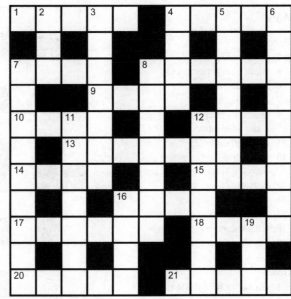

454

Across

1 Show off (5)
4 Missives used as birthday or Christmas greetings (5)
7 Beloved person (4)
8 Flummox, confuse (6)
9 Horse colouring (4)
10 Allude to (4)
12 Priggish (4)
13 Acorn-producing plant (3,4)
14 Ringlet (4)
15 Back end (4)
16 Marshes (4)
17 Major river flowing through Brazil (6)
18 Portent (4)
20 One's ancestry (coll) (5)
21 Keen (5)

Down

2 Metal-bearing mineral (3)
3 Resembling a dream (7)
4 Greenish-blue colour (4)
5 Official who is expected to ensure fair play (7)
6 Tool used to press clothes (5,4)
7 Folding seat for use outdoors (9)
8 Citadel (7)
11 Whirlwind (7)
12 Facade one presents to the world (7)
16 Curtsies (4)
19 Biblical first woman (3)

455

Across

3 Square hole made to receive a tenon (7)
6 Ardent male lover (5)
7 Make amorous advances towards (7)
8 Waterfall slide (5)
10 Snuggle (6)
12 Estimate the value (4)
14 Russian emperor (4)
17 Watchman (6)
19 Eagle's nest (5)
20 Provincial capital of Nova Scotia (7)
21 Humble (5)
22 Alphabetic characters (7)

Down

1 Merchant who sells foodstuffs (6)
2 Quantity (6)
3 Prophet who led the Israelites towards the Promised Land (5)
4 Cosmetic preparation (8)
5 Mark of infamy (6)
9 Close-fitting casual top (3,5)
11 Prepare leather (3)

13 Scour a surface (6)
15 Native of Aleppo or Palmyra, for example (6)
16 Stank (6)

18 Lone Star State of the USA (5)

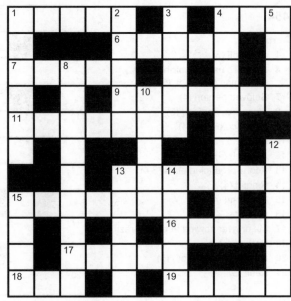

456

Across

1 Sorcery (5)
4 Steal from a person (3)
6 Abundant (5)
7 Appears to be (5)
9 Musical effect produced by rapid alternation of tones (7)
11 Ask earnestly (7)
13 Woman skilled in aiding the delivery of babies (7)
15 Bluster (7)
16 Caller (5)
17 Stand-in doctor (5)
18 Catch sight of (3)
19 Take part in a row (5)

Down

1 Gather or bring together (6)
2 Hindu social class (5)
3 Distress (5)
4 Make peace, come to terms (9)
5 Brand name of a ballpoint pen (4)
8 Deserving of respect or high regard (9)
10 Fanatical (5)

12 Soft and mild (6)
13 Month of the year (5)
14 Code of beliefs accepted as authoritative (5)

15 Formal offers at an auction (4)

457

Across

1 Political organisation (5)
4 Injures badly by beating (5)
8 Nought (4)
9 Go by boat (4)
10 Province of Indonesia (5)
11 Ms Chanel, fashion designer (4)
12 Neuter (a female cat, for example) (4)
14 Reveals (5)
15 Ooze (4)
16 Country once called Persia (4)
17 Wading bird with a long neck (5)
18 At rest (4)
19 Not many (1,3)
20 Contributions to state revenue (5)
21 Person afflicted with Hansen's disease (5)

Down

2 Woodland flower (7)
3 Lowest atmospheric layer (11)
5 Murder, especially a socially prominent person (11)
6 Having a smooth, soft surface (5)
7 Storage areas (9)
13 Scholarly life (7)
15 Garment worn on the upper half of the body (5)

458

Across

1 Noise made by a mouse, for example (6)
6 African antelope with ridged curved horns (6)
7 Precious red gemstones (6)
8 Gunk, slime (6)
10 Stonecutter (5)
13 Cleft (7)
16 Detection and location device (5)
18 Smear with ointment (6)
20 Enthusiastic and warm in manner (6)
21 Order of business (6)
22 Makes a logical connection (4,2)

Down

1 Plasma (5)
2 News chief (6)
3 Osculate (4)
4 Encrusted with sugar (7)
5 Light-beam intensifier (5)
9 Animal's den (4)
11 Child's two-wheeled vehicle operated by foot (7)
12 Gas used in lighting (4)
14 Decanter (6)
15 Apostolic (5)
17 Synthetic fabric (5)
19 Not this! (4)

459

Across

1 Derek ____, British actor who was knighted in 1994 (6)
4 Part of the lower jaw (4)
6 Discovery that proves to be illusory (5,4)
8 Flow back (3)
10 Method (6)
13 Army division (4)
14 Cook in a marinade (5)
16 Two considered together (4)
17 Express astonishment or surprise (6)
20 Source of metal (3)
21 Frightened greatly (9)
22 Clubs used in the game of cricket (4)
23 Period of ten years (6)

Down

1 ____ Cagney, Hollywood star who died in 1986 (5)
2 Toothed implements for arranging the hair (5)
3 Island to the north of Java (6)
4 Put down by force or authority (7)
5 Negative word (3)
7 Black eye (slang) (6)
9 Well in the past (6)
11 Casual tops (1-6)
12 Informal term for a mother (3)
15 Containing salt (6)
18 Hard drink originating in Russia (5)
19 Depart (5)
21 Bill in a restaurant (3)

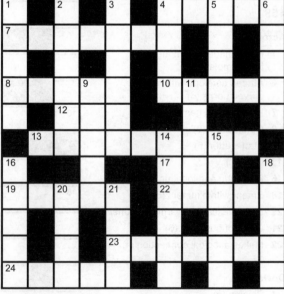

460

Across

4 Cleaner of chimneys (5)
7 Ascetic Muslim monk (7)
8 Groom with elaborate care (5)
10 After the expected time (5)
12 To and ___ (3)
13 Of a triangle, having two sides of equal length (9)
17 And not (3)
19 Bid (5)
22 Characterised by dignity and propriety (5)
23 Penalty or fine for wrongdoing (7)
24 Choose by a vote (5)

Down

1 Dexterous (5)
2 Short underpants (6)
3 Keyboard instruments (6)
4 Become closed (4)
5 Arabian ruler (4)
6 Growth on the surface of a mucous membrane (5)
9 Become ground down (5)
11 Assign (5)
14 Guarantee (6)
15 Pencil mark remover (6)
16 Dome-shaped dessert (5)
18 Ms Cavell, English nurse executed by the Germans in World War I (5)
20 Smoke duct (4)
21 Narrow fissure in rock (4)

232

461

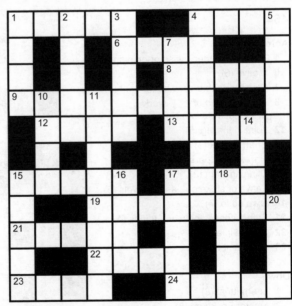

Across

1 Primitive fish with long jaws with needle-like teeth (3)
3 Native to the UK (7)
6 Front legs (9)
8 Excessive, extreme (inits) (3)
10 Artist of consummate skill (6)
13 Very dark black (4)
14 Abhorrence (5)
16 Biblical twin of Jacob (4)
17 Break through (6)
20 ___ Orbison, singer (1936–88) (3)
21 Mournful (9)
22 Container for coal (7)
23 Division of an ocean (3)

Down

1 Atmosphere of depression (5)
2 Vessels made of logs strung together (5)
3 Kept out (6)
4 Ancient Greek or Roman warship (7)
5 Possesses (3)
7 Unbroken mustang (6)
9 Bunch of cords fastened at one end (6)
11 One who travels for pleasure (7)
12 Chest bone (3)
15 Relating to or similar to bears (6)
18 Regions (5)
19 Doglike nocturnal mammal (5)
21 Suppuration (3)

462

Across

1 Close-fitting (5)
4 Stepped (4)
6 High male voice (4)
8 Battleground (5)
9 Prudent (8)
12 Item of footwear (4)
13 Castrated male chicken (5)
15 Leg joints (5)
17 Inlet (4)
19 River that flows through the Grand Canyon (8)
21 Paved area that adjoins a house (5)
22 Card game (4)
23 Squad (4)
24 Item of bed linen (5)

Down

1 Of the highest quality (4)
2 Product of seabirds, used as a fertiliser (5)
3 Implied (5)
4 Bullfighter (8)
5 Waste pipe (5)
7 Bath powder (4)
10 Very dark black (4)
11 Socially awkward or tactless act (8)
14 Was in debt to (4)
15 Destroyed or killed (sl) (5)
16 Before long (4)
17 Army unit of two or more divisions (5)
18 Indistinct (5)
20 Drum out (4)

463

Across

1. Rod carried as a symbol (5)
4. Bedtime beverage (5)
7. Meadow (3)
8. Line spoken by an actor to the audience (5)
10. Search, as with a dragnet (5)
11. Fireside mat (3)
12. Large basket (usually one of a pair) carried by a beast of burden (7)
13. Allege (3)
15. One of the supports for a table (3)
17. Foolish (7)
20. Egg cells (3)
21. Yellowish-brown colour (5)
22. Compare (5)
23. Light mid-afternoon meal (3)
24. Frightening (5)
25. Capable of flowing (5)

Down

1. Musical symbol (5)
2. Make parallel (5)
3. Quality of being adaptable or variable (11)
4. Larva of a butterfly or moth (11)
5. Covers the surface of (5)
6. Lessen the intensity (5)
9. Debonair (5)
14. Existing (5)
15. Inland bodies of water (5)
16. Tropical fruit with a yellow skin and pink pulp (5)
18. Souvenir (5)
19. Sweet made of flavoured sugar (5)

464

Across

1. Yield to another's wish or opinion (6)
6. Motive (6)
7. Slender double-reed instrument (4)
8. *On the Origin of ___*, work by Charles Darwin (7)
12. Joint in the leg (5)
13. Sharp knock (3)
14. Harass with persistent ridicule (3)
15. Clinging plant (3)
17. Leave or strike out, as of vowels (5)
18. Own up to (7)
21. Empty spaces between things (4)
22. Sealed in a tin (6)
23. In a slumber (6)

Down

1. Intermittent (8)
2. Master Beckham (8)
3. Journey (4)
4. Secular (4)
5. Asian peninsula separating the Yellow Sea and the East Sea (5)
8. Dish out (5)
9. Boundaries (5)
10. Bother, chafe (8)
11. Gets faster (6,2)
16. Spoken (5)
19. Reserve of money (4)
20. Drink often mixed with alcohol (4)

465

Across
1 Offensively malodorous (5)
4 Make sore by rubbing (5)
7 Regret (3)
8 Musical pace (5)
10 Edgar Allan ___, writer (3)
11 Domed recess (4)
12 Demands (5)
14 Pulse vegetables (5)
17 Attack on all sides (5)
20 Ring-shaped bread roll (5)
22 Caustic (4)
23 Directed or controlled (3)
24 Commit to memory (5)
26 Fall behind (3)
27 Corrode (5)
28 Hard black wood (5)

Down
1 Sofa bed of Japanese design (5)
2 Male cat (3)
3 Falls (5)
4 Famous person (abbr) (5)
5 First letter of the Greek alphabet (5)
6 Pitchers (5)
9 Military chaplain (5)
13 Augment (3)
15 Circumvent (5)
16 Maiden name indicator (3)
17 Tired of the world (5)
18 Of sound (5)
19 Correspond (5)
20 Where the sides of a ship curve in to form the bottom (5)
21 Ungracefully tall and thin (5)
25 Bustle (3)

466

Across
1 Outer area of a city (6)
4 In a competent manner (4)
6 City in northern Scotland (9)
8 Be in possession of (3)
10 Title given to a former ruler of Germany (6)
13 Mountain goat (4)
14 Rotate rapidly (5)
16 Primitive chlorophyll-containing, mainly aquatic organism (4)
17 Natural spring which gives out steam (6)
20 Promissory note (inits) (3)
21 Escapade (9)
22 Resembling a web (4)
23 Area set back or indented (6)

Down
1 Trembled (5)
2 Russian pancake (5)
3 Appraisal (6)
4 Income from investment paid regularly (7)
5 Affirmative answer (3)
7 Designating sound transmission from two sources (6)
9 Emitted long loud cries (6)
11 Elegant, imposing (7)
12 Manipulate in a fraudulent manner (3)
15 Safe (6)
18 Sift (5)
19 Ladder steps (5)
21 Each and every (3)

467

Across

1 Fragrant oily resin used in perfumes (6)
6 Printed mistakes (6)
7 Void (4)
8 Couch (6)
10 Bisect (5)
13 Inanely foolish (7)
16 Measure of gold's purity (5)
18 Supply or impregnate with oxygen (6)
20 Eject fluid from the mouth (4)
21 Court game (6)
22 Dreamlike state (6)

Down

1 Public announcement of a proposed marriage (5)
2 Finds an answer to (6)
3 Clutter (4)
4 At a more distant point (7)
5 Identification tab (5)

9 Heroic (4)
11 Tramp (7)
12 Public violence (4)
14 Sickness (6)
15 Coat with fat during cooking (5)
17 Identifying appellation (5)
19 Compass point (4)

468

Across

1 In the area or vicinity (5)
4 Relish served with food (5)
7 Golf club with a relatively narrow metal head (4)
9 Thoroughbred animal (9)
11 Poke or thrust abruptly (4)
13 Medium for radio and television broadcasting (8)
15 Person's second self (5,3)
16 Latin name of two constellations (4)
19 Contrariwise (4,5)
22 Decree ____, stage in divorce proceedings (4)
23 Strong coffee with a frothed milk topping (5)
24 Sediment that has settled at the bottom of a liquid (5)

Down

1 Kingsley ____, 20th century author (4)
2 Gumbo (4)
3 Nervous twitch (3)
4 Note in the tonic sol-fa scale (3)
5 Deviating from the general or common order (9)
6 Large water jugs with wide spouts (5)

8 Gets back (9)
10 Interruption in the intensity or amount of something (9)
12 Cash register (4)
14 Greek god of love (4)
15 Blacksmith's block (5)
17 Garden tool (4)
18 Regrettably (4)
20 Contend (3)
21 Disencumber (3)

469

Across

1 Contented (5)
4 Animal with two feet (5)
8 Indigent (4)
9 Hydrophobia (6)
10 In the past (3)
11 Depletes (4)
13 Kin group (4)
14 Anticipate (7)
15 Christmas (4)
16 Ancient Greek harp (4)
17 Expert (3)
18 Cargo ship designed to carry crude oil in bulk (6)
19 Expectorated (4)
21 Founded upon law (5)
22 Fusilli, for example (5)

Down

2 Much ___ about Nothing, Shakespeare play (3)
3 Sun umbrella (7)
5 Soft wool fabric with a colourful swirled pattern of curved shapes (7)
6 Rid of disease-causing bacteria (9)
7 One-humped camel (9)
8 Occurring immediately after birth (9)
12 Former German coin (7)
13 Percussion instrument (7)
20 Toward the stern of a ship (3)

470

Across

1 Captivate (5)
5 Seedcase (3)
7 Hawaiian greeting (5)
8 Makes tea (5)
9 Fragrant rootstock of various irises (5)
12 Particular look on someone's face (10)
16 Scottish hillside (4)
17 Upon (4)
19 Hypothesis that is taken for granted (10)
22 Abnormal swellings on the body (5)
23 Board used with a planchette (5)
24 Of the countryside (5)
25 Belonging to him (3)
26 Advanced slowly (5)

Down

1 Gossamer structure (6)
2 Intruders (11)
3 Overly eager speed (5)
4 Spool-and-string toys (2-3)
5 Treating with an apparent kindness which betrays a feeling of superiority (11)
6 Raised platform (4)
10 Uproar (4)
11 Keen on (4)
13 Medical 'photograph' (1-3)
14 Cease activity in order to relax (4)
15 Add together (3)
18 Moving in the direction ahead (6)
20 Appropriate (5)
21 Town in Dorset (5)
22 Money (4)

471

Across

1 High-pitched signal (5)
5 Exclude (3)
7 Missing portion in a book or manuscript (6)
8 Divisions of the school year (5)
10 Elegance and beauty of movement (5)
11 Issue forth (7)
14 Oblivious (7)
16 Country on the Iberian Peninsula (5)
17 Salvers (5)
19 Former British gold coin worth 21 shillings (6)
20 Colouring agent (3)
21 ___ Cup, golf tournament played every two years (5)

Down

1 Swimmer (6)
2 Deciduous tree (3)
3 Flour and water dough (5)
4 Shift, move very slightly (5)
5 Knitted hat covering the head and neck, with an opening for the face (9)
6 Feeling of intense anger (4)
9 Place in a different order (9)
12 Large wine cask or beer barrel (3)
13 Container for burning incense (6)
14 Out of condition (5)
15 Change (5)
16 Exchanged for money (4)
18 Beam (of light) (3)

472

Across

4 Fill quickly beyond capacity (5)
7 Push in (7)
8 Large monkey (3)
10 Brand of fine English porcelain (5)
12 Currency (5)
13 Honk (4)
15 Without end, unremitting (9)
19 Protrude the lips (4)
21 Carrying weapons (5)
24 Give a speech (5)
25 A person in general (3)
26 Inclined to show mercy (7)
27 Very small spot (5)

Down

1 Combat between two mounted knights (5)
2 Scientific instrument that provides a flashing light (6)
3 Reduces to pulp (6)
4 Crease (4)
5 Prayer-ending word (4)
6 Samuel ___, diarist (1633–1703) (5)
9 One who behaves affectedly in order to impress others (6)
11 Make numb (6)
14 Liveliness and energy (3)
16 Relax (6)
17 Lines on which musical notes are written (6)
18 Traditional pantomime, ___ in the Wood (5)
20 Bunk in a ship, train, etc (5)
22 Fashion (4)
23 Floor on a boat (4)

473

Across

1 Pry into another's private affairs (5)
4 Engraving or carving in relief (5)
7 Insect's feeler (7)
8 Melancholy (3)
9 Arctic sled dog (5)
11 Sycophant (5)
12 Flat spear-shaped leaf, especially of grass (5)
14 Applauds (5)
16 Small sharp bite (3)
17 Japanese art of folding paper into shapes (7)
19 Burn superficially or lightly (5)
20 Platform (5)

Down

1 Space created by the swing of a scythe (5)
2 Choose (3)
3 Large-flowered garden plant (5)
4 Shore of a sea (5)
5 Make-up used on the eyelashes (7)
6 In a peculiar manner (5)
10 Hone (7)
12 Fillip, incentive (5)
13 Conjure up in the memory (5)
14 Counters used to represent money when gambling (5)
15 Take by force (5)
18 Mother of the ancient Irish gods (3)

474

Across

1 Word used in an apology (5)
4 Bringing death (5)
7 Statement that makes something clear (11)
8 Journey in a vehicle (4)
11 Lowest regions (6)
14 Only, just (6)
17 Takes in food (4)
21 Very close in resemblance (11)
22 Melodies (5)
23 Outer surfaces of an object (5)

Down

1 Implement with a shaft and barbed point (5)
2 Quick (5)
3 Twelve months (4)
4 Candle light (5)
5 Contort (5)
6 Organs located in the chest (5)
9 Slang term for diamonds (3)
10 Calm central region of a cyclone (3)
11 Division of a week (3)
12 Food in a pastry shell (3)
13 Headgear (3)
14 Implied (5)
15 Develop fully (5)
16 Coils (5)
18 Accolade (5)
19 Garden buildings used for storage (5)
20 Is victorious (4)

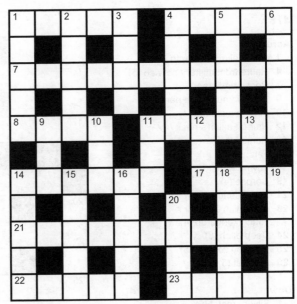

475

Across

1 Long-barrelled, muzzle-loading shoulder gun (6)
6 Cultivating tool (6)
7 Capital of modern Macedonia (6)
9 Ultimate client for which a thing is intended (3,4)
13 Impulses (5)
14 Battery terminal (5)
15 Bronze (3)
16 Type of fruit (5)
19 Country, capital Santiago (5)
20 Earmark (7)
22 Line on a weather map (6)
23 Television receiver (6)
24 Marked by excessive self-indulgence (6)

Down

1 Brawny (8)
2 Temporary substitutes (8)
3 At that time (4)
4 Eva ___, German mistress of Adolf Hitler (5)
5 Took part in a ballot (5)
8 Court clown (6)
10 Moves to music (6)
11 Friendly and outgoing (8)
12 Practise (8)
17 ___ out, dwindle (5)
18 Founder of the Bolsheviks (5)
21 Foul or loathsome (4)

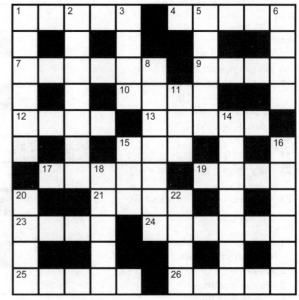

476

Across

1 Nautical unit of depth (5)
4 Retire from military service (5)
7 Rocky and steep (6)
9 Showy and festive party (4)
10 Marine mammal (4)
12 Hair on a lion's neck (4)
13 Hunts for (5)
15 Fetched (3)
17 Yawns wide (5)
19 Corpse (4)
21 In the centre of (4)
23 Australian term for a young kangaroo (4)
24 Deep ditch (6)
25 Cowboy contest (5)
26 Harvest (5)

Down

1 Silvery metal (6)
2 Plant with waxy, brightly coloured flowers (7)
3 Optical organs (4)
5 Bird of prey (5)
6 Bird's bill (4)
8 Down payment (7)
11 Painting, sculpture, etc (3)
14 Capital of Cameroon (7)
15 Precious or semi-precious stone (3)
16 Large snake (6)
18 Recipient of money (5)
20 Partly open (4)
22 Pull, haul (4)

240

477

Across
1 Holy book (5)
3 Skewered meat dish (5)
6 Small firearm that shoots pellets (3,6)
10 Expression of dislike (4)
12 With unflagging vitality (8)
14 Winner of a competition (8)
15 Item used to carry many cups at once (4)
18 Place endowed for the support and lodging of the poor (9)
21 Firm open-weave fabric used by window-cleaners (5)
22 Aromatic herb (5)

Down
1 Washtub (4)
2 Prejudice (4)
3 Colourful ornamental carp (3)
4 Club (3)
5 Beaks (5)
7 Narrow strip of land connecting two larger land areas (7)
8 Covered and often columned entrance to a building (7)
9 Thin slivers of wood (7)
11 Unit of length (4)
13 Asian plant widely cultivated for its oily beans (4)
14 Talons (5)
16 Depend (4)
17 US university (4)
19 Make imperfect (3)
20 Son of Noah (3)

478

Across
1 Helix (6)
6 Breadwinner (6)
8 Tree such as the cedar or larch (7)
9 Heavenly body (4)
10 Pigment prepared from the ink of cuttlefishes (5)
13 Riotous crowd (3)
14 Certify (7)
16 Unit of sound intensity (3)
17 Alpine vocal call (5)
19 Coloured part of the eye (4)
21 Family appellation (7)
22 Jubilant (6)
23 Ironic parody (6)

Down
1 Fires from a job (5)
2 Dried grape (6)
3 Sediment in wine (4)
4 Without weapons (7)
5 Tiny morsel of bread or cake (5)
7 Blood vessel (6)
11 Large water bird (7)
12 Offer suggestions (6)
15 Poem of fourteen 10- or 11-syllable lines (6)
16 One stroke over par in golf (5)
18 Belgian city (5)
20 Soap froth (4)

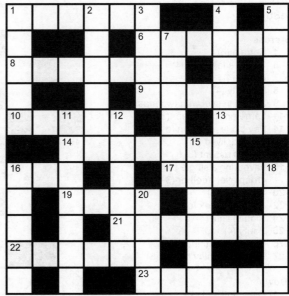

479

Across

1 Actor's lines (6)
6 Interruption in the intensity or amount of something (6)
7 Three-dimensional shape (4)
8 Grade of excellence (7)
10 Former name of Tokyo, Japan (3)
12 Instrument for measuring the distance of an object (11)
15 Anger (3)
16 Localised sore (7)
19 Act presumptuously (4)
20 Contribute (6)
21 Spite (6)

Down

1 Shoot arising from a plant's roots (6)
2 Decorative strip (6)
3 Archaic form of the word 'you' (4)
4 Release after a security has been paid (4)
5 To a greater extent (7)
8 Line of people or vehicles (5)
9 Farewell remark (5)
11 Accounts journal in which transactions are entered for later transfer to a ledger (7)
13 Hindu Festival of Lights (6)
14 Be in awe of (6)
17 Partially burn (4)
18 Thin part of a wine glass (4)

480

Across

1 Refrain (6)
5 Stitches together (4)
7 Barrel (4)
8 Horsefly (4)
9 Sailing vessel with two masts (4)
11 Large northern deer (3)
14 Pay close attention to (4,4)
16 Existed, lived (3)
18 Sign of assent (3)
19 Favouring a single person or group over another (3-5)
20 Went first (3)
22 Second Greek letter (4)
24 Ring of light (4)
25 Booty (4)
26 Press down tightly (4)
27 Plant with spiny bracts (6)

Down

1 Over, finished (4)
2 Draw into the mouth by creating a vacuum (4)
3 Synopsis of a play (8)
4 Children's game (3)
5 Outer space as viewed from Earth (3)
6 Figured out (6)
10 At another time (4)
12 Incline (4)
13 Conference attendee (8)
15 Heavy book (4)
16 Australian animal (6)
17 Chair (4)
20 Deprivation (4)
21 Distribute playing cards (4)
23 High mountain (3)
24 Very warm (3)

242

481

Across

1 David ____, whose first hit was *Space Oddity* (5)
3 Date-producing trees (5)
6 Units of land area (5)
7 Pedal digit (3)
8 Jar of glass or porcelain (4)
9 Flowers commonly seen on a lawn (7)
12 Force by impact (3)
14 Knotted item of clothing (3)
15 Do needlework (3)
17 Replies (7)
20 Nocturnal birds of prey (4)
21 Belonging to us (3)
22 Inland waterway (5)
23 Addition, division, etc (abbr) (5)
24 Component parts of a necklace, usually round in shape (5)

Down

1 Name given to a product (5)
2 Individual units in a list (5)
3 Gives delight (7)
4 Not now! (5)
5 Rise as vapour (5)
8 Vessels that carry blood to the heart (5)
10 Hatchet (3)
11 Slanted letters (7)
13 Broadcast (3)
15 Tempest (5)
16 Most unfit (5)
18 Make cloth by interlacing threads (5)
19 Garments of a jockey (5)

482

Across

1 Air cavity in the skull (5)
4 In a cold manner (5)
7 Style of design popular in the 1920s and 1930s (3,4)
8 Adversary (5)
10 Work of art that imitates the style of some previous work (8)
13 Long-necked bird (4)
15 British nobleman (4)
17 Supplement sometimes found at the end of a publication (8)
19 Eastern county (5)
20 Seat behind the rider of a motorbike (7)
21 Demon (5)
22 Clemency (5)

Down

1 Reduces to thin strips (6)
2 Jotter (7)
3 Neuters (an animal) (5)
5 Insignia used by the medical profession (8)
6 Storage cabinet (6)
9 Stringed instrument (8)
11 Cardinal number (3)
12 Pet rodent (7)
14 Large North American deer (6)
16 Great comfort (6)
18 Jeans fabric (5)

483

Across

1 Lines where pieces of fabric are sewn together (5)
4 Adult males (3)
6 Banal (5)
7 Forum in Ancient Greece (5)
9 Extended area of land (5)
10 Not devious (7)
13 Consider in detail (7)
15 Take exception to (5)
16 Order of Greek architecture (5)
17 Fires from a job (5)
18 Acquired (3)
19 River that flows through Paris (5)

Down

1 Doctor-priest or medicine man working by magic (6)
2 Look at intently (5)
3 Sweets with a menthol flavour (5)
4 Award for winning a championship (9)
5 Clean or orderly (4)
8 Situated at the farthest possible point from a centre (9)
11 Either of male or female (3)
12 Free from harm or evil (6)
13 Perpendicular (5)
14 Haywire (5)
15 Pull, haul (4)

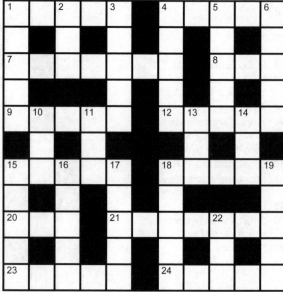

484

Across

1 Croatian city on the Adriatic Sea (5)
4 Popular Mexican palm-like plant (5)
7 Bureaucratic procedure (3,4)
8 Assistance (3)
9 Be worthy or deserving (5)
12 Public dance hall (5)
15 Old Testament prophet (5)
18 Dripping wet (5)
20 Shortened forename of US president Lincoln (3)
21 Engage in boisterous, drunken merrymaking (7)
23 Heave (5)
24 Egyptian water lily (5)

Down

1 Idly play a guitar (5)
2 Hallucinogenic drug (inits) (3)
3 Crisp bread (5)
4 End resistance (5)
5 Common crustaceans (5)
6 Relating to sound (5)
10 Self-esteem (3)
11 Frozen water (3)
13 Artificial language, a simplification of Esperanto (3)
14 Part of a gearwheel (3)
15 Has in mind (5)
16 Blaspheme (5)
17 Stony hillside (5)
18 Ability (5)
19 Back gardens (5)
22 Tit for ___, getting even (3)

485

Across
1. Russian country house (5)
4. Adult female (5)
7. Sour-tasting (6)
9. Wading bird of warm and tropical climates (4)
10. Deserve by one's efforts (4)
11. Visible suspension in the air (6)
13. Fail to include (4)
15. Adult female hogs (4)
17. Arch of the foot (6)
20. Informal greeting used on meeting or parting (4)
21. Leg joint (4)
22. Fissure in the Earth's crust (6)
23. Insurrectionist (5)
24. Sharpened with a whetstone (5)

Down
1. Legendary creatures resembling tiny old men (7)
2. Intelligent ape of equatorial African forests (abbr) (5)
3. Au revoir (5)
5. Indicating impending bad luck (7)
6. Defence plea of being elsewhere (5)
8. Of the heart (7)
12. Designed to incite to indecency (7)
14. Narrowed to a point (7)
16. One sixteenth of a pound (5)
18. *Our Friends in the* ____, TV series (5)
19. Mythological giant (5)

486

Across
1. Capital of Cuba (6)
4. Roman cloak (4)
6. Large, strong animal suitable for heavy work (9)
8. Extinct flightless bird of New Zealand (3)
10. Boundary line (6)
13. Lacking hair (4)
14. Principle (5)
16. Charitable gifts (4)
17. Penetrate with a sharp implement (6)
20. ____ Lavender, Private Frank Pike in *Dad's Army* (3)
21. Disparaging remark (9)
22. Erotic desire (4)
23. Fire-breathing dragon used in medieval heraldry (6)

Down
1. Atomic exploding device (1-4)
2. Parson (5)
3. Looked after during an illness (6)
4. Problem (7)
5. Reverence (3)
7. Mineral such as quartz (6)
9. Loads, an abundance (coll) (6)
11. Disagree (7)
12. Fabric with prominent rounded crosswise ribs (3)
15. In a flippant manner (6)
18. Use water to remove soap (5)
19. With the extremity facing the observer (3,2)
21. Pointed tool (3)

487

Across
1 Bone in the leg (5)
4 Tree with rot-resistant wood (5)
7 Swerves off course momentarily (4)
8 Puts into a letterbox (5)
9 Expressed in words (4)
10 Free from danger (4)
12 Spigots (4)
15 Bird's construction (4)
17 Hostelries (4)
19 Landscaped complex of shops (4)
20 Church passage (5)
22 Biblical first man (4)
23 Thin porridge (5)
24 Become rotten, as of an egg, for example (5)

Down
1 Inferior (especially of a country's leadership) (6)
2 Heating elements in an electric fire (4)
3 Bottomless gulf (5)
5 Diminish (6)
6 Science of morals in human conduct (6)
11 Beard found on a bract of grass (3)
13 Icon representing a person, used in internet chat and games (6)
14 Fodder harvested while green (6)
16 From that place (6)
18 Latin American dance (5)
21 Grains on the beach (4)

488

Across
1 Group delegated to consider some matter (9)
8 Reminiscent of the past (fashion) (5)
9 Periods of play in cricket (5)
10 Items of footwear (5)
11 Forest god (5)
12 Bedtime drink (5)
15 Clear (5)
17 Jewish sacred writings and tradition (5)
18 Cardinal number (5)
19 Social unit living together (9)

Down
2 Get the better of (5)
3 Berths, ties up (5)
4 Runs at a moderately swift pace (5)
5 Force out (5)
6 Institute legal proceedings against (9)
7 Alienated (9)
13 Consignment (5)
14 Cinders (5)
15 Property of sound with variation in the frequency of vibration (5)
16 Month with 30 days (5)

489

Across
1 Dance moves (5)
4 Dairy product (5)
7 Visual receptor cell sensitive to dim light (3)
8 Law established by following earlier judicial decisions (9)
9 Gammon (3)
10 Last Commandment (5)
11 Border of cloth doubled back and stitched down (3)
15 Find repugnant (9)
16 Little rascal (3)
17 Provide a remedy (5)
18 Corroded (5)

Down
1 Range (5)
2 Devoured (5)
3 Strongroom in which valuables may be securely stored (4-7)
4 Machine with a revolving drum used in making concrete (6,5)
5 Third planet from the Sun (5)
6 Formal title used when addressing a woman (5)
11 Robbery at gunpoint (5)
12 Leaf that adorns the Canadian flag (5)
13 Trousers (5)
14 Small, round and gleaming (of eyes) (5)

490

Across
1 Verdigris (6)
6 Exclusive circle of people (6)
7 Fellow (4)
8 Made up one's mind (7)
10 Harden to (5)
12 Cure-all (7)
15 Condensed but memorable saying (5)
16 Attendant on an aeroplane (7)
19 Talk easily or familiarly (4)
20 Fondle (6)
21 In accord with the latest fad (6)

Down
1 Remaining scraps or leftovers (8)
2 Drinking vessel (6)
3 Disease of the skin (4)
4 Restricted (7)
5 Offspring of a male donkey and a female horse (4)
8 Hideout (3)
9 Without deviation (8)
11 Period at universities during which money is raised for charities (3,4)
13 Morally reprehensible person (3)
14 German city known to the French as Aix-la-Chapelle (6)
17 Rupture (4)
18 Oxidisation caused by moisture in the air (4)

491

Across

1 Fertilised egg (6)
6 Feasible (6)
7 Capital of Zimbabwe (6)
9 Enter uninvited (7)
10 Seventh letter of the Greek alphabet (3)
12 Place where food is dispensed to the needy (4,7)
17 Compass point at 67.5 degrees (inits) (3)
18 Hard to catch (7)
20 Feeling of ill-will arousing active hostility (6)
21 Goes in (6)
22 Plaid associated with Scotland (6)

Down

1 Reflected sounds (6)
2 Agency, department (6)
3 Cooker (4)
4 Material (6)
5 Become happy (7)
8 Stack of hay (4)
11 Doing arduous or unpleasant work (7)
13 Artist's crayon (6)
14 Adolescent (4)
15 Armoured hat (6)
16 British naval hero (6)
19 Enormous (4)

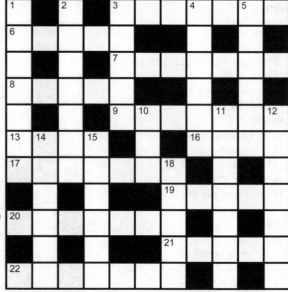

492

Across

3 Effusive (7)
6 Species of bacteria that can threaten food safety (1,4)
7 Pasta 'cushions' (7)
8 Ellipses (5)
9 Prepared by a compositor for printing (7)
13 Depicted (4)
16 Aspersion (4)
17 Grave (7)
19 Long journeys on foot (5)
20 Point at which to retire for the night (7)
21 Tolerate (5)
22 Frightened (7)

Down

1 Divisions of a minute (7)
2 Widow woman (7)
3 Foremost (5)
4 Grins (6)
5 Environmental condition, surroundings (6)
10 Thee (3)
11 Alcoholic beverage flavoured with the fruit of the blackthorn (4,3)
12 Legal guardian (7)
14 Go back on one's promise (6)
15 Cold season (6)
18 Purloin (5)

493

Across

1 Construction built by a spider (6)
6 Warm up again (6)
7 Point in orbit (6)
9 Jersey (7)
13 Sarcastic pessimist (5)
14 Come up (5)
15 Having the leading position (5)
18 Eighth letter of the Greek alphabet (5)
19 Moving and bending with ease (7)
21 Intense feeling of love (6)
22 Admittance (6)
23 Clouded as with sediment (6)

Down

1 Dark grey colour (8)
2 Small squares of rich chocolate cake (8)
3 Make beer (4)
4 Cut the wool from (5)
5 Projecting edge of a roof (5)
8 Former monetary unit of Portugal (6)
10 Time of celebration in the Christian calendar (6)
11 Preset explosive device (4,4)
12 Put in working order (8)
16 Snag, difficulty (5)
17 Poplar tree (5)
20 Sturdy upright pole (4)

494

Across

1 Clump of trees (5)
4 Hearty enjoyment (5)
7 Copy (7)
8 Hardy and sure-footed animal (3)
9 Left over, superfluous (5)
11 Undersides of shoes (5)
12 Restrains (5)
14 Coagulated milk used to make cheese (5)
16 Expire (3)
17 Run or skip about briskly (7)
19 Display stand for a painting (5)
20 Cornstalks (5)

Down

1 Tight waves in the hair (5)
2 Worthless or oversimplified ideas (3)
3 Class of people enjoying superior status (5)
4 Plant grown as a lawn (5)
5 Machine that inserts metal fasteners into sheets of paper (7)
6 Fertile tract in the desert (5)
10 Lacking freshness (atmosphere) (7)
12 Framework of a military unit (5)
13 Rope-making fibre (5)
14 Pandemonium (5)
15 Small mouselike mammal (5)
18 Equality (3)

495

Across

3 Diffusing warmth and friendliness (7)
6 Movies (5)
8 At a convenient or suitable time (9)
9 Japanese rice dish (5)
10 Peninsula of Ukraine, on the Black Sea (6)
13 As a result (4)
16 Fit of shivering or shaking (4)
18 Greenfly, blackfly, etc (6)
20 House for travellers (5)
22 First regiment of household infantry, ___ Guards (9)
23 Cooks in fat or oil (5)
24 Beetroot soup (7)

Down

1 Counterbalance (6)
2 At short range (5,2)
3 Savoury jelly (5)
4 Respiratory disorder (6)
5 Four-wheel covered carriage (6)
7 Rate of travel (inits) (3)
11 Colour (3)
12 Image boost (3-4)
14 Coiffure (6)
15 Gleams brightly (6)
17 Join the military (6)
19 Budge (5)
21 Throughout a period of time, poetically (3)

496

Across

1 Wire device used to straighten the teeth (6)
6 Ever (6)
7 Delivered a blow to (6)
9 Elongated dirigible powered balloon (7)
10 Vertical part of a stair (5)
12 Small axe with a short handle (7)
17 Addictive narcotic extracted from poppies (5)
18 Strategy (7)
20 Device that supplies warmth (6)
21 Decoration along a wall (6)
22 Marine mammal with downward-pointing tusks (6)

Down

1 Small informal restaurant (6)
2 Again but in a new or different way (6)
3 South American monkey with a long bushy tail (4)
4 Ballroom dance in double time (3-4)
5 Meant to be sung (5)
8 Heavy open wagon (4)
11 Made of clay (7)
13 Stockings, socks and tights (4)
14 Laugh nervously (6)
15 Stings (6)
16 Iraq's second largest city (5)
19 Gnaw (4)

497

Across

1 Decoration consisting of a ball of tufted wool (6)
6 Nocturnal lemur of Madagascar (3-3)
8 Feeling of righteous anger (7)
9 Madman (6)
10 Cocktail made of orange liqueur, lemon juice and brandy (7)
13 Umberto ___, author of *Foucault's Pendulum* (3)
14 Moldovan monetary unit (3)
17 Tomboys (7)
20 Shrub mainly used for garden hedging (6)
21 Stick vegetable, eaten as a fruit (7)
22 Starter course of a meal (6)
23 Contrite (6)

Down

1 Goads (5)
2 Astronomical unit of distance (6)
3 Molten rock in the Earth's crust (5)
4 Tiredness (7)
5 Area of sand sloping down to the water (5)
7 Annually, every twelve months (6)
11 Swerve (7)
12 Stick or hold together (6)
15 Comestible (6)
16 Higher in position (5)
18 Alternative (5)
19 Roman prophetess (5)

498

Across

1 Russian prison camp for political prisoners (5)
4 In addition (4)
6 Angle between a stem and a leaf (4)
7 Units (1/6 inch) used in printing (3)
9 Graven image (4)
10 Form of the Hebrew name of God used in the Bible (6)
12 Frighten greatly (7)
15 Book of maps (5)
16 Marine plant (7)
17 Dark grey cloud (6)
20 Biblical patriarch, Jacob's third son (4)
21 Mischievous little fairy (3)
22 Inventory (4)
23 Scottish island, capital Portree (4)
24 Mistake (5)

Down

1 Lady Jane ___, queen for nine days (4)
2 Growing luxuriously (4)
3 Newspaper or official journal (7)
4 Tool used for bending wire (6)
5 Aunt ___, game played by throwing sticks at a doll (5)
8 Indian corn (5)
11 Mythological beauty, ___ of Troy (5)
13 Exude (7)
14 Public meeting for open discussion (5)
15 For a short time (6)
16 Grain stores (5)
18 Stand to support a coffin (4)
19 Box lightly (4)

499

Across
1 Trinket (5)
4 Muscle cramp (5)
7 Early form of modern jazz (3)
8 Raises up (5)
10 Occupied a chair (3)
11 Leak through (4)
12 Eddy (5)
14 Australian wild dog (5)
15 Metal currency units (5)
16 Broker (5)
19 O ___ All Ye Faithful, Christmas carol (4)
20 Sleeveless outer garment worn by Arabs (3)
21 Fill with high spirits (5)
23 Neither (3)
24 Turn inside out (5)
25 Sacred table in a church (5)

Down
1 Small compartments (5)
2 Branch of the British armed forces (inits) (3)
3 Out of date (11)
4 Roadside device triggered by fast-moving vehicles (5,6)
5 It's said to make the heart grow fonder (7)
6 Paris underground railway (5)
9 High rocky hill (3)
13 Mimic (7)
15 Desire strongly (5)
17 Mousse (3)
18 Belonging to those people (5)
22 Products of human creativity (3)

500

Across
1 Feeling remorse for (5)
4 Garments worn primarily by Hindu women (5)
7 Hard durable wood (3)
8 Release, relinquish (3,2)
9 Conclude by reasoning (5)
10 Female parent of an animal (3)
11 Emblem of Christianity (5)
14 Gather into a ruffle (5)
17 Beautify (5)
20 Capture (5)
23 Burned remains (3)
24 Gives the cry of an ass (5)
25 Seraph (5)
26 High rocky hill (3)
27 Pile fabric used to make bath towels (5)
28 Perform a wedding ceremony (5)

Down
1 Object that has survived from the past (5)
2 Presentation, briefly (5)
3 Articles of commerce (5)
4 Subsist on a meagre allowance (5)
5 Firearm (5)
6 Very small fish (5)
12 Angling pole (3)
13 Man's title (3)
15 Meadow (3)
16 The alphabet (inits) (3)
17 Range, scope (5)
18 Elated (2,3)
19 Malicious (5)
20 Allure (5)
21 Large cat (5)
22 Shrub with prickly leaves (5)

501

Across

1 Foundation (5)
4 ___ board, used to shape fingernails (5)
7 In total (3,4)
9 Silky-coated sheepdog (6)
10 Elongated cluster of flowers (6)
12 Swarm (4)
15 Foolish (coll) (4)
17 Noisy quarrel (6)
19 Residential district, often run-down (6)
20 Bride-to-be (7)
21 Aromatic resin used in perfume and incense (5)
22 Sensations of acute discomfort (5)

Down

1 Small lynx of North America (6)
2 Protection (7)
3 Step (5)
5 Bevelled (6)
6 Alleviation (6)
8 Unwanted discharge of a fluid (7)
11 Cocktail of vermouth and gin (7)
13 Representation of a person (6)
14 Mode of procedure (6)
16 Prickles (6)
18 Woolly mammals (5)

502

Across

1 Bohemian dance (5)
4 Group of islands, capital Apia (5)
7 Cut (the grass, for example) (3)
8 Tennis stroke (3)
10 Insincerely emotional, maudlin (11)
11 Devoured (3)
13 Strong, lightweight wood (5)
14 Stocky short-legged harness horse (3)
18 Not working (11)
19 Propel with oars (3)
20 Billiards stick (3)
21 Lofty nest of a bird of prey (5)
22 Rise rapidly, rush (5)

Down

1 Money bag (5)
2 Deviating from the truth (5)
3 Mixed feelings or emotions (11)
4 Lotteries in which the prizes consist of the monies paid by the participants (11)
5 Mediterranean island, capital Valletta (5)
6 Stroll, saunter (5)
9 Commitment to tell the truth (4)
12 Something which must not be done, said, etc (coll) (2-2)
14 Approximately (especially of a date) (5)
15 Climbing plant supporter (5)
16 Motorcycle rider (5)
17 Capital of Switzerland (5)

503

Across

1 Triangular part of a wall (5)
4 Appear suddenly or unexpectedly (3,2)
8 Do physical harm or damage (6)
9 Implant (5)
10 Morsel (5)
12 Secondary and usually adverse symptoms of a drug (4,7)
13 Arousing or holding the attention (11)
15 Outerwear items (5)
18 Type of beer (5)
19 Chewy sweet (6)
20 Frighten away (5)
21 Dig deeply into (5)

Down

1 Estimate (5)
2 Polygraph used in interrogation (3,8)
3 Come to a halt (3)
4 Fluid product of an inflammation (3)
5 Plan and control how a complex undertaking is done (11)
6 For every (3)
7 Devices used for smoking tobacco (5)
11 Later on (5)
13 Peruvian tribe at the time of the Spanish conquest (5)
14 Canyon (5)
16 Mother of the ancient Irish gods (3)
17 Girl's name (3)
18 Boy (3)

504

Across

1 Haemorrhage (5)
3 Wild animal (5)
7 Brine-cured (6)
9 Wind direction pointer (4)
10 Recuperate after an illness or medical treatment (10)
14 Abbreviation for hundredweight (3)
16 City famous for its casino (5,5)
19 Large luxurious car (abbr) (4)
20 Tension (6)
22 George ____, Archbishop of Canterbury (1991–2002) (5)
23 Durable aromatic wood (5)

Down

1 Cut in two (6)
2 Consume (3)
4 Mischievous fairies (5)
5 Tall perennial woody plant (4)
6 Alpine perennial plant (9)
8 Language, jargon (5)
11 Law passed by Parliament (3)
12 And so forth (abbr) (3)
13 Cut thinly (5)
15 Light tanker for supplying water or fuel (6)
17 Not a single person (2-3)
18 Group of countries in a special alliance (4)
21 Fish eggs (3)

505

Across

1 Hurry (6)
6 Cultural (6)
8 City besieged by Joshua (7)
9 Vulgar (6)
10 Coy, shy (7)
13 Sicken (3)
14 Female sheep (3)
17 Hold spellbound (7)
20 Short, pointed beard (6)
21 Butchery (7)
22 UK city in which the Met Office is based (6)
23 According with custom or propriety (6)

Down

1 Headscarf worn by Muslim women (5)
2 Chinese system of slow meditative physical exercise (3,3)
3 Prime minister of India from 1947 to 1964 (5)
4 Dispenser that produces a vapour to relieve congestion (7)
5 Moves along quickly (5)
7 Bathroom fixture (6)
11 Attacked brutally (7)
12 Sheep's coat (6)
15 Complain peevishly in an annoying or repetitive manner (6)
16 Woman's name, old-fashioned (5)
18 Approaches (5)
19 Suspicious, untrusting (5)

506

Across

1 Impaired in skill by neglect (5)
3 Elevates (5)
6 Twist of strands of hair (5)
7 In the past (3)
8 Single article (4)
9 Period between sunrise and sunset (7)
12 Consume food (3)
14 Automobile (3)
15 Gammon (3)
17 Took no notice of (7)
20 Formerly (4)
21 Exclude (3)
22 Android (5)
23 Stories (5)
24 Newly made (5)

Down

1 Quick, fast (5)
2 Wind round and round (5)
3 Portable lamp (7)
4 Blaze (5)
5 Low in stature (5)
8 Mental picture (5)
10 Farmhouse cooker (3)
11 Frozen spikes of water (7)
13 Imitate (3)
15 Custom (5)
16 Significance of a story (5)
18 Perfume (5)
19 Drainage channel (5)

507

Across

1 Barrage balloon (5)
4 Sailing vessels (5)
7 Perennial herb (3)
8 Brownish black colour (5)
9 Roused from sleep (5)
10 Earth's nearest star (3)
11 Board game (5)
14 Talk (5)
17 Mock attack (5)
20 Essential oil or perfume obtained from flowers (5)
23 Hen's produce (3)
24 Narrow to a point (5)
25 Fragrant rootstock of various irises (5)
26 Immoral act (3)
27 Dig deeply into (5)
28 Arabian country (5)

Down

1 Fundamental (5)
2 Permeate (5)
3 Newspaper writers and photographers, collectively (5)
4 Pulse vegetables (5)
5 On your own (5)
6 Very small spot (5)

12 Tinge (3)
13 One-hundredth of a yen (3)
15 Cooking vessel (3)
16 Alias (inits) (3)
17 Destined (5)

18 Force (5)
19 Concise in manner (5)
20 Acute pain (5)
21 Make a rhythmic sound (5)
22 Plant exudation (5)

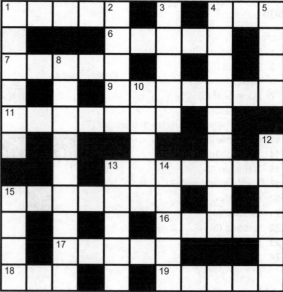

508

Across

1 Loft (5)
4 Cry (3)
6 Severe and intense (5)
7 Lesson (5)
9 Line touching a curve (7)
11 Dentist's consulting room (7)
13 Idealistic (but usually impractical) social reformer (7)
15 Person with a record of failing (2-5)
16 Move to music (5)
17 Anoint with oil (5)
18 Melancholy (3)
19 Picture puzzle (5)

Down

1 Confront, solicit (6)
2 Hindu social class (5)
3 Bright and pleasant (5)
4 Formal separation from an alliance or federation (9)
5 Thai currency unit (4)
8 Pointed tip of a dart-like weapon (9)

10 Sharp, narrow ridge found in rugged mountains (5)
12 Not if (6)
13 Distressed (5)

14 Arrange (5)
15 Tidings (4)

509

Across

4 Colourless alcoholic spirit (5)
7 Come into possession of (7)
8 Rises upward into the air (5)
10 Contend (5)
12 Her (3)
13 Doctor (9)
17 Excessive, extreme (inits) (3)
19 Cockeyed (5)
22 Eye covering (5)
23 Out of the ordinary (7)
24 One sixteenth of a pound (5)

Down

1 Strong, lightweight wood (5)
2 Flatten (6)
3 Osculates (6)
4 ___ Lynn, wartime songstress (4)
5 Medicine (4)
6 Britain's only native venomous snake (5)
9 Piece of poetry (5)
11 Indian side dish of yogurt and chopped cucumbers (5)
14 Metallic reddish-brown element (6)
15 Accomplish (6)
16 Fruit with aromatic pulp and a large seed (5)
18 Large marine snail (5)
20 Oven for firing pottery (4)
21 Sagacious (4)

510

Across

1 Mooring (5)
4 John Quincy ___, sixth President of the United States (5)
8 Epic tale (4)
9 Inhabit (6)
10 Slang term for diamonds (3)
11 Symbol of the zodiacal sign Leo (4)
13 Marquee (4)
14 Magazine article (7)
15 Encountered generally, especially at the present time (4)
16 Edge tool used to cut and shape wood (4)
17 Portion of a circumference (3)
18 Submerged (6)
19 Shades of colour (4)
21 Subdivision of an act of a play (5)
22 Cat with a grey or tawny coat mottled with black (5)

Down

2 Seventh letter of the Greek alphabet (3)
3 Apprentice (7)
5 Liquorice-flavoured herb (7)
6 Climbing plants with fragrant flowers (5,4)
7 Large dog (5,4)
8 Pathological hardening or thickening of tissue (9)
12 Action of attacking an enemy (7)
13 Windpipe (7)
20 Wane (3)

511

Across

1 Fragrant oily resin used in perfumes (6)
6 Heart condition marked by chest pain (6)
7 Bird house (6)
10 Betrayal of trust (9)
12 Form of theological rationalism (5)
13 US musician and record producer, former husband of Tina Turner (3)
15 Cook in an oven (5)
18 Measure or standard used for comparison (9)
20 Agree (6)
21 Travelling show (6)
22 Martial art (6)

Down

1 Long, thin, flat piece of wood (5)
2 Marks left by old wounds (5)
3 Ancient South American civilisation (4)
4 Fully alert and watchful (4,5)
5 One of a class of woodland deities (5)
8 Planned route or journey (9)
9 Failing in what duty requires (6)
11 Priest or religious leader (6)
14 Kill without legal sanction (5)
16 Arise (5)
17 Particular items (5)
19 Chore (4)

512

Across

1 Self-defence discipline (4)
3 Edging of small loops, as on lace (5)
6 Give a cat-like sound of pleasure (4)
7 Part of a church that contains the altar (4)
9 Force of workers available (3)
10 Remove the fastenings from (7)
12 Hollow, flexible structure resembling a bag (3)
13 Frequently, poetically (3)
14 Evergreen conifer (7)
15 Maiden name indicator (3)
16 Mr Geller, spoon-bender (3)
18 Child's two-wheeled vehicle operated by foot (7)
20 Owns (3)
21 Introduce to solid food (4)
22 White-tailed sea eagle (4)
23 Globe, planet (5)
24 Back end (4)

Down

1 Close-fitting trousers of heavy denim (5)
2 Exposed (4)
3 Lustful, salacious (8)
4 Steadiness of mind under stress (9)
5 Article of faith (5)
8 Descendant (9)
11 Hypothesised (8)
15 Not in any way (5)
17 Interior (5)
19 Large container (4)

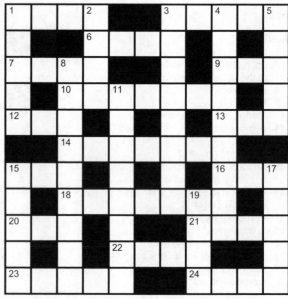

513

Across

1 Accumulation caused by clogging or a stoppage (4-2)
6 State of commotion and noise (6)
7 Emergence (6)
9 Frame supporting the body of a car (7)
13 Doglike nocturnal mammal (5)
14 Heave, regurgitate (5)
15 To hinder or preclude, in law (5)
18 Robbery at gunpoint (5)
19 Trace (7)
21 Proposal (6)
22 Native of Sana'a, for example (6)
23 Prods (6)

Down

1 Leonid ___, former president of the Soviet Union (8)
2 Puts right (8)
3 Thrust (4)
4 Open by force of leverage (5)
5 Legerdemain (5)
8 Norway lobsters (6)
10 Bowed, curved (6)
11 Walking with long steps (8)
12 Breaks into fragments (8)
16 Number considered lucky (5)
17 Different (5)
20 Acquire through effort (4)

514

Across

1 Forced out (6)
6 No particular person (6)
7 Gesture (4)
9 Enquiry into the finances of a person applying for monetary aid (5,4)
13 Absolute (5)
15 Flurry (3)
16 Opaque gems (5)
20 Sailing boat with two parallel hulls (9)
23 Cereal grass (4)
24 Central area in a building that is open to the sky (6)
25 Orb, globe (6)

Down

1 Start, commencement (5)
2 Ringworm (5)
3 Wish harm upon (4)
4 Catholic Holy Father (4)
5 Flesh used as food (4)
8 Local time at the 0 meridian passing through Greenwich (inits) (3)
10 Clock that wakes a sleeper at a preset time (5)
11 Scent (5)
12 Go by boat (4)
14 Vegetable known as lady's fingers (4)
17 Cause to wither (5)
18 Tropical black cuckoo of central America (3)
19 Setting (5)
20 Fossil fuel (4)
21 Port in southern Lebanon on the Mediterranean Sea (4)
22 Official symbols of a family, state, etc (4)

515

Across

3 Display of bad temper (7)
6 Inundated (5)
7 Discourteous, impolite (7)
8 ___ pole, North American emblem (5)
9 Swollen, distended (7)
13 Exploiter (4)
16 Deposit of valuable ore (4)
17 Low wall along the edge of a roof (7)
19 Tapering block (5)
20 Confined, imprisoned (7)
21 Bring to bear (5)
22 Having hair on the chin (7)

Down

1 Composition of flat objects stuck on a board (5-2)
2 Associate who works with others (7)
3 Digit of the hand (5)
4 Characteristic of a clan (6)
5 Combined (6)
10 Bruce ___, expert kung fu actor who died in 1973 (3)
11 Child learning to walk (7)
12 Arid regions of the world (7)
14 Barbaric, violent (6)
15 Carnivorous bird, such as the eagle (6)
18 River that flows through Kelso (5)

516

Across

1 Small round bread which can open into a pocket (4)
3 Disease of the skin (6)
6 Hyphen (4)
7 Country, capital Lomé (4)
8 Organised persecution of an ethnic group (6)
9 Not definitely settling something (10)
14 Stargazer (10)
17 Form a queue (4,2)
19 Rubbish receptacles (4)
20 Cab (4)
21 Ocean floor (6)
22 As a result (4)

Down

1 Regional dialect (6)
2 Love intensely (5)
3 Clairvoyance (inits) (3)
4 Cuts into pieces (5)
5 Large northern deer (5)
10 God of the underworld; counterpart of the Greek Pluto (3)
11 Artificial language, a simplification of Esperanto (3)
12 Vigour (3)
13 Total disaster (6)
14 In existence (5)
15 Course (5)
16 Celestial path (5)
18 Fill out (3)

517

Across
1 Noisy altercation (5)
4 Mail (4)
6 Former communist country (inits) (4)
8 Wanderer (5)
9 Blow that renders the opponent unconscious (8)
12 Not at home (4)
13 Informal term for a British policeman (5)
15 State of depression (5)
17 Associated with a divine power (4)
19 Fervent supporter of a person or institution (8)
21 Heavens (5)
22 Presently (4)
23 Amount by which the cost of a business exceeds its revenue (4)
24 Propel through the air (5)

Down
1 Play music in a public place and solicit money for it (4)
2 Dart (5)
3 Auspicious (5)
4 Diplomatic etiquette (8)
5 Present time or age (5)
7 Rebuff (4)
10 Carpentry pin (4)
11 Slipshod (8)
14 Young men (4)
15 Aromatic herb (5)
16 Neither good nor bad (2-2)
17 Pursue like a ghost (5)
18 Covering that protects an inside surface (5)
20 Unfreeze (4)

518

Across
1 Sudden flash (as of lightning) (6)
4 Becomes older (4)
8 Device used to control a flow (5)
10 General line of orientation (5)
11 Native of Stockholm, for example (5)
12 Chemist or physicist, for example (9)
18 Accumulate (5)
19 Sloping mass of loose rocks at the base of a cliff (5)
21 Hawaiian greeting (5)
22 Produced tones with the voice (4)
23 Almost not (6)

Down
1 Saline (5)
2 Dance party that lasts all night (4)
3 ___ Lang Syne, Scottish song (4)
5 Any leafy plants eaten as vegetables (6)
6 Conduit for carrying off waste products (5)
7 Attack on all sides (5)
9 Against (4)
13 Wax drawing implement (6)
14 Literary composition (5)
15 Advance slowly (4)
16 Natives of Aarhus or Odense, for example (5)
17 Type of boat used to transport people and cars (5)
19 Couch (4)
20 Sudden attack (4)

519

Across

1 Calvin ____, fashion designer (5)
3 Encounters (5)
6 Oil platforms (4)
8 Hard to comprehend, solve or believe (6)
9 Chafe (3)
11 Nigerian monetary unit (5)
12 Locate (5)
14 Arranged in close-packed rows (7)
15 Get the better of (5)
16 Growing older (5)
18 Consume (3)
19 Saucepan stand (6)
20 Take care of (4)
21 Actors' parts (5)
22 In a poor way (5)

Down

1 Holy book of Islam (5)
2 Covered against loss (7)
3 Small or minor details (8)
4 Hand over to the authorities of another country (9)
5 Fashion (5)
7 Machine for grinding grain (9)
10 Female hereditary title (8)
13 Meeting for boat races (7)
15 Further from the centre (5)
17 Divine (5)

520

Across

1 Kidnap (6)
7 Arrange differently (7)
8 Ever (6)
9 Short, abrupt (4)
10 Dome-shaped dessert (5)
11 Shade of blue tinged with green (4)
13 Ascend (4)
15 Grilled food on a skewer, served with peanut sauce (5)
16 ___ Christian Andersen, storyteller (4)
18 Move rapidly (6)
20 Turns into (7)
21 Clandestine (6)

Down

1 Rhododendron-like shrub (6)
2 Daybreak (4)
3 Loud utterance of emotion (3)
4 International games, especially in cricket (4,7)
5 Shop where foodstuffs are sold (7)
6 One of four playing-card suits (6)
10 Double-reed instrument (7)
12 Musical note having the time value of an eighth of a whole note (6)
14 Bring about (6)
17 Celestial body (4)
19 Consumption (3)

521

Across

1 Savagely cruel (6)
6 Request for a repeat performance (6)
7 Make moist (6)
8 Blur (6)
10 Forbidden (5)
13 Go backwards (7)
16 Printer's mark, indicating an insertion (5)
18 Rectifies (6)
20 Hurt or upset (6)
21 Ancient Greek city, site of the Temple of Apollo (6)
22 Hypothesis (6)

Down

1 Bathroom fixture (5)
2 Walk silently (6)
3 Transparent optical device (4)
4 Small, graceful animal of the woods (3,4)
5 Confused scuffle (5)
9 Refuse of processed grapes, etc (4)
11 For a short time (7)
12 Roman love poet, born in 43 BC (4)
14 Ironic parody (6)
15 Bamboo-eating mammal (5)
17 Hot alcoholic drink (5)
19 Eject fluid from the mouth (4)

522

Across

1 Coffee shops (5)
4 Rubbish (5)
7 Creature (6)
9 Largest and most southerly island in the Marianas (4)
10 Feel concern (4)
11 Abrupt (6)
13 Group of musicians (4)
15 Lean-fleshed fish, often farmed (4)
17 Calculating machine (6)
20 Former unit of money in Italy (4)
21 Amusement or pastime (4)
22 Solidified carbon dioxide, used mainly as a refrigerant (3,3)
23 ___ out, dwindle (5)
24 Advanced slowly (5)

Down

1 Timeless (7)
2 Cooked in oil (5)
3 Empty area (5)
5 Branch of mathematics (7)
6 Educate in a skill (5)
8 Cord worn around the neck to hold a knife or whistle (7)
12 Exhaust, use up (7)
14 Move downward and lower (7)
16 Plant also known as the century plant (5)
18 Canal boat (5)
19 Adhere, stick (5)

523

Across
1 Chafe at the bit, like a horse (5)
3 Region of complete shadow (5)
6 Berkshire town, famous for its racecourse (5)
9 Furze (5)
10 Sprang up (5)
12 Screenplay (6)
13 Cut back on certain foods (4)
14 Part of a necklace (4)
15 Sudden sharp pain in the side of the body (6)
19 County (5)
20 Decorative ruffle (5)
21 Rebound after hitting (5)
22 Piquant (5)
23 Financial obligations (5)

Down
1 Forms a layer over (5)
2 Native New Zealander (5)
3 Egg on (4)
4 Lawyer who speaks in the higher courts of law (9)
5 Broker (5)
7 Plant such as the clove pink (9)
8 Pinnacle (3)
11 Save up for future use (5)
14 Accord or comport with (5)
16 Nervous twitch (3)
17 Angry (5)
18 Organic component of soil (5)
19 Kill (4)

524

Across
1 Army doctor (5)
4 Pungent spice, popular in apple pies (5)
7 Bustle (3)
8 Item which enables something to be used in a way different from that for which it was intended (7)
9 Frighten away (5)
10 Relative magnitude (5)
12 Trade (5)
14 Alcoholic drink (coll) (5)
16 Localised sore (7)
18 Be equal, draw (3)
19 Aromatic herb (5)
20 Cleaned with a broom (5)

Down
1 Complains (5)
2 Series of pictures representing a continuous scene (7)
3 Discontinue (5)
4 Common crustaceans (5)
5 Cereal grass (3)
6 Eagle's nest (5)
11 Original disciple (7)
12 Intonate (5)
13 In that place (5)
14 Motor coaches (5)
15 Select by a vote (5)
17 Enclosure for swine (3)

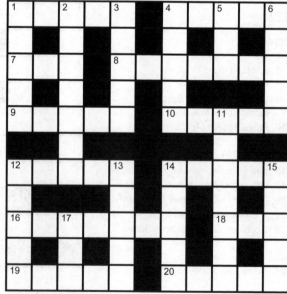

525

Across

1 U-shaped curve in a stream (5)
4 *The Fall of the House of ___*, story by Edgar Allan Poe (5)
7 Annual publication giving weather forecasts, etc (7)
9 Full in quantity or extent (6)
10 Front of a building (6)
12 Top cards (4)
15 Bulge or swelling (4)
17 Line on a weather map (6)
19 State of being male or female (6)
20 Cattle farmer (7)
21 Framework of a military unit (5)
22 Offensive (5)

Down

1 Daniel ___, Nicaraguan president (6)
2 'Fab' group associated with the 1960s (7)
3 Dock (5)
5 Sailor (6)
6 Jubilant (6)
8 Unwanted discharge of a fluid (7)
11 Draws aimlessly (7)
13 Stout-bodied insect that produces a loud, chirping sound (6)
14 Football (6)
16 Hearty and lusty, crude (6)
18 Repeat performance (5)

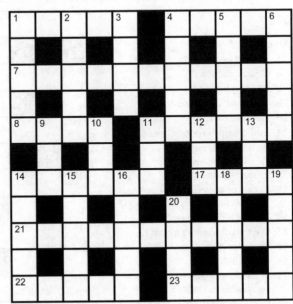

526

Across

1 Wharves (5)
4 Junk (5)
7 Based on or involving resemblance (11)
8 Mark left by a wound (4)
11 Muddles (6)
14 Declared as a fact (6)
17 Binds (4)
21 Set of questions evaluating knowledge (11)
22 Locates (5)
23 Cinders (5)

Down

1 Evades (5)
2 Punctuation mark (5)
3 Make tight (4)
4 Apportion (5)
5 Falls in droplets (5)
6 Removes the rind from (5)
9 Baby's bed (3)
10 Informer (3)
11 Angry (3)
12 Posed for artistic purposes (3)
13 Calm central region of a cyclone (3)
14 Horizontal support (5)
15 Anew (5)
16 Departs (5)
18 Celtic language (5)
19 Kitchen or bathroom basins (5)
20 Collection of facts (4)

527

Across

4 Mayhem (5)
7 Discharge (7)
8 Night of 31 December (3,5,3)
12 Alliance (9)
15 Ready-to-wear (3-3-5)
20 Shore next to the coast (7)
21 Judge tentatively (5)

Down

1 Structure for open-air sports (5)
2 Exhaled with force (4)
3 Female pantomime character (4)
4 Listen (4)
5 Long depression in the surface of the land (4)
6 Highland Games pole (5)
9 Leavening agent (5)
10 Nimble, spry (5)
11 English explorer said to have been saved by Pocahontas (5)
13 In an early period of life (5)
14 Behind (5)
16 Front of the human head (4)
17 Expression of dislike (4)
18 Drench (4)
19 Make changes in text (4)

528

Across

1 Look at intently (5)
4 Motor coaches (5)
8 Building block (4)
9 Tool used with a mortar (6)
10 Gentle blow (3)
11 Soft creamy French cheese (4)
13 By word of mouth (4)
14 Graceful antelope of Africa and Asia (7)
15 Period of 40 weekdays from Ash Wednesday to Holy Saturday (4)
16 Type of food shop (abbr) (4)
17 Division of a tennis match (3)
18 Decanter (6)
19 Skin irritation (4)
21 In an unfortunate or deplorable manner (5)
22 Unrestrained merrymaking (5)

Down

2 Metal container (3)
3 Place affording peace and quiet (7)
5 Release (3,4)
6 Mollusc or crustacean, for example (9)
7 Burdened psychologically or mentally (9)
8 Belly button (9)
12 Snubbed (7)
13 Attractively quaint, but not necessarily authentic (3-4)
20 Prompt (3)

529

Across

1 Creator (5)
3 Capital of South Korea (5)
7 Indian bread, baked in a clay oven (4)
8 Dispel gloom (5)
9 Magnificent (5)
11 Device operated by the insertion of a coin (4,7)
14 Lower-ranking assistant (11)
16 Alleviates (5)
19 Paved area that adjoins a house (5)
20 Skin of a fruit (4)
21 Astute (5)
22 Lure (5)

Down

1 Protective secretion of bodily membranes (5)
2 Political campaigner (11)
3 Droop (3)
4 Coarse pottery (11)
5 Smallest whole number (3)
6 Machine tool (5)
10 Fop (5)
12 Romanian monetary unit (3)
13 Mesh (3)
14 Stalks of a plant (5)
15 Black wood (5)
17 Health resort near a spring (3)
18 Film props and scenery (3)

530

Across

2 Television set, colloquially (6,3)
6 Attempted (5)
8 Celestial bodies (5)
11 Portable sets of steps (7)
12 Act of going in (5)
13 Proportion (5)
14 Block of metal (5)
17 Extract (metals) by heating (5)
19 Feeling uneasy and self-conscious (7)
20 Arabian country (5)
21 Make parallel (5)
22 Person who tends to shrink from social contacts (9)

Down

1 Part of a limb farthest from the torso (9)
2 Culpability (5)
3 Light-headed (5)
4 Light-beam amplifier (5)
5 Animal (5)
7 Fleshy pendulous part of the hearing organ (7)
9 Restraint that confines freedom (7)
10 Abridged (9)
15 Range (5)
16 Ballroom dance (5)
17 Partial darkness (5)
18 Authoritative proclamation (5)

531

Across

1 Off-colour (5)
3 State in north-eastern India (5)
7 Fit for cultivation (6)
9 Elaborate song for a solo voice (4)
10 Excessively sentimental tale (4-6)
14 Mineral (3)
16 Faint star of enormous density (5,5)
19 Being in a tense state (4)
20 Fortress (6)
22 Leisurely walk (5)
23 Swamped with water (5)

Down

1 Sparse (6)
2 Present a knighthood (3)
4 Cut of meat from the upper part of the leg (5)
5 Intend to express or convey (4)
6 Veneration (9)
8 Cause to feel self-conscious (5)
11 Speck (3)
12 Flushed (3)
13 Accurate (5)
15 Again but in a new or different way (6)
17 Short descriptive poem of rural life (5)
18 Catherine ____ Jones, actress (4)
21 Female pig (3)

532

Across

1 Popular number puzzle (6)
6 Provide what is desired or needed (6)
8 Puts up with (7)
9 Cut or eliminate (6)
10 Occupy (a dwelling) illegally (5)
13 Deal with in a routine way (7)
16 Time of life between the ages of 13 and 19 (5)
18 Fruit with yellow flesh (6)
20 Sauce served with fish (7)
21 Poem of fourteen 10- or 11-syllable lines (6)
22 Despot (6)

Down

1 Vehicles used to travel over snow (5)
2 Relating to or using sight (6)
3 Second-hand (4)
4 Gain the good will of (7)
5 Varieties (5)
7 System of newsgroups on the worldwide web (6)
11 Improving or increasing trend (7)
12 Up until now (2,4)
14 Area, zone (6)
15 Cramp (5)
17 Slumbered (5)
19 Unit of power (4)

533

Across

1 Small amount of food eaten between meals (5)
3 Commandeer (5)
7 Make possible (6)
9 Deserve by one's efforts (4)
10 Be unwell (3)
11 God of love, also known as Cupid (4)
13 Number in a brace (3)
15 Plume (7)
17 And so forth (abbr) (3)
18 Barrier consisting of a horizontal bar and supports (4)
20 Regret (3)
21 Alleviate (4)
22 Wet-nurse (6)
24 Multiplication (5)
25 French secondary school (5)

Down

1 Spit for holding meat in place (6)
2 Train driver's compartment (3)
4 Industrial plant for extracting metal from ore (7)
5 Section of glass (4)
6 Callous (9)
8 At great height (5)
12 Place out of sight (7)
14 Dried seaweed (5)
16 Verbally report or maintain (6)
19 Financial obligation (4)
23 Affectedly modest (3)

534

Across

1 Cut finely (5)
4 Encourage to do wrong (4)
6 Chooses (4)
7 Expectorated (4)
8 Equestrian display (8)
12 Male parent (4)
14 Manufactures (5)
15 Container for a bird (4)
16 International organisation that cares for the sick in wartime (3,5)
20 European mountain range (4)
21 Birthplace of mankind (4)
22 Skill and sensitivity in dealing with others (4)
23 Grunt (5)

Down

1 Wearing footgear (4)
2 Debauched old man (4)
3 Crash out (4)
4 Valuer, estimator (8)
5 Identifying appellation (5)
9 __ Parks, African American civil rights activist (4)
10 County in southern England (8)
11 Enquired (5)
13 Furrows, grooves (4)
15 Shore of a sea (5)
17 Cheats, swindles (4)
18 Anise-flavoured Greek liqueur (4)
19 Pimple (4)

535

Across
1 Removes (5)
4 Packs to capacity (5)
7 Armed struggle (3)
8 Corrupt (5)
10 Hoot with derision (3)
11 Additional (4)
12 Emit an odour (5)
14 Assignation between lovers (5)
17 Gusset (5)
20 Climbing plant supporter (5)
22 Cuckoo pint, for example (4)
23 Affirmative word (3)
24 Passing from physical life (5)
26 Domestic swine (3)
27 Plant with daisy-like flowers (2-3)
28 Throw out (5)

Down
1 Pipes (5)
2 Colourful ornamental carp (3)
3 Expand abnormally (5)
4 Bottle that holds oil or vinegar for the table (5)
5 Church associated with a convent (5)
6 Recreational pastime (5)
9 Beautiful young woman (5)
13 Chaps (3)
15 Spacious (5)
16 Her (3)
17 Adult insect (5)
18 Velvety leather (5)
19 Brown-grey colour (5)
20 Shift (5)
21 Brightest star in the constellation Orion (5)
25 Mischievous little fairy (3)

536

Across
1 Garment worn on the upper half of the body (5)
4 Go in (5)
7 Drum out (4)
8 Pungent vegetable (5)
9 Spring month (5)
11 Feasible alternative (11)
15 Egg of a louse (3)
16 Gift of prophetic vision (6,5)
19 Projecting bay window (5)
21 Mild Dutch cheese (5)
22 Rise upward into the air (4)
23 Wrinkled (5)
24 Deviating from the truth (5)

Down
1 Spy (5)
2 One's ancestry (coll) (5)
3 Large cask or barrel (3)
4 Seventh Greek letter (3)
5 Changing direction (7)
6 Automobile race run over public roads (5)
10 Tolerate (5)
12 Force produced by a pressure difference (7)
13 Hostelry (3)
14 Of a thing (3)
16 Backless chair (5)
17 Colour of bleached bones (5)
18 Exaggerated nasality in speech (5)
20 Hallucinogenic drug (inits) (3)
21 Young woman (coll) (3)

537

Across

1 Paces (5)
4 Distance downwards (5)
8 Domain (4)
9 Improvement (6)
10 Title (3)
12 Eastern marketplace (6)
14 Gelling agent (4)
15 Confer dignity or honour upon (7)
17 Nipple (4)
18 Brownish-yellow colour (6)
19 Reverence (3)
20 Measure (6)
21 Taunt (4)
23 Eastern county (5)
24 Wooden pin (5)

Down

2 Seaman (3)
3 Lowly agricultural labourer (7)
5 Dropped steeply (7)
6 Impediment (9)
7 Person who takes the place of another (9)
8 Act as a mediator (9)
11 Boy's name (3)
13 Avid (7)
14 Brisk and lively tempo (7)
16 Decorative tie (3)
22 Fatal disease of cattle (inits) (3)

538

Across

1 Girl's name (5)
5 Evil (3)
7 Clyster (5)
8 Falls (5)
9 Contaminated (5)
12 Female sibling with whom one has a parent in common (10)
16 Aluminium silicate mineral (4)
17 Greek and Roman muse of history (4)
19 Means of support (10)
22 Cap made of soft cloth (5)
23 Exhales audibly (5)
24 Deep serving spoon (5)
25 Affirmative word (3)
26 Kingdom in the South Pacific (5)

Down

1 Pleasure obtained by inflicting harm on others (6)
2 Megalithic monument (5,6)
3 Birds' homes (5)
4 Repairs (5)
5 Instrument that makes music by rotation of a cylinder studded with pegs (6,5)
6 Confront with resistance (4)
10 Irritation (4)
11 Group of three (4)
13 Thin rectangular block (4)
14 Lay slabs (4)
15 Ailing (3)
18 City of south-central Ukraine (6)
20 Musical study (5)
21 Gusset (5)
22 Greek letter (4)

539

Across

1 Prepared for something difficult or unpleasant (6)
6 Inconsistent in quality (6)
7 Enter forcibly (6)
9 Ugly object (7)
10 Cone-bearing evergreen (3)
12 Contemptibly narrow in outlook (5-6)
17 Before, poetically (3)
18 Square hole made to receive a tenon (7)
20 Large North American deer (6)
21 Crescent-shaped yellow fruit (6)
22 Father or mother (6)

Down

1 Short underpants (6)
2 Break of day (6)
3 Import tax (4)
4 Diminish (6)
5 More festive (7)
8 Toll of a bell (4)

11 Violating principles of right and wrong (7)
13 Deadly (6)
14 Estimation (4)
15 Make up one's mind (6)
16 Portray (6)
19 Exchange (4)

540

Across

1 Hanging cloth used as a blind (5)
3 Expect (5)
6 Tired of the world (5)
7 Take exception to (5)
10 Not having enough money to pay for necessities (11)
13 Arousing or holding the attention (11)
15 Flatfish (5)
18 Presentation, briefly (5)
19 Sing the praises of (5)
20 Second planet from the Sun (5)

Down

1 City in the United Arab Emirates on the Persian Gulf (5)
2 Law established by following earlier judicial decisions (9)
3 Assist (3)
4 Branch (3)
5 Limited periods of time (5)
8 Being (9)
9 Hand tool for boring holes (5)

11 Adult male person (3)
12 Large vase (3)
13 Come forth (5)
14 Very rude or coarse; vulgar (5)
16 Social insect (3)
17 Old cloth measure (3)

541

Across

1 Issue commands or orders for (9)
8 Modify (5)
9 Sepals of a flower (5)
10 Grazing land (3)
11 Bill for an amount due (5)
13 Flour and water dough (5)
15 Many times (5)
18 Ecstasy (5)
20 Mature (3)
21 Tilt (5)
22 Harmless tropical house-lizard (5)
23 Fill something previously emptied (9)

Down

2 Nocturnal badger-like carnivore (5)
3 Inclined to anger or bad feelings (5)
4 Provide a brief summary (5)
5 Hollow devices that make a ringing sound when struck (5)
6 Draught animal (9)
7 Enlargement (9)

12 Falsehood (3)
14 Each and every (3)
16 Commerce (5)
17 Of birth (5)
18 Commence (5)

19 Peruvian tribe at the time of the Spanish conquest (5)

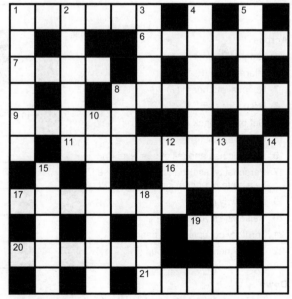

542

Across

1 Deliberately causes a delay (6)
6 Pleasantly occupied (6)
7 Estimate the value (4)
8 Official who watches a game or match closely to ensure that the rules are adhered to (7)
9 Adversary (5)
11 Acute and highly contagious viral disease (7)
16 Relating to birds (5)
17 As an alternative (7)
19 Head honcho (4)
20 North American native dog (6)
21 Deep gorge (6)

Down

1 Surface on which pictures can be projected (6)
2 Song of devotion or loyalty (6)
3 Preserve (4)
4 Rudolf ___, Russian-born ballet dancer and choreographer (1938–93) (7)
5 Precious gem (5)
8 Scandinavian type of knotted pile rug (3)

10 Bring up in conversation (7)
12 Boy (3)
13 Trading in ecclesiastical privileges (6)

14 Coincidence, accord (6)
15 Bother (5)
18 ___ Guinness, actor (1914–2000) (4)

543

Across
1. Stick or hold together (6)
6. Windcheater (6)
7. Electric razor (6)
9. Cross-brace that supports a rail on a railway track (7)
13. Former French coin (5)
14. Small rodent (5)
15. Spherical object (3)
16. Alternative (5)
19. Informal term for money (5)
20. Cover, surround or encircle (7)
22. Diacritical mark (two dots) placed over a vowel in German (6)
23. Diminishes gradually to a point (6)
24. To a very great extent (6)

Down
1. Excess of revenue over outlay in a given period of time (4,4)
2. Migraine symptom (8)
3. British nobleman (4)
4. Cowboy contest (5)
5. Earnings (5)
8. Accompany (6)
10. Insignia (6)
11. Buy (8)
12. Of late (8)
17. Experiment (5)
18. Projecting edge of a roof (5)
21. Fall silent (4)

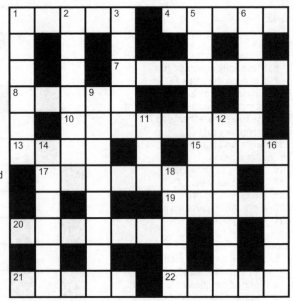

544

Across
1. Jangle (5)
4. Intermission (5)
7. Hospital attendant (7)
8. Exchanges (5)
10. Get on the back of (8)
13. River deposit (4)
15. Periodic rise and fall of sea level (4)
17. Personality disturbance characterised by a state of unconscious conflict (8)
19. Underway (5)
20. Raise one's voice (5,2)
21. Territory occupied by a nation (5)
22. Senior member of a group (5)

Down
1. French sweet blackcurrant liqueur (6)
2. Diffusing warmth and friendliness (7)
3. Give a shine to (5)
5. Pre-dinner drink (8)
6. Brine-cured (6)
9. Peevish (8)
11. Also (3)
12. Refuse to follow orders (7)
14. Writing fluid receptacle (3-3)
16. Dines at home (4,2)
18. Full of flavour (5)

545

Across

1 Moving staircase (9)
8 Provide (5)
9 Link up, connect (3,2)
10 Resin-like substance (3)
11 Freedom from disputes (5)
13 Flexible joint (5)
15 Show appreciation (5)
18 Common gastropod (5)
20 Zero (3)
21 Dwelling (5)
22 Very tired (coll) (3,2)
23 Alpine perennial plant (9)

Down

2 Finnish steam bath (5)
3 Common fruit (5)
4 The letter 'H' written as a word (5)
5 Large body of salt water (5)
6 Continuing indefinitely (9)
7 Emphasise (9)
12 Is able to (3)
14 Charged particle (3)
16 Audibly (5)
17 Rest on bended legs (5)
18 Quench (5)
19 Collection of maps (5)

546

Across

1 Austrian composer, ___ Schubert (5)
4 Point directly opposite the zenith (5)
7 Relating to letting of a property (6)
9 City on the river Tiber (4)
10 Departed, went (4)
12 Young herring (4)
13 Crisp bread (5)
15 Consumed (3)
17 Large wading bird (5)
19 Completed (4)
21 Missile that is thrown (4)
23 Hard outer layer of a fruit (4)
24 Highly seasoned fatty sausage (6)
25 Slumber (5)
26 Domestic birds (5)

Down

1 Dense woodland (6)
2 Shaped like a ring (7)
3 Ardour (4)
5 Large artery (5)
6 Ridge of rock, coral, etc (4)
8 Alphabetic characters (7)
11 Adversary (3)
14 Depository for goods (7)
15 Mother of the ancient Irish gods (3)
16 Describe the meaning of (6)
18 Mix up or confuse (5)
20 Coloured part of the eye (4)
22 Savoury taste experience (4)

547

Across

1 Gentle, indulgent (4)
3 Fish-eating bird (6)
5 Uncooked (3)
6 Part of the ear (4)
7 Form of communication (6)
9 Plot to carry out some harmful or illegal act (10)
14 Turning on a pivot (10)
17 Paying customer (6)
19 Endorsement made in a passport (4)
20 Bladed chopping tool (3)
21 Insect with large pincers at the rear of the abdomen (6)
22 Volcanic rock (4)

Down

1 Choose (6)
2 Lock of hair (5)
3 Bird that hoots (3)
4 Mineral used as an abrasive (5)
8 Beverage (3)
10 Novel (3)
11 Frost (3)
12 Breath or spirit in Chinese philosophy (3)
13 Herbivorous lizard of tropical America (6)
14 Spicy tomato sauce (5)
15 Strong anger (3)
16 Flush (5)
18 Children's game (3)

548

Across

1 Respected leader in national or international affairs (9)
8 Historical object (5)
9 Distinctive smell (5)
10 Ailing (3)
11 Deceive (5)
13 Espresso coffee with milk (5)
15 Acute (5)
18 Rich brown pigment (5)
20 Israeli submachine-gun (3)
21 ___ Wilde, dramatist (5)
22 Knave (5)
23 Confused multitude of things (5-4)

Down

2 Fine net used for tutus (5)
3 Implied (5)
4 Will (5)
5 Terminate before completion (5)
6 Exactness (9)
7 Implanted device that controls heartbeat (9)
12 Atmosphere (3)
14 ___ Maria, prayer to the Virgin Mary (3)
16 Capital of Ghana (5)
17 Rid of impurities (5)
18 Enchantress (5)
19 Leaves of a book (5)

549

Across
1 Melvyn ____, presenter of TV's *The South Bank Show* from 1978–2010 (5)
4 Religious paintings (5)
8 Implement used to clean the barrel of a firearm (6)
9 Appellations (5)
10 Construct (a building) (5)
12 Happening without apparent external cause (11)
13 Container for clothing, sheets, etc that need washing (5,6)
15 Annoying insects (5)
18 Planetary satellites (5)
19 40th President of the US (6)
20 Eddy (5)
21 Prepared for action (5)

Down
1 Premium (5)
2 Popular fruit used as a vegetable in cooking (5,6)
3 Oxygen, for example (3)
4 Wrath (3)
5 Fundamental assumption from which something is begun (11)
6 Lyric poem (3)
7 Locations (5)
11 Young sheep (5)
13 Lennox ____, retired heavyweight boxing champion (5)
14 Easily irritated (5)
16 ____ Lanka, country (3)
17 ____ volatile, smelling salts (3)
18 Impair (3)

550

Across
1 Shaft of light (4)
3 Dissimilar (6)
5 Lummox (3)
6 Cause the ruin or downfall of (4)
7 Loud utterance; often in protest (6)
9 State of financial comfort or security (coll) (4,6)
14 Irritate (3)
15 Broadcast (3)
17 Bad luck (10)
20 Indicates the direction of (6)
22 Belonging to me (4)
23 Liveliness and energy (3)
24 ____ and the Beast, famous fairy-tale (6)
25 Printed characters (4)

Down
1 Sultanate in Borneo (6)
2 Morose (5)
3 Vehicle from another world (inits) (3)
4 Protein found in hair, feathers, nails and hooves (7)
8 Golfing device (3)
10 Opening to which a sleeve can be attached (7)
11 Travel on the piste (3)
12 As well (3)
13 ____ de Cologne, perfumed liquid (3)
16 Go back on one's promise (6)
18 Boy (3)
19 Entice (5)
21 Engage in espionage (3)

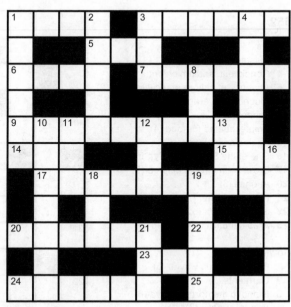

551

Across

1 Early form of modern jazz (3)
3 Long, narrow deposit of beach material (4,3)
6 Dispersed (9)
8 Negative word (3)
10 Piece of material inset to enlarge a garment (6)
13 Fill to satisfaction (4)
14 Bodily waste water (5)
16 Behaves in a particular way (4)
17 Aim at (6)
20 At all times, poetically (3)
21 A movement upward (9)
22 Produce milk for a baby to drink (7)
23 Augment (3)

Down

1 Fetch (5)
2 Nuisances (5)
3 Drool (6)
4 Chest of drawers (7)
5 Disencumber (3)
7 Starter course of a meal (6)
9 Units of weight (6)
11 Imagine to be the case (7)
12 Small insectivorous bird (3)
15 Indigenous person (6)
18 Aladdin's spirit (5)
19 Copy on thin paper (5)
21 Hand tool (3)

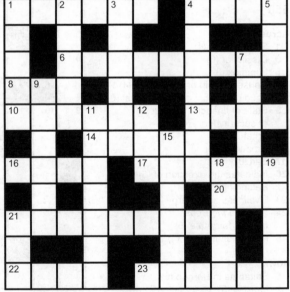

552

Across

1 Pulsates (6)
4 Condiment, sodium chloride (4)
6 Absence of culture and civilisation (9)
8 Alcoholic beverage (3)
10 Tenant (6)
13 Animal hunted for food (4)
14 Equine animal (5)
16 One of the Seven Deadly Sins (4)
17 Brown with a reddish tinge (6)
20 At once (3)
21 Fine porcelain (4,5)
22 Succeed in an examination (4)
23 Area set back or indented (6)

Down

1 Relating to sea waves (5)
2 Garments (5)
3 Island to the north of Java (6)
4 Bands, streaks (7)
5 Woollen cap of Scottish origin (3)
7 Designating sound transmission from two sources (6)
9 Rough shelter at the side of a house (4-2)
11 Timidity (7)
12 Make a mistake (3)
15 Lying face upward (6)
18 Trap for birds or small mammals (5)
19 Two offspring born from the same pregnancy (5)
21 Small loaf or roll of soft bread (3)

553

Across

3 J D Salinger novel, *The ___ in the Rye* (7)
6 Mendicant monk (5)
7 Imaginary animal (7)
8 Authorises (coll) (5)
9 Immense (4)
11 Podium (4)
14 Russian emperor (4)
17 Slightly open (4)
19 Employees' representative body (5)
20 Substance taken to counter indigestion (7)
21 Reside (5)
22 Seeds used to flavour a traditional seedcake (7)

Down

1 Have the financial means to buy something (6)
2 Hindu Festival of Lights (6)
3 Flatten (5)
4 Seal of approval (6)
5 "I have found it" (6)
10 Country, capital Washington DC (inits) (3)
12 Order of business (6)
13 African desert (6)
15 Black eye (slang) (6)
16 Cause to feel aggrieved (6)
18 Reddish colour often associated with good health (5)

554

Across

1 Place where vehicles halt to take on and discharge passengers (3,4)
7 Fluid product of inflammation (5)
9 Maxim (5)
11 Means of returning something by post (inits) (3)
12 Private conversation (4-1-4)
13 Harnesses (5)
14 Pressured, compelled (7)
18 Lagoon encircled by a coral reef (5)
20 Regions on opposite sides of the Earth (9)
23 Former name of Tokyo (3)
24 Plays, theatre (5)
25 Woodland plants (5)
26 World's highest mountain (7)

Down

1 Tony ___, former prime minister (5)
2 Motionless (6)
3 Bloodsucking African fly (6)
4 City with a famous tower (4)
5 Old-fashioned form of 'you' (4)
6 Lacking mercy (5)
8 Thin flexible tube inserted into the body (8)
10 Racial extermination (8)
15 Golfing attendant (6)
16 Quantity of medication taken at any one time (6)
17 Prickly plants (5)
19 Smallest amount (5)
21 Move in large numbers (4)
22 Assume a stance, as for artistic purposes (4)

555

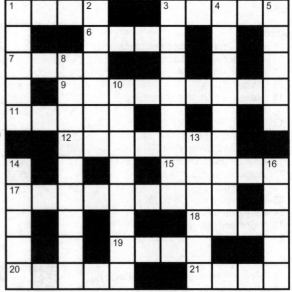

Across

1 Cavalry unit (5)
4 Hanging loosely (5)
7 Filled tortilla (4)
9 Pit viper with horny segments at the end of the tail (11)
10 Stings (6)
12 Necessitate (4)
13 Hitch, unforeseen problem (4)
14 Coarse food (especially for cattle and horses) (6)
17 Generated form of energy (11)
20 In this place (4)
21 Money bag (5)
22 Decorate (5)

Down

1 Changes direction (5)
2 Aquatic creature (5)
3 Close friend (3)
4 Distress signal (inits) (3)
5 Proceed (2,5)
6 Bear fruit (5)
8 Armistice, truce (9)
11 Lacking professional skill (7)
13 Woolly mammals (5)
15 Chopped into cubes (5)
16 Synthetic fabric (5)
18 Definite article (3)
19 Brother of George Gershwin (3)

556

Across

1 Writing implements (4)
3 Contrite (5)
6 Ready money (4)
7 Spanish sparkling white wine (4)
9 Former, onetime (9)
11 Tendon connecting muscle to bone (5)
12 Large imposing building (7)
15 Farm with facilities for livestock (5)
17 Person displaying ostentatious or smug cleverness (coll) (5,4)
18 Badgers' den (4)
19 Drink often mixed with alcohol (4)
20 Hibernated (5)
21 Red eruption of the skin (4)

Down

1 Chooses (5)
2 Frightened (6)
3 Woman who dances in a chorus line (8)
4 Dwelling place (9)
5 Country bumpkin (5)
8 Impressive by reason of age (9)
10 Most fast moving (8)
13 Form of address for Roman emperors (6)
14 Drug addicts (5)
16 Snag, difficulty (5)

557

Across

3 Fixing permanently in place (7)
6 Native of Baghdad, for example (5)
7 Score with a sharp point (7)
8 Disorderly outburst (coll) (3-2)
10 Country, capital Warsaw (6)
12 Expresses in words (4)
14 Shape (4)
17 Explosive device used to break down a gate or wall (6)
19 Damp (5)
20 French castle (7)
21 Condiment (5)
22 Confectionery made from sugar, butter and nuts (7)

Down

1 Combats (6)
2 Old car in a dilapidated condition (coll) (6)
3 Plant fibre used to make rope (5)
4 Back and forth (2,3,3)
5 Flower 'juice' (6)
9 Medical institution (8)
11 Toward the stern of a ship (3)
13 Item that prevents a ship from moving (6)
15 Abominable (6)
16 Female parent (6)
18 Entertain (5)

558

Across

1 Obvious and dull (5)
5 Chest for the Covenant (3)
7 Egyptian statesman who nationalised the Suez Canal (6)
8 Form of civil disobedience (3-2)
10 Brief description accompanying an illustration (7)
12 Spanish conquistador who conquered Mexico (6)
13 Fireside mat (3)
16 Well-seasoned stew (6)
17 Marine plant (7)
19 Belgian port famous for its cloth industry (5)
21 Chinese fruit having a thin brittle shell (6)
22 Very small (3)
23 Armistice (5)

Down

1 Cut in two (6)
2 Tropical black cuckoo of central America (3)
3 Cavalryman (6)
4 Request on an invitation (inits) (4)
5 Thistle-like flower head with edible fleshy leaves (9)
6 Eager (4)
9 Platform that rotates a phonograph record (9)
11 Shade of blue (5)
14 Contraption (6)
15 Figurine (6)
17 Demonstrate (4)
18 Apiece (4)
20 Of a female (3)

559

Across

2 Evaluating (9)
6 Bulgarian capital (5)
7 Girl who features in Lewis Carroll's famous stories (5)
9 Pin (3)
10 Grin (5)
12 Enrol (5)
14 Off the cuff (2-3)
17 Grate (teeth) (5)
19 Melody (3)
20 Voice qualities (5)
21 Famous American battle (5)
22 Refuse to stop (9)

Down

1 Helper (9)
2 Civilian dress worn by a military person (5)
3 With the mouth wide open, as in wonder or awe (5)
4 Employment (5)
5 Imbecile (5)
8 Creature found in the soil (9)

11 Hawaiian floral garland (3)
13 Grandmother (3)
15 Ocean-going vessel (5)

16 Coat in fat (5)
17 Level (5)
18 Speedily (5)

560

Across

1 Regions (5)
5 Public transport vehicle (3)
7 Disorder characterised by fear (6)
8 Right-hand page of a book (5)
10 Judder (5)
11 Economics (7)
14 Staying power (7)
16 Baked to a cinder (5)
17 Lacking enthusiasm or concern (5)
19 Written order directing a bank to pay money (6)
20 One of the two symbols used in Morse code (3)
21 Traditional stories accepted as history (5)

Down

1 Floating aimlessly (6)
2 Appropriate (3)
3 Fleeced (5)
4 Excessively fat (5)
5 Stringed Russian instrument (9)
6 Free from danger (4)

9 Build (9)
12 Feline mammal (3)
13 Stroke lovingly (6)
14 Alloy of iron and carbon (5)

15 Book for collecting stamps (5)
16 Lacking hair (4)
18 Pasture (3)

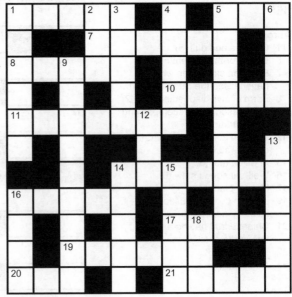

561

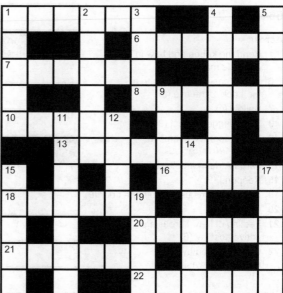

Across
1 Religious doctrine (5)
4 Flat-bottomed boat (4)
7 Manufacturer (5)
8 Timid (3)
10 Large, edible marine fish (4)
11 Powdered type of sugar (6)
13 Ability to walk steadily on the deck of a pitching ship (3,4)
16 Burn superficially or lightly (5)
17 Cut off (7)
18 Without much speed (6)
21 Boundary (4)
23 Wing of an insect (3)
24 Chris ___, ex-husband of Billie Piper (5)
25 Affectedly dainty or refined (4)
26 Fertilised plant ovules (5)

Down
1 Flat round object (4)
2 Chaps (4)
3 Loss of memory (7)
4 Land (6)
5 French group of vineyards (3)
6 Brings on to solid food (5)
9 Chops roughly (5)
12 Leases out (5)
14 Perpetually young (7)
15 Cook by radiated heat (5)
16 Small case into which an object fits (6)
17 Clumsy (5)
19 Walk through water (4)
20 Deviates erratically from a set course (4)
22 Unit of gravitational force (3)

562

Across
1 According to the timepiece (6)
6 Block the passage through (6)
7 Fills with high spirits (6)
8 Join together by overlapping (6)
10 Rise as vapour (5)
13 Itinerant Australian labourer (7)
16 Trick (5)
18 Drill used to shape or enlarge holes (6)
20 Joined by treaty or agreement (6)
21 English author of satirical novels, ___ Waugh (6)
22 Extreme fear (6)

Down
1 Periods of play in cricket (5)
2 Declare illegal (6)
3 Expression of love (4)
4 Boldly resisting authority or an opposing force (7)
5 Mechanical bar (5)
9 American feline (4)
11 Someone who breaks free (7)
12 Spice made from the covering of the nutmeg (4)
14 Deer horn (6)
15 Carrying weapons (5)
17 Durable aromatic wood (5)
19 Harangue (4)

563

Across

1 Plant life (5)
4 Be in direct physical contact with (5)
7 Forces out (6)
9 Wash with a mop (4)
11 Lawful, legitimate (5)
12 Copyist (6)
14 Army division (4)
16 Disease of the skin (4)
19 Intensify (6)
21 Large group or crowd (5)
22 Heavy open wagon (4)
23 Establish an association (6)
25 Relating to punishment (5)
26 Flaming (5)

Down

1 Plant valued for its fragrant tubular flowers (7)
2 Flexible twig of a willow tree (5)
3 Law passed by Parliament (3)
5 Little-known (7)
6 American raccoon (5)
8 Slim (7)
10 Be victorious (3)
13 Motionlessness (7)
15 Place where leather is made (7)
17 Go after with the intent to catch (5)
18 And not (3)
20 Location, whereabouts (5)
24 Brownie (3)

564

Across

1 Bend the knees and bow in a servile manner (6)
6 Light-sensitive membrane at the back of the eye (6)
7 Bellow (4)
9 Many-legged insect (9)
12 Italian operatic composer (1813–1901) (5)
13 Large African antelope (3)
15 Respond (5)
18 Suite of rooms usually on one floor (9)
20 Close (4)
21 Feeling of ill-will arousing active hostility (6)
22 Characterised by insincerity, evasive (6)

Down

1 Russian city on the Vyatka River (5)
2 Exhausted (5)
3 Court order (4)
4 Sleep during winter (9)
5 Ring-shaped bread roll (5)
8 Vigorously active, gymnastically (9)
10 Dark period (5)
11 Harden (5)
14 Cold vegetable dish (5)
16 Boredom (5)
17 Linger (5)
19 Overlook (4)

565

Across

1 Composer whose works include *The Clock* and *London symphonies* (5)
5 Large wild ox (5)
8 Elderly person (inits) (3)
10 Bring into harmony with (6)
11 Fewer (4)
14 Cook over an open fire (8)
15 Cotton fabric used on wounds (4)
16 Red gem (4)
17 Chief port of Yemen (4)
20 Ring slowly (4)
21 Reply of denial (8)
23 Canter (4)
24 Make unauthorised alterations (6)
25 Unit of electric current (abbr) (3)
26 Very recently (5)
27 Indicate (5)

Down

2 Cancellation of civil rights (9)
3 Uncertainty (5)
4 Name of the dog in Peter Pan (4)
6 Deadbeat (5)
7 Inquisitive (5)
9 Latin phrase meaning 'for each person' (3,6)
12 Former French coin (3)
13 Army officer below the rank of captain (9)
17 Mr Mosimann, famous chef (5)
18 Inflated pride (3)
19 Connected with birth (5)
20 Musical pace (5)
22 Piece of leather forming the front upper of a shoe (4)

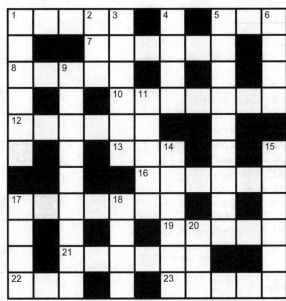

566

Across

1 Ascent (5)
5 Diving bird of northern seas (3)
7 Lots and lots (coll) (6)
8 Type of parrot (5)
10 Crocus stigmas used in flavouring food (7)
12 Construction built by a spider (6)
13 Massage (3)
16 Comfort in disappointment or misery (6)
17 Contract, abridge (7)
19 Demands (5)
21 Book of the Old Testament (6)
22 Intestine (3)
23 Bird of prey's claw (5)

Down

1 Children's magazines (6)
2 Flightless bird, now extinct (3)
3 Water tanker (6)
4 Musical mark indicating the pitch of notes (4)
5 Early form of sextant (9)
6 Incisive (4)
9 Small two-wheeled horse-drawn carriage (9)
11 Evil or corrupt practice (5)
14 Hat tied under the chin (6)
15 Time of year (6)
17 Close-fitting (4)
18 Capacious bag or basket (4)
20 Long period of time (3)

567

Across

1 Rudolf ___, WWII Nazi leader (4)
3 Coagulated milk used to make cheese (5)
6 Roman cloak (4)
7 Female horse (4)
9 Instant (9)
11 Over-worked horse (3)
12 Ideal future husband (2,5)
14 Type, kind (3)
16 Overbearing pride (9)
18 In the quickest time (inits) (4)
19 Source of illumination (4)
20 Food often named the 'staff of life' (5)
21 Variety (4)

Down

1 Mortal (5)
2 Part of a flower (4)
3 Knitted jacket (8)
4 Payments to a copyright holder (9)
5 Glossy, smooth (5)
8 Long, complicated and confusing procedure (9)
10 Popular garden plant with showy yellow or orange flowers (8)
13 Biblical brother of Esau (5)
15 Destroyed or killed (sl) (5)
17 Tight-fitting hats (4)

568

Across

1 Person who comes before one in time (11)
7 Predict from an omen (5)
8 Fuses, adheres (5)
9 Self-importance (3)
10 Behave towards (5)
12 Circular frame with spokes (5)
14 Instances (5)
17 Avowed (5)
19 Add up (3)
20 Loose garment worn by Muslim women (5)
21 Liquorice-flavoured seeds (5)
22 Means of the rapid escape of a pilot from an aircraft (7,4)

Down

1 Usable for a specific purpose (11)
2 Emblem representing power (5)
3 Type of heron (5)
4 Arm joint (5)
5 From that time (5)
6 Richly and brilliantly colourful (11)
11 Shortened forename of US president Lincoln (3)
13 In what way? (3)
15 Twilled woollen fabric (5)
16 Come into being (5)
17 Step (5)
18 Fruit, an important source of oil (5)

286

569

Across

1 Insincere talk about religion or morals (4)
3 Security (6)
5 Garden tool (3)
6 Delicate, woven and decorative fabric (4)
7 Real (6)
9 Scatter among or between other things (11)
14 Noblewoman ranking below a duchess (11)
18 Ice-cream container (6)
20 Capital of Latvia (4)
21 Tiny insect (3)
22 Decapitate (6)
23 Habitation for bees (4)

Down

1 White metallic element that burns with a brilliant light (7)
2 Melodic subject of a musical composition (5)
3 Body of salt water (3)
4 Holds fast (5)
8 Foot digit (3)
10 High rocky hill (3)
11 Glide over snow (3)
12 Fish eggs (3)
13 Bring into servitude (7)
15 In a higher position (5)
16 Dupe, swindle (3)
17 Compass point (5)
19 Small amount (3)

570

Across

1 Humble (5)
4 Circus entertainer (5)
7 Not accurate (7)
8 Painting, sculpture, etc (3)
9 Plain dough cake, often griddled (5)
11 Amount by which a salary is increased (5)
12 Addition, subtraction, division, multiplication, etc (abbr) (5)
14 Burn with steam (5)
16 Seize suddenly (3)
17 Give life to (7)
19 Bout, period of indulgence (5)
20 Distinctive spirit of a culture (5)

Down

1 Haywire (5)
2 Plural of the word 'am' (3)
3 Circumvent (5)
4 Provide food for an event (5)
5 Musical toy (7)
6 Saltpetre (5)
10 Tenth month of the year (7)
12 Devices that explode on contact (5)
13 Remove body hair (5)
14 River that flows through Paris (5)
15 Clothing (5)
18 Fire's remains (3)

571

Across
1 Hackneyed (5)
3 Japanese dish (5)
6 Swimming pool (4)
8 Musical composition of three or four movements of contrasting forms (6)
9 Aspire (3)
11 Oscar ___, Irish writer and wit (1854–1900) (5)
12 Space between two planes that intersect (5)
13 Large deer (3)
14 Avoid one's assigned duties (5)
15 Frosting (5)
18 Completely (3)
19 Astonished (6)
20 Acorn-producing trees (4)
21 Drinking vessel (5)
22 Muscular and heavily built (5)

Down
1 Rule made by a local authority (2-3)
2 Stay clear of (5)
3 Country, capital Bratislava (8)
4 Place of complete bliss (7-2)
5 Complacently foolish (5)
7 Head of the Tibetan Buddhist hierarchy (5,4)
10 Disposition to be patient and long suffering (8)
14 Informal language (5)
16 Genetic copy (5)
17 Extravagantly and emotionally demonstrative (5)

572

Across
1 Welsh political party, ___ Cymru (5)
4 Horde (5)
7 Protection (7)
8 Japanese currency unit (3)
9 Card game (5)
11 Causes emotional distress (5)
12 A A ___, creator of Pooh Bear (5)
14 Professional cooks (5)
16 Coaster (3)
17 Room (7)
19 Growl (5)
20 Branchlet (5)

Down
1 Baffling question or problem (5)
2 Expert (3)
3 Simple song (5)
4 Beat with a piece of leather (5)
5 At no particular moment (7)
6 Sweets with a menthol flavour (5)
10 Civilians trained as soldiers (7)
12 Acts out without words (5)
13 Be superior to (5)
14 Confusion, disarray (5)
15 Gesture involving the shoulders (5)
18 Rigid piece of metal (3)

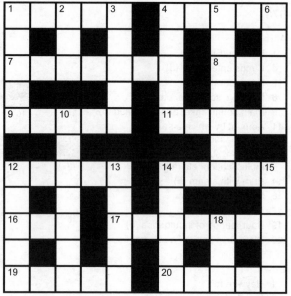

573

Across

1. Unrefined (5)
3. Inventories (5)
6. Sternwards (5)
7. Kingdom in the South Pacific (5)
10. Deserving reward or praise (11)
13. Autonomous (4-7)
15. In a peculiar manner (5)
18. Wireless (5)
19. Tempest (5)
20. Fence formed by a row of closely planted shrubs (5)

Down

1. Enchant (5)
2. Double-dealing, intending to mislead (9)
3. Ignited (3)
4. Boy child (3)
5. Closes with a bang (5)
8. Bring into being (9)

9. One stroke over par in golf (5)
11. Adam's wife (3)
12. Container for ashes (3)
13. Catches sight of (5)
14. Treasure of unknown ownership (5)
16. Singing couple (3)
17. Sweet potato (3)

574

Across

1. Not long before the present (6)
6. Rupture in smooth muscle tissue (6)
7. Traditional knowledge (4)
8. Catch fire (6)
10. Not affected by alcohol (5)
13. Former (3-4)
16. Month of the year (5)
18. Ductile, malleable (6)
20. Bathroom fixtures (4)
21. Peruser of text (6)
22. In a spooky manner (6)

Down

1. Bread buns (5)
2. Number represented by the Roman XI (6)
3. Native of Bangkok, for example (4)
4. Person in an organisation who has access to exclusive information about it (7)
5. Desert animal (5)
9. Dismal, dour (4)
11. Basic unit of money in Venezuela (7)
12. Harness strap (4)
14. Substance (6)
15. Separated (5)
17. Loose woman (5)
19. Weedy annual grass (4)

575

Across

4 Emblem (5)
7 One more (7)
8 Liturgical vestment worn by priests (3)
10 Held back, as of breath (5)
12 Artist's tripod (5)
13 Domesticated bovine animals (4)
15 Destruction of tissue by freezing (9)
19 Sharpen (a blade) (4)
21 Blackbird (5)
24 Landed estate of a lord (5)
25 School organisation for families and staff (inits) (3)
26 Goat-like antelope (7)
27 Arctic canoe (5)

Down

1 Jewish spiritual leader (5)
2 Physician (6)
3 Shelters from light (6)
4 Scottish hillside (4)
5 Slang term for fingerprints (4)
6 Before due time (5)
9 Thin plate or layer of bone (6)
11 Guided anti-ship missile (6)
14 To the ___ degree (to the utmost) (3)
16 Former name of Mumbai (6)

17 Band of tissue connecting a muscle to bone (6)
18 Coin equal to one hundredth of a rouble (5)
20 Get up (5)
22 Neuter (a female cat, for example) (4)
23 Be without (4)

576

Across

1 Capital of Tibet (5)
4 Former Nigerian capital (5)
7 Give up work (6)
9 Type of sousaphone (4)
10 Gambling stake (4)
12 Not many (1,3)
13 Main part of the human body (5)
15 Ironic (3)
17 Coffee-chocolate drink (5)
19 Heating elements in an electric fire (4)
21 Hanker (4)
23 Lowest female singing voice (4)
24 Three times (6)
25 Twilled cloth used especially for military uniforms (5)
26 Cardinal number (5)

Down

1 Long noosed rope (6)
2 Style of design popular in the 1920s and 1930s (3,4)
3 City, site of the Taj Mahal (4)
5 Daisy-like flower (5)
6 Cleansing agent (4)

8 Participant in some activity (7)
11 Non-functional replica of something else (3)
14 Dramatisation (7)
15 Which person? (3)

16 Characteristic to be considered (6)
18 Timepiece (5)
20 Rear, posterior part (4)
22 Clarified butter used in Indian cookery (4)

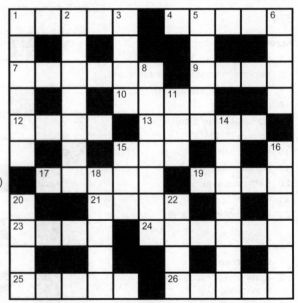

577

Across

1 Leapt (6)
6 Person who handles equipment for travelling entertainers (6)
7 Void (4)
8 Dash a liquid upon or against (7)
12 Elf or fairy (5)
13 (They) exist (3)
14 Manipulate in a fraudulent manner (3)
15 Hostel (3)
17 Mass of eggs deposited by frogs (5)
18 Drop a hint (7)
21 Presidential assistant (4)
22 Psychiatric hospital (6)
23 One who transmits a message (6)

Down

1 Sketchy summary of the main points of a theory (8)
2 Taking it easy (8)
3 Wire hairpin (4)
4 Decoy, lure (4)
5 Large natural stream of water (5)
8 Twilled woollen fabric (5)

9 Acute but unspecific feeling of anxiety (5)
10 Tropical tree with yellow flowers and long brown seed pods (8)

11 Arctic ruminants (8)
16 Dentist's assistant (5)
19 Fête (4)
20 Adds together (4)

578

Across

1 Dish of mutton, potatoes and onions (5,4)
8 Pop music not issued by a major record company (5)
9 Vigilant, awake (5)
10 Yearly assembly of shareholders (inits) (3)
11 Vertical part of a stair (5)
13 Ski run densely packed with snow (5)
15 Graph (5)
18 Savoury jelly (5)
20 Scottish port (3)
21 Painful eyelid swellings (5)
22 Clear space in an area of woodland (5)
23 Crucial (9)

Down

2 Travels as a passenger (5)
3 Smudge, daub (5)
4 Scallywag (5)
5 Level betting (5)
6 Miniature model of something (9)

7 Litter used as a means of transporting sick people (9)
12 Fruiting spike of a cereal plant (3)
14 Of a thing (3)

16 Bottomless gulf (5)
17 Appreciation (5)
18 Jargon (5)
19 Shopping centre (5)

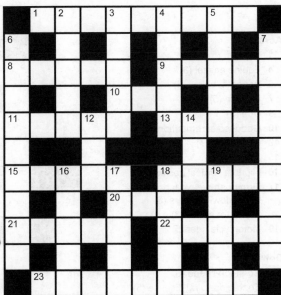

579

Across
1 Low land that is seasonally flooded (5)
3 Measure the depth of something (5)
7 Influence in an unfair way (4)
8 Egyptian water lily (5)
10 Large water jugs with wide spouts (5)
11 One of the supports for a table (3)
13 One of two actors who are given the same status in a film (2-4)
15 Implores (4)
16 Crazy (3)
18 Standard (4)
19 Decorative bunch of cords (6)
21 Young newt (3)
22 German empire (5)
25 Offering of a tenth part of some personal income (5)
26 Loose earth (4)
27 Belgian city (5)
28 Shafts of light (5)

Down
1 Willpower, restraint (4-7)
2 Cast off hair (5)
3 Pastry dish (3)
4 Principle (3)
5 Devoid of practical purpose (7)
6 Books that retail in large numbers (11)
9 Line formed by joining two pieces (4)
12 Frame of iron bars to hold a fire (5)
14 Conjecture (7)
17 Foolish (coll) (4)
20 Gateway in a fence (5)
23 Part of a gear wheel (3)
24 Hasten (3)

580

Across
1 Scarper (5)
4 Equine animal (3)
6 Beneath, below (5)
7 Domain (5)
9 Due (5)
10 Goddess of retribution (7)
13 Be false to (7)
15 At liberty (5)
16 Flip to a vertical position (5)
17 Firm open-weave fabric used by window-cleaners (5)
18 Signal for action (3)
19 Motorcycle rider (5)

Down
1 Go at top speed (6)
2 Contagious viral disease (5)
3 Farewell remark (5)
4 Truce (9)
5 Garden pest (4)
8 Place endowed for the support and lodging of the poor (9)
11 Nickname of US president Eisenhower (3)
12 Seller (6)
13 Express strong disapproval of (5)
14 Tiny morsel of bread or cake (5)
15 Secular (4)

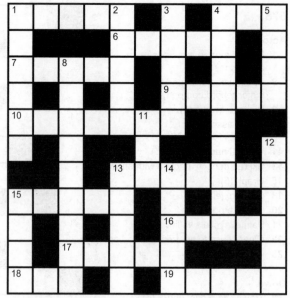

581

Across

1. Underground tunnels (5)
4. Possibly (5)
7. Speak softly or indistinctly (6)
9. Cut, as of wood (4)
10. Bill of fare (4)
11. Loves intensely (6)
13. Landscaped complex of shops (4)
15. Cease (4)
17. Dark blue colour (6)
20. Man-eating giant (4)
21. Divisions of a week (4)
22. Remove by cutting out (6)
23. Cake-maker (5)
24. Suburban residences (abbr) (5)

Down

1. Direction indicator (7)
2. Star sign between Leo and Libra (5)
3. Foam or froth on the sea (5)
5. Adopted in order to deceive (7)
6. Intestine (5)
8. Breathe (7)
12. Rejoinder (7)
14. Big feline (7)
16. Royal headdress (5)
18. Connected series or group (5)
19. Mode of expression (5)

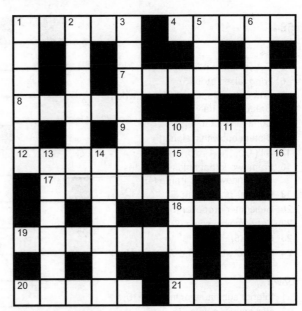

582

Across

1. Broom made of twigs (5)
4. Discharge, throw out (5)
7. Incorporate, embody (7)
8. Small, savoury Spanish snacks (5)
9. Make certain of (6)
12. Pointed projection on a fork (5)
15. Contaminate (5)
17. Single-celled, water-living protozoon (6)
18. Boy's name (5)
19. Made up one's mind (7)
20. Yield to another's wish or opinion (5)
21. Choral work (5)

Down

1. Circus tent (3,3)
2. Indication, usually of a disease (7)
3. Knead (7)
5. Israelite leader who destroyed Jericho (6)
6. Borough in inner north London (6)
10. Fame (7)
11. Curled lock of hair (7)
13. Elongated cluster of flowers (6)
14. Beginner, initiate (6)
16. Small tower extending above a building (6)

583

Across

1 Restraint used to slow a vehicle (5)
3 Scratches left by a glacier on rocks (5)
7 Male of domestic cattle (4)
9 Reach a destination (6)
10 Comes to the assistance of (4)
11 Town and port in north-west Israel (4)
12 Fleshy root (5)
15 Prices (5)
17 In golf, played a hole in one stroke (4)
19 At rest (4)
20 On a ship (6)
21 Sean ___, US film actor and director (4)
22 Mixture of rain and snow (5)
23 Farm storage buildings (5)

Down

1 Small lynx of North America (6)
2 Ms Minogue (5)
4 Pound, pulse (5)
5 Figure-skating jump involving a turn in mid air (4)
6 Reject, turn down (4,5)
8 *Key* ___, 1948 film (5)
13 Compere (coll) (5)
14 Handsome youth loved by Aphrodite (6)
16 Roofing material (5)
17 First letter of the Greek alphabet (5)
18 Enthusiastic devotees (4)

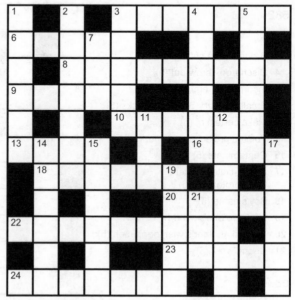

584

Across

3 Covered with hair (7)
6 Long raised strip (5)
8 Arm of the Mediterranean between Greece and Italy (6,3)
9 Communion table (5)
10 Distant but within sight (6)
13 Nil (4)
16 Framework that holds the panes of a window in the frame (4)
18 Express agreement (6)
20 Helicopter propeller (5)
22 Very small in scale (9)
23 Scour (5)
24 Predatory black-and-white whale (7)

Down

1 Inferior substitute or imitation (6)
2 Newspaper chiefs (7)
3 Name of several kings of England (5)
4 Church councils (6)
5 Belonging to those people (6)
7 Indian state, capital Panaji (3)
11 Be in possession of (3)
12 From the Orient (7)
14 Less difficult (6)
15 Hard, brittle element; the heaviest known metal (6)
17 As a result of this (6)
19 Bind (5)
21 Imaginary monster or ogre (3)

585

Across

1 Cleanse the entire body (5)
4 Hidden storage space (5)
7 Bituminous pitch (7)
8 Observe (3)
9 Jack in a pack of cards (5)
11 Lift (5)
12 Pack of cards used for fortune-telling (5)
14 Be overcome by a sudden fear (5)
16 Organ of locomotion and balance in fishes (3)
17 Study of the body (7)
19 Battleground of World War I (5)
20 Boundary (5)

Down

1 Cartridge containing an explosive charge but no bullet (5)
2 Bathroom fixture (3)
3 Wipe off (5)
4 Snag (5)
5 Buffer (7)
6 Something that happens at a given place and time (5)

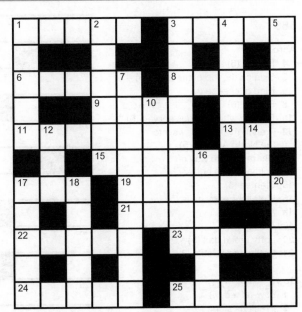

10 Word formed from the initial letters of a multi-word name (7)
12 Bunches of feathers or hair (5)
13 Tantalise (5)
14 Product of an oyster (5)
15 Church cellar (5)
18 Unit of electrical resistance (3)

586

Across

1 Condition marked by uncontrollable tremor (5)
3 Acute (5)
6 Growth on the surface of a mucous membrane (5)
8 Comical in a whimsical way (5)
9 Actor's portrayal of someone (4)
11 Sporting dog (7)
13 Charge (3)
15 Small bone in the middle ear (5)
17 Step in dancing (especially in classical ballet) (3)
19 Flimsy (7)
21 Sediment in wine (4)
22 Endure (5)
23 Place where milk, butter, cheese, etc is produced (5)
24 Brains (5)
25 Courtyard (5)

Down

1 Tubes (5)
2 Port city in western Turkey (6)
3 Placed into an inferior position (9)
4 Detached (5)
5 Heartbeat (5)
7 Serving no useful purpose (9)
10 Barrier constructed to keep out the sea (5)
12 Green vegetable (3)
14 Flightless bird (3)
16 Capital of Zambia (6)
17 Religious song (5)
18 Descendant (5)
20 Authoritative declaration (3-2)

587

Across

1 Remain cheerful in the face of adversity (4,2)
6 Impart knowledge to (6)
7 Drag the bottom of a lake (6)
9 Umpire (7)
10 Norwegian composer (1843–1907) (5)
12 Verbal defamation (7)
17 Give a speech (5)
18 Hearing distance (7)
20 Instruction to go away (4,2)
21 Country which borders Belize, Guatemala and the USA (6)
22 Work a way into someone's affections (6)

Down

1 Hispanic shop selling wine and groceries (6)
2 Joan Collins' rôle in *Dynasty*, ___ Carrington (6)
3 Jetty (4)
4 Member of a police force (7)
5 Groom with elaborate care (5)
8 'Lady' whose real name is Stefani Joanne Angelina Germanotta (4)
11 Stretchy fabric (7)
13 Show excessive affection (4)
14 Baby's toy (6)
15 Alloy of tin and lead (6)
16 Smooth surface (as of a cut gemstone) (5)
19 Double-reed woodwind instrument (4)

588

Across

1 Freight (5)
3 Skin on the top of the head (5)
6 Kind of cheese (4)
8 Furrow (6)
10 Dish on which food is served (5)
12 French river that flows into the North Atlantic (5)
14 Characteristic way of holding one's body (7)
15 Slanted (5)
16 Metal currency units (5)
18 Assorted (6)
19 Ale (4)
20 Lofty proud gait (5)
21 Settle one's debts (3,2)

Down

1 Low-priced (5)
2 Precious stone (3)
3 Loose-fitting white ecclesiastical vestment (8)
4 Native Australian (9)
5 Bit (5)
7 Onyx marble (9)
9 Protective strap in a car (4,4)
11 Number (3)
13 Yoko ___, widow of John Lennon (3)
15 Hobbles (5)
17 Disrobe (5)
19 Woman's garment (abbr) (3)

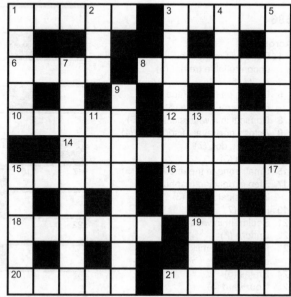

589

Across

2 Food-fish, the young of herring, sprat, etc (9)
7 By way of (3)
8 Inspiring admiration or wonder (7)
10 Male relative (7)
12 Root vegetable from which sugar is derived (4)
13 Light fluffy dish of egg yolks and stiffly beaten egg whites (7)
14 Instrument sounded to announce a meal (4)
16 Formerly the basic unit of money in Greece (7)
19 Artist's workroom (7)
20 Association of criminals (3)
21 Factory where workers do piecework for poor pay (9)

Down

1 Conjure up in the memory (5)
2 Notify of danger (4)
3 Muslim prayer leader (4)
4 Constant (4)
5 Point in orbit (6)
6 Act of stealing (5)
9 Military conflict (7)
11 Mixture of fog and smoke (4)
12 Group of countries in a special alliance (4)
13 Expulsion of air from the nose (6)
14 Pasture (5)
15 Wounding or pointed remarks (5)
16 Muck, filth (4)
17 Curved gateway (4)
18 Protuberance (4)

590

Across

1 Moves unobtrusively or furtively (6)
6 Tropical American fruit-eating bird (6)
7 Dread (4)
8 Prepared by a compositor for printing (7)
12 Product derived from cane or beet (5)
13 Sound off (5)
14 ___ and buts, objections (3)
15 Ancient Mexican civilisation (5)
18 More genuine (5)
19 Have (7)
21 Capital of Azerbaijan (4)
22 Rich and elaborate cake (6)
23 Mr De Niro, actor (6)

Down

1 Persuade someone through flattery (coll) (4-4)
2 Board game (8)
3 Remain, sit tight (4)
4 Drink of bourbon and sugar and mint over crushed ice (5)
5 Place of safety or sanctuary (5)
8 Instant (5)
9 Puts into a letterbox (5)
10 Feign, imitate (8)
11 Passage from the eye to the nose (4,4)
16 Divided into regions (5)
17 Organic compound (5)
20 Branch line (4)

591

Across

1 Rolling treeless highland (5)
4 Tree with rot-resistant wood (5)
7 Musical composition (4)
8 Method of producing designs on cloth by covering with wax, then dyeing (5)
9 Blackleg (4)
10 Border (4)
12 Called on the phone (4)
15 Boorish (4)
17 Jointed appendage (4)
19 Musical finale (4)
20 Wife of a rajah (5)
22 Star that ejects material (4)
23 Woody ___, US film-maker and comic actor (5)
24 Carnivorous mammal of the weasel family (5)

Down

1 Wooden planting tool (6)
2 Blow gently (4)
3 Fume (5)
5 Smaller in amount (6)
6 Mission (6)
11 Barrier that contains the flow of water (3)
13 Without usual standards or principles (6)
14 Brief look (6)
16 Excepted (6)
18 Alloy of copper and zinc (5)
21 'Fiddling' Roman emperor (4)

592

Across

1 Envelop (6)
4 Decorated with frosting (4)
6 Flat tableland with steep edges (4)
7 Genghis ___, founder of the Mongol empire (4)
9 Colouring agent (3)
12 Lessen the intensity of (8)
14 Swarm of young fishes (3)
16 Equality (3)
17 Excessively devoted to a single faction (3-5)
18 Animal's foot (3)
20 Absorbed, engrossed (4)
22 Daddy (4)
23 Deliberate trickery intended to gain an advantage (4)
24 Cure (6)

Down

1 Expressed in words (4)
2 Highest level attainable (4)
3 Belonging to the past (8)
4 Fluid used for writing (3)
5 Performer who moves to music (6)
8 Mound (4)
10 Narration, story (4)
11 Sing and play for somebody (8)
13 Standard monetary unit of Bangladesh (4)
14 Quarter (6)
15 Bark in a high-pitched tone (4)
18 Leaf of a book (4)
19 Keenly cautious (4)
21 Make heavy demands on (3)

593

Across

1 Midnight meeting of witches (6)
6 Declining gradually (6)
8 Group of people attractively arranged (7)
9 Chivalrous nobleman (6)
10 Samuel ___, English diarist (1633–1703) (5)
13 Product of coal tar extensively used in dyeing (7)
16 Hooded jacket (5)
18 Argentine plain (6)
20 Large ape (7)
21 Hired (6)
22 Uncle's wife (6)

Down

1 Assemble (3,2)
2 Anne ___, second wife of Henry VIII (6)
3 Hard durable timber (4)
4 One given to fits of laughter (7)
5 Semi-precious stone with streaked colouring (5)
7 Fabulous monster of swamps and lagoons (6)
11 Remuneration (7)
12 Fodder harvested while green (6)
14 Country, state (6)
15 Steeple (5)
17 Not in a state of sleep (5)
19 Salt of carbonic acid, used in soap powders (4)

594

Across

1 Gradient (5)
3 Large ladle (5)
7 Fanciful but graceful asymmetric ornamentation (6)
9 Panache (4)
10 Hardy annual cereal grass (3)
12 Prayer-ending word (4)
13 Moderately warm (5)
15 British system of medical care (inits) (3)
17 Loosen (5)
19 Smoke duct (4)
21 Sleeveless outer garment worn by Arabs (3)
22 Juicy, gritty-textured fruit (4)
23 Remain awake beyond one's normal bedtime (4,2)
25 African country, capital Tripoli (5)
26 Struggle for breath (5)

Down

1 Shriek (6)
2 For, in favour of (3)
4 Grovel (5)
5 Languish (4)
6 Compass point (5-4)
8 Dirt-free (5)
11 Affirmative word (3)
14 Filling (5)
15 Pen tip (3)
16 Folk (6)
18 After the expected time (5)
20 Gemstone (4)
24 Deciduous tree (3)

595

Across

1 South American rodent resembling a small beaver (5)
4 Modify (5)
7 Glassware made of quartz (7)
8 Location detector (5)
10 Relating to the Sun (5)
12 Consecrate (5)
14 Kingly, majestic (5)
16 Digression (5)
17 Give tongue to (5)
19 Outstanding musician (7)
20 Weight equivalent to 16 ounces (5)
21 Very steep, almost vertical (5)

Down

1 Little angel (6)
2 Measure of three feet (4)
3 Of legs, to take out of a folded position (7)
5 Circumspect (8)
6 Colourless watery fluid of blood (6)
9 Hired murderer (8)
11 Gruelling (7)
13 Without breaks between notes, in music (6)
15 Greater (6)
18 Tall perennial woody plant (4)

596

Across

1 Two-sixths (5)
3 Long noosed rope used to catch animals (5)
7 Examine (6)
8 Mosque official (4)
9 Loops of soft yarn, cut to give a tufted pattern (10)
13 Reacting quickly and positively (10)
17 Shaft on which a wheel rotates (4)
18 Breadwinner (6)
19 Assembly of witches (5)
20 Bike (5)

Down

1 Themes (6)
2 Ball-shaped (5)
4 Defence of some offensive behaviour or failure to keep a promise (5)
5 Units of electrical resistance (4)
6 Became technologically advanced (9)
10 Scottish form of 'no' (3)
11 Greek letter (3)
12 Extent (6)
14 Sift (5)
15 Flower arrangement of a single branch (5)
16 Bath powder (4)

597

Across

1 Formal offers at an auction (4)
3 Young eel (5)
6 ___ and ends (4)
7 Catch sight of (4)
9 Chocolate treat associated with a spring festival (6,3)
12 Domestic fowl (3)
14 Truck with an enclosed cargo space (3)
15 Inflicts punishment (9)
16 Morsel (3)
17 Number of turns in 60 seconds (inits) (3)
19 Citadel in ancient Greek towns (9)
21 Contains the flow of (usually water) (4)
22 Have supper (4)
23 Blockade (5)
24 Soap froth (4)

Down

1 Deciduous tree (5)
2 Asian plant widely cultivated for its oily beans (4)
3 Surpassing what is common (8)
4 Contrariwise (4,5)
5 Govern (5)
8 Sink in (9)
10 Rush (8)
11 Short intake of breath (4)
13 Large-scale (4)
16 Edges of a river (5)
18 Old Testament prophet (5)
20 The ___ of March, 2011 film (4)

598

Across

1 Assigned to a station (5)
5 The Mill on the ___, George Eliot novel (5)
8 Andean mammal (5)
9 Formal school or college balls (5)
10 Mark ___, US novelist (5)
11 Serving to identify a species or group (11)
15 Scrupulously neat and tidy in appearance (4-7)
19 Ballroom dance (5)
21 Mike ___, former heavyweight champion boxer (5)
23 Groups of three (5)
24 Idly play a guitar (5)
25 Bottomless gulf or pit (poetic) (5)

Down

1 Animal with two feet (5)
2 Fruits of the blackthorn (5)
3 Common type of tree (3)
4 Smart and stylish (7)
5 Overweight (3)
6 Native of Muscat, for example (5)
7 Sound practical judgment (5)
12 Water frozen in the solid state (3)
13 Country, capital Zagreb (7)
14 Contend (3)
15 Functions (5)
16 Madagascan primate (5)
17 Dirty and disorderly (5)
18 Jeans fabric (5)
20 Cash machine outside a bank (inits) (3)
22 Aggressive, rude and noisy troublemaker (3)

599

Across

1 Spoken (5)
4 Ordain (5)
7 Lax (7)
8 Extreme (5)
9 Food provider (7)
13 Grave (4)
16 Certain (4)
17 Not in good condition (7)
19 Firearm (5)
20 Antonio ____, Italian composer and violinist (1675–1741) (7)
21 Coloured transparent gemstone (5)
22 Colour slightly (5)

Down

1 Volcanic island republic in Melanesia (7)
2 Traditions (7)
3 Pale purple colour (5)
5 Sounds (6)
6 Sign of the zodiac (6)
10 Beard found on a bract of grass (3)
11 Brutal fellow (7)
12 Daydream (7)
14 Punctual (2,4)
15 Study of plants (6)
18 Float (5)

600

Across

1 Unemotional person (5)
4 Acute abdominal pain (5)
7 Chemical compound (7)
8 Chinese communist leader (1893–1976) (3)
9 Popular game played with pieces of stiffened paper (5)
12 Blasphemed (5)
15 Suspicious, not as expected (coll) (5)
18 Ticks over (5)
20 ____ Tolstoy, Russian writer (3)
21 With legs stretched far apart (7)
23 Beauty parlour (5)
24 Imperial (5)

Down

1 Of sound (5)
2 Known (3)
3 Gambling game using two dice (5)
4 Professional cooks (5)
5 State of being disregarded or forgotten (5)
6 Ugly evil-looking old woman (5)
10 ____ Baba, fictional character in *One Thousand and One Nights* (3)
11 First note in the tonic sol-fa scale (3)
13 Small mass of soft material (3)
14 Wheat-like cereal plant (3)
15 Drops down (5)
16 Destroy or ruin (5)
17 Ache, long (5)
18 Lay to rest (5)
19 Carapace (5)
22 Clinging plant (3)

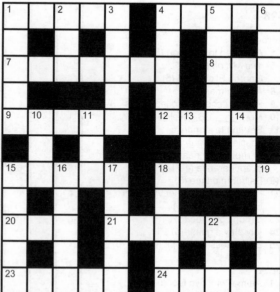

601

Across

1. Strongboxes for valuables (5)
4. Coconut flesh (5)
7. Currency used in Kabul, for example (7)
8. Select as an alternative (3)
9. Edible spread (5)
11. Unstable (5)
12. Defender (5)
14. Pair of game birds (5)
16. Rented out (3)
17. Noisy outcry (7)
19. Digress (5)
20. Limbless reptile (5)

Down

1. Fill quickly beyond capacity (5)
2. Mediterranean tree or its edible fruit (3)
3. Garden tool used for digging (5)
4. Counters used to represent money when gambling (5)
5. In proportion (3,4)
6. Suitably (5)
10. Break into many pieces (7)
12. Strong winds (5)
13. Dukedom (5)
14. Gives the cry of an ass (5)
15. Spooky (5)
18. Reproductive cells (3)

602

Across

1. Sour-tasting (6)
6. Lapis ___, azure blue semi-precious stone (6)
8. Seek out and bring together (5,2)
9. Fencing sword (4)
10. Moves through water (5)
13. Malleable metallic element that resists corrosion (3)
14. Educational institution (7)
16. Owing (3)
17. Hinged lifting tool (5)
19. German composer (1685–1750) (4)
21. Capital of Uganda (7)
22. Force used in pushing (6)
23. Join the military (6)

Down

1. Measures of land (5)
2. Generator (6)
3. Hint (4)
4. Make calm or peaceful (7)
5. Become broader (5)
7. Computer application program that uses the client's web browser to provide a user interface (6)
11. Large mass of frozen water (7)
12. Trousers for casual wear (6)
15. New Testament book telling the story of Christ (6)
16. Demise (5)
18. Vertical passage into a mine (5)
20. Dislike intensely (4)

603

Across

1 Convenient (5)
3 Sightless (5)
7 Floor covering (abbr) (4)
9 Finger-shaped cream cake (6)
11 Deduce (5)
13 Avid (5)
14 Sun-dried brick (5)
15 Prowess (3)
16 Lucifer (5)
17 Electronic message (5)
20 Measure of gold's purity (5)
22 Guide (6)
23 Male sheep (4)
24 Find the answer to (5)
25 In a bashful way (5)

Down

1 Cut in two (5)
2 Low humming sound (5)
4 Italian word for a woman loved or loving (9)
5 Funereal lament (5)
6 Four-winged insect (3)
8 Onset of darkness (9)
10 Fissure in the Earth's crust (6)
12 European country (6)
16 Cut-price events (5)
18 Fen (5)
19 Hearty (5)
21 Boat built by Noah (3)

604

Across

1 Removes the central part of an apple (5)
4 Chair used as a carriage (5)
7 Explosive initials! (3)
8 Primitive plant forms (5)
10 Add together (3)
11 Agitate (4)
12 Mr Richardson, knighted actor (1902–83) (5)
14 ___ faithfully, letter ending (5)
15 Available (3)
16 Boasts (5)
17 Follow as a result (5)
20 US composer and lyricist of musical comedies, ___ Porter (4)
21 Pistol, for example (3)
22 Depart (5)
24 Edgar Allan ___, US writer and poet (3)
25 Heave (5)
26 Hazardous (5)

Down

1 Position of professor (5)
2 Harass with persistent ridicule (3)
3 Medical instrument (11)
4 Narrator (11)
5 Talk about in detail (7)
6 Makes impervious to feeling (5)
9 Snake (3)
13 Apprentice (7)
16 Fake (5)
18 Surnamed before marriage (3)
19 Lament for the dead (5)
23 Beast of burden (3)

605

Across
- 1 Large ladle (5)
- 4 Sag (5)
- 7 Repent (3)
- 8 Get up (5)
- 9 Perfect type (5)
- 10 Juvenile newt (3)
- 11 Stonecutter (5)
- 14 Bear fruit (5)
- 17 Exorbitant (5)
- 20 Fleshy root (5)
- 23 Geological time period (3)
- 24 Transmitting live from a studio (2,3)
- 25 Organisation of employees (5)
- 26 Is able to (3)
- 27 Cultivated land (5)
- 28 Experiment (5)

Down
- 1 Horde (5)
- 2 Leaves out (5)
- 3 Groom (5)
- 4 Divine being (5)
- 5 Corpulent (5)
- 6 Heaped (5)
- 12 Toward the stern of a ship (3)
- 13 A single (3)
- 15 Promissory note (inits) (3)
- 16 Side sheltered from the wind (3)
- 17 Pathfinder (5)
- 18 Electronic message (5)
- 19 Roost (5)
- 20 Jeer at (5)
- 21 Russian pancake (5)
- 22 Of the kidneys (5)

606

Across
- 3 Struck with fear or apprehension (7)
- 6 Beg earnestly (5)
- 7 Lump of frozen water (3,4)
- 8 Closely packed (5)
- 9 Completely (7)
- 13 Decays (4)
- 16 Japanese form of wrestling (4)
- 17 Hang freely (7)
- 19 Once more (5)
- 20 Huge destructive wave (7)
- 21 No longer new, uninteresting (5)
- 22 Sharply (7)

Down
- 1 Arachnids (7)
- 2 Popular snack, often salted (7)
- 3 Au revoir (5)
- 4 Wealth (6)
- 5 Preserve a dead body (6)
- 10 Metal container (3)
- 11 Fugitive, escapee (7)
- 12 More immature (7)
- 14 Beginning (6)
- 15 Lightweight item used in bathing (6)
- 18 Lawn flower (5)

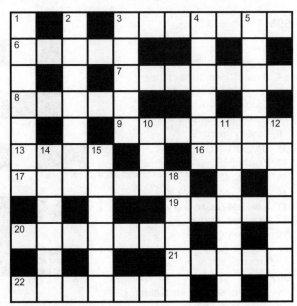

607

Across

1 Fruiting spikes of cereal plants (4)
3 Screenplay (6)
5 Leguminous plant (3)
6 Game played on horseback (4)
7 Recognition (6)
9 Name given to an alert and energetic person (5,6)
14 Dignity, esteem for one's own person (4-7)
18 Capital of Croatia (6)
20 Partially burn (4)
21 Visitor from space? (inits) (3)
22 Population count (6)
23 Trampled (4)

Down

1 Fast train that makes a limited number of stops (7)
2 Reproductive body produced a fern (5)
3 Hollow, flexible, bag-like structure (3)
4 Number indivisible by another (5)
8 Seventh Greek letter (3)
10 Mousse (3)
11 Four-winged insect (3)

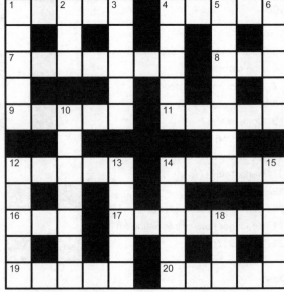

12 Compete for something (3)
13 No longer active in one's profession (7)
15 Fill with high spirits (5)
16 Cone-bearing evergreen (3)
17 Looped edging on a ribbon (5)
19 Public transport vehicle (3)

608

Across

1 Award for winning (5)
4 Saying: "He who pays the ___ calls the tune" (5)
7 Clinging part of a plant (7)
8 Garland of flowers (3)
9 Cavalry sword (5)
11 On your own (5)
12 Plait hair (5)
14 Perhaps (5)
16 Short-lived fashion (3)
17 Inflatable plastic ring worn as a swimming aid (7)
19 Canyon (5)
20 Smudge (5)

Down

1 Addition, division, etc (abbr) (5)
2 Cacophony (3)
3 Above average in size (5)
4 Bohemian dance (5)
5 Criticise harshly or violently (7)
6 River that flows through Bonn (5)
10 Lodger (7)

12 Make less visible, obscure (5)
13 First Englishman to circumnavigate the globe (5)
14 Contagious viral disease (5)
15 Duck valued for its soft down (5)
18 Grow old (3)

609

Across

1 Series of seats on a cable for carrying people up a mountain (9)
8 Targeted (5)
9 Give personal assurance, guarantee (5)
10 Augment (3)
11 County that borders the Thames estuary (5)
13 Play out (5)
15 Love affair (5)
18 Assign (5)
20 Known (3)
21 Tertiary (5)
22 With the extremity facing the observer (3,2)
23 Pleasure (9)

Down

2 Organic component of soil (5)
3 List of contents of a book (5)
4 Barrier constructed to keep out the sea (5)
5 All animal life of a place (5)
6 Move or act quickly (4,5)
7 Item for sharpening edged tools or knives (9)
12 Australian running bird (3)
14 Nothing (3)
16 Aromatic edible bulb (5)
17 Cowboy contest (5)
18 Group of elite soldiers (1-4)
19 Burdened (5)

610

Across

1 Apartments (5)
4 Domain (5)
9 Stead (4)
10 Period during which some action is awaited (4,3)
11 Linger (5)
12 Go back to a previous state (6)
15 Female operatic star (4)
18 Gas used in lighting (4)
20 Located beneath something else (6)
22 Ellipses (5)
23 Sweet pepper (7)
25 Chief Norse god (4)
26 Native of Dallas, for example (5)
27 Apportion (5)

Down

1 Installed (6)
2 Authorise (7)
3 Forest god (5)
5 Number indicated by the Roman XI (6)
6 Be unwell (3)
7 Rough shelter at the side of a house (4-2)
8 Drinking vessel (3)
13 Day before a festival (3)
14 Emblems of high office (7)
16 Interior (6)
17 Greek goddess of wisdom (6)
19 Snuggle (6)
21 Sources (5)
23 Cooking vessel (3)
24 Mingle (3)

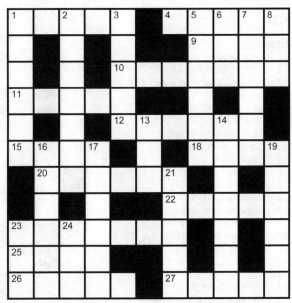

611

Across

1 Moved slowly and stealthily (5)
3 Hits with an open hand (5)
6 Amy Winehouse hit of 2007 (5)
8 Indian side dish of yogurt and chopped cucumbers (5)
9 The smallest quantity (4)
10 Sir Walter ___, British author (1771–1832) (5)
12 Enclosure for swine (3)
14 Woolly mammals (5)
16 Existed, lived (3)
18 Judge's hammer (5)
20 Harness strap (4)
21 City in India (5)
22 Mound of stones piled up as a memorial (5)
23 Incorrect (5)
24 Writing material (5)

Down

1 Shows concern (5)
2 Tresses of hair woven together (6)
3 Integral to a plan of action, especially in war (9)
4 Assumed name (5)
5 Sheltered from light or heat (5)
7 Troubling oneself (9)
11 US government unit (inits) (3)
13 Be equal, draw (3)
15 Central American canal (6)
16 Bereaved wife (5)
17 Outburst resembling the discharge of firearms (5)
19 Person who avoids the company of others (5)

612

Across

1 Moves in large numbers, swarms (5)
5 Hackney carriage (3)
7 Greek muse of love poetry (5)
8 Ran easily (5)
9 Joan ___, MBE, author (1924–2004) (5)
12 Not in accordance with scientific laws (10)
16 Gyrate (4)
17 Sadly (4)
19 Resolution (10)
22 Aladdin's spirit (5)
23 Long-distance walker (5)
24 Become ground down (5)
25 Explosion that fails to occur (3)
26 High, thin in tone (5)

Down

1 Bulbous plants (6)
2 Having gained knowledge through practise (11)
3 Chair used as a carriage (5)
4 Country, capital Doha (5)
5 Scottish soup (4-1-6)
6 Capital of the former West Germany (4)
10 Mosque official (4)
11 Panache (4)
13 Vaulted recess (4)
14 Not in favour of (4)
15 Nocturnal bird (3)
18 Floor of a house (6)
20 Projection at the end of a piece of wood (5)
21 Gas formerly used as an anaesthetic (5)
22 Decorate with precious metal (4)

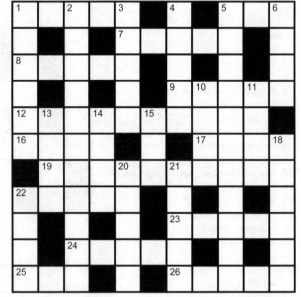

613

Across
1 Vendor (6)
4 Directs a weapon (4)
6 16th century V-shaped panel of stiff material worn over the chest (9)
9 Brandy measure (3)
10 Vertical post or rod used as a support (9)
12 Commercial, passenger-carrying planes (9)
13 Buddy (3)
15 Proclaimer of public announcements (4,5)
17 Rabbit's tail (4)
18 Protein that acts as a catalyst (6)

Down
1 Receptacle for a coin (4)
2 Final irritation that stretches one's patience beyond the limit (coll) (4,5)
3 Person with an abnormal sense of self-importance (9)
4 The alphabet (inits) (3)
5 Calm, with no emotional agitation (6)
7 Increase by natural growth or addition (9)
8 Commercial preparation used to keep coiffure in place (9)
11 Insect that rests with forelimbs raised as if in prayer (6)
14 Racing sled for one or two people (4)
16 Snare, trap (3)

614

Across
1 Widespread (6)
4 Airborne soldier (abbr) (4)
7 Necessitate (4)
9 Exactly right (4,2)
11 Flour and water dough (5)
13 Compress into small folds or ridges (5)
14 Recruit into an army (5)
15 Hand tool (3)
16 Blaspheme (5)
17 Depart, go (5)
20 Step (5)
22 Rain channel (6)
23 Unit of heredity (4)
24 Waterside plant (4)
25 Uneven in quality, texture, etc (6)

Down
1 Sarcastic pessimist (5)
2 Formal title used when addressing a woman (5)
3 Bird's home (4)
5 Treatment of a convalescent patient (9)
6 Abrogate (5)
8 Point directly above the focus of an earthquake (9)
10 Spanish rice dish (6)
12 Thinly distributed (6)
16 Sweet substance (5)
18 Cardinal number (5)
19 Each one, without exception (5)
21 Journey (4)

615

Across

1 Muscle cramp (5)
4 Anoint with oil (5)
8 Young bird of prey (6)
9 Criticism disguised as praise (5)
10 Coherent (5)
12 Church member (11)
15 Men's loose underpants (5,6)
17 Right-hand page (5)
20 Type of firearm (5)
21 Bone of the forearm (6)
22 Sir Fred ___, English astrophysicist (1915–2001) (5)
23 Attitude, beliefs (5)

Down

1 Subsist on a meagre allowance (5)
2 Insincerely emotional, maudlin (11)
3 Month with 31 days (3)
4 Completely (3)
5 Nerve specialist (11)
6 And so forth (abbr) (3)
7 Large northern sea duck (5)
11 Selected (5)
13 Bustle (3)
14 Feed (3)
15 Common tree (5)
16 Outstanding players in a tournament (5)
18 Weep (3)
19 Lyric poem (3)
20 Strong-scented perennial herb (3)

616

Across

1 Not easy to swallow (5)
3 Gateaux (5)
7 Throughout the time of (6)
10 Finishing line for a foot race (4)
11 Broad smile (4)
12 Common black-fruited shrub (10)
15 Everyday speech of the people (10)
20 Fix, put right (4)
21 Primitive, mainly aquatic organism (4)
22 Fertilised egg (6)
23 Banal (5)
24 Point directly opposite the zenith (5)

Down

1 Club that is used as a weapon (6)
2 Talk in a tearful manner (5)
4 Essential oil or perfume obtained from flowers (5)
5 Eject in large quantities (4)
6 Kitchen utensil used for mixing or whipping (3,6)
8 Address of a page on the World Wide Web (inits) (3)
9 Long raised strip (5)
13 Measuring stick (5)
14 Fervency (6)
16 Respond to a stimulus (5)
17 Darkest part of a shadow (5)
18 None in particular (3)
19 Component (4)

617

Across

1 To the opposite side (6)
6 Necktie (6)
7 Rear (4)
8 Fan, supporter (7)
9 Lessens the rate of (5)
11 Written account (7)
16 Hummock (5)
17 Officer of the court (7)
19 Bird symbolising peace (4)
20 Flat metal tumblers that revolve in locks (6)
21 Make a thrusting forward movement (6)

Down

1 Take into custody (6)
2 Implement used to clean the barrel of a firearm (6)
3 Move very quickly (4)
4 Italian astronomer and mathematician (7)
5 Belly button (5)
8 Beast of burden (3)
10 Fabric made from the hair of sheep (7)
12 UN agency dealing with banking and finance (inits) (3)
13 Become used up (3,3)
14 Resist separation (6)
15 Projecting edge of a roof (5)
18 Water-dwelling creature (4)

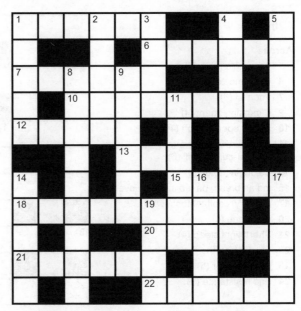

618

Across

1 Electronic image made of pixels (6)
6 Firstborn (6)
7 Earlier, more in advance (6)
10 Able to speak two languages fluently (9)
12 Desert in north-eastern Egypt (5)
13 Baby's bed (3)
15 Fasten by passing rope through a hole (5)
18 Measurement around the body between the ribs and hips (9)
20 Pulled suddenly (6)
21 Gender that refers to inanimate objects (6)
22 Revised before printing (6)

Down

1 Motor coaches (5)
2 Mood disorder (5)
3 Persian fairy (4)
4 Aromatic seeds used as seasoning especially in curry (9)
5 Lagoon encircled by a coral reef (5)
8 Causing disapproval or protest (9)
9 Derive by reason (6)
11 Aquatic South American rodent resembling a small beaver (6)
14 Lightweight cord (5)
16 Boredom (5)
17 Ceased (5)
19 Ancient Greek harp (4)

619

Across

- 4 Natives of Iraq, for example (5)
- 8 Appeared again (2-7)
- 9 Wing of an insect (3)
- 10 Authoritative proclamation (5)
- 13 Inclined surfaces connecting different levels (5)
- 14 Winnie-the-____, A A Milne's famous bear (4)
- 15 Alpine perennial plant (9)
- 19 Common sense, intellect (4)
- 21 Study intensively, as before an exam (coll) (3,2)
- 24 Acute pain (5)
- 25 Sleeveless outer garment worn by Arabs (3)
- 26 Moored boat with a warning beacon (9)
- 27 Elegance and beauty of movement (5)

Down

- 1 Grovel (5)
- 2 Amount of time (6)
- 3 Drum, pound (4)
- 4 Gelling agent (4)
- 5 Taking it easy (8)
- 6 Biblical first man (4)
- 7 Spicy tomato sauce (5)
- 11 Female deer (3)
- 12 Having a sweet nature befitting an angel (8)
- 16 Comfort, solace (6)
- 17 Earth's nearest star (3)
- 18 In the centre of (5)
- 20 Slender, graceful young woman (5)
- 22 Fête (4)
- 23 Leaf of a book (4)
- 24 High male voice (4)

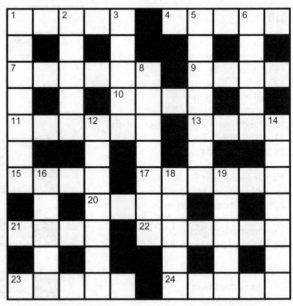

620

Across

- 1 Assemble (3,2)
- 4 Gibe, mock (5)
- 7 Vocalist (6)
- 9 Cleansing agent (4)
- 10 Heavy open wagon (4)
- 11 Shorebird with a slender upward-curving bill (6)
- 13 Belonging to us (4)
- 15 Indian bread, baked in a clay oven (4)
- 17 Country, capital Moscow (6)
- 20 Kin group (4)
- 21 Short, light sleep (4)
- 22 Buccaneer (6)
- 23 Bread maker (5)
- 24 End resistance (5)

Down

- 1 Provide with nourishment (7)
- 2 Ballroom dance (5)
- 3 Chunk (5)
- 5 Traditions (7)
- 6 Stylistic talent (5)
- 8 Device for catching rodents (3,4)
- 12 Acknowledge defeat (7)
- 14 Marine plant (7)
- 16 Bouquet (5)
- 18 Oneness (5)
- 19 Money risked on a gamble (5)

621

Across
1 Pursue like a ghost (5)
4 Reduce to small pieces by pounding (5)
7 Terminal section of the alimentary canal (6)
9 Daddy (4)
10 Went on horseback (4)
12 In one's sleeping place (4)
13 Daughter of a sibling (5)
15 Concert (3)
17 Brook (5)
19 Centre of an apple (4)
21 Bump into (4)
23 Strong positive emotion (4)
24 Narrow steep-sided valley (6)
25 Sepals of a flower (5)
26 Aroma (5)

Down
1 Plant-derived (6)
2 Ambiguous (7)
3 Extended journey (4)
5 Indian currency unit (5)
6 Distribute playing cards (4)
8 Familiar name for a person (7)
11 Archaeological site (3)

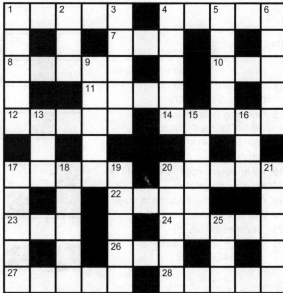

14 Coated, frozen dessert in the shape of a brick (4,3)
15 Word of surprise (3)
16 Refuse to accept or acknowledge (6)
18 ___ board, used to shape fingernails (5)
20 Group of countries in a special alliance (4)
22 Bathroom fixtures (4)

622

Across
1 Substance used to make cheese (5)
4 Scandalise (5)
7 ___ and outs, details of a situation (3)
8 Use water to remove soap (5)
10 Novel (3)
11 Stare at lustfully (4)
12 Cider fruit (5)
14 Malicious (5)
17 In a state of uncertainty (2,3)
20 Sharp part of a knife (5)
22 Brand name of a ballpoint pen (4)
23 Hoot with derision (3)
24 Conscious, aware (5)
26 God of the underworld; counterpart of the Greek Pluto (3)
27 Native American tent (5)
28 Less than the correct amount (5)

Down
1 Approximately (especially of a date) (5)
2 Dashed (3)
3 Military blockade (5)
4 Anaemic-looking (5)
5 Gasps for breath (5)
6 English painter, L S ___ (1887–1976) (5)
9 Figure out (5)
13 Put a snooker ball down a hole (3)
15 Softly radiant (5)
16 Small amount (3)
17 Chief monk (5)
18 Sailing vessel with a single mast (5)
19 Dwelling house (5)
20 Common alloy (5)
21 Turn inside out (5)
25 Farmhouse cooker (3)

623

Across
1 Chortle (5)
4 Swift descent through the air (5)
7 Explodes with a bang (4)
8 Field on which a university's buildings are situated (6)
9 Ejected saliva from the mouth (4)
10 Follower of Hitler (4)
12 Become soft or liquid, usually by heating (4)
13 Implements, puts into service (7)
14 Charitable gifts (4)
15 Yob deterrent (inits) (4)
16 Soap froth (4)
17 Warns of danger (6)
18 Young girl (4)
20 Band of material used to support an injured arm (5)
21 Enquired (5)

Down
2 Gone by (3)
3 Rumourmongers (7)
4 Chair (4)
5 Tyrannise (7)
6 Locations (9)
7 Police vehicles, colloquially (5,4)
8 Insensitive or heartless (7)
11 African river flowing into the Indian Ocean (7)
12 Acute and highly contagious viral disease (7)
16 Adult male deer (4)
19 Catch sight of (3)

624

Across
1 Mediterranean tree with edible pods used as a chocolate substitute (5)
4 Connected with sea-going forces (5)
7 Clap one's hands (7)
9 One who suffers for the sake of principle (6)
10 Withdraw from an organisation (6)
12 Jetty (4)
15 Rich-looking, upper-class (coll) (4)
17 Free of charge (6)
19 Determines the direction of travel (6)
20 At a more distant point (7)
21 Identification tab (5)
22 Oscar ___, Irish writer and wit (1854–1900) (5)

Down
1 Refuse to talk (4,2)
2 Arrange differently (7)
3 Gives the cry of an ass (5)
5 In a slumber (6)
6 Entertains or diverts (6)
8 Exact (7)
11 Expressive of grief or suffering (7)
13 Herbivorous lizard of tropical America (6)
14 Baby's plaything (6)
16 Persuade a person to buy worthless property (6)
18 Cornstalks (5)

625

Across

1 Cleanse the entire body (5)
3 Pedestal (5)
7 Eager (4)
8 In the area or vicinity (5)
10 Flexible appendages of animals (5)
11 Branch of the British armed forces (inits) (3)
13 Unwholesome atmosphere (6)
15 Introduce to solid food (4)
16 Object used in the game of skittles (3)
18 Secret scheme (4)
19 Person who handles equipment for travelling entertainers (6)
21 High-pitched bark (3)
22 Part of the leg between the hip and the knee (5)
25 Cut in two (5)
26 Sheltered and secluded place (4)
27 Slang of thieves and vagabonds (5)
28 Begin (5)

Down

1 River that flows from the Himalayas to join the Ganges in Bangladesh (11)
2 Divisions of a day (5)
3 Division of a tennis match (3)
4 Beverage (3)
5 Liquorice-flavoured herb (7)
6 Impartiality (11)
9 Press down tightly (4)
12 Magical being (5)
14 Idolising (7)
17 Biblical ark-builder (4)
20 At a distance (5)
23 Gunge (3)
24 Peppery (3)

626

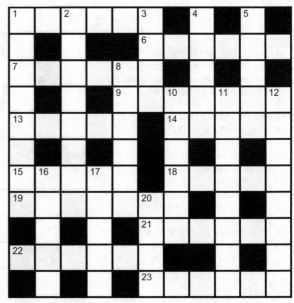

Across

1 Able to absorb fluids (6)
6 Public speaker (6)
7 Be preoccupied with something (6)
9 Woman who invites guests to a social event (7)
13 Earthy metallic oxide (5)
14 Article of faith (5)
15 Fit out (5)
18 Maxim ____, Russian playwright (5)
19 Ironical language (7)
21 Long noosed rope (6)
22 Derek ____, British actor who was knighted in 1994 (6)
23 Only, just (6)

Down

1 Annoys continually or chronically (8)
2 Time of day when most people are travelling to or from work (4,4)
3 Average (2-2)
4 Hindu social class (5)
5 Furze (5)
8 Inhabitant of the Tibetan Himalayas (6)
10 Mark of infamy (6)
11 Cause to be alert (8)
12 In a stringent manner (8)
16 Country, capital Doha (5)
17 Fluid said to flow in the veins of the gods (5)
20 Slender (4)

627

Across
1 Exhaled with force (4)
3 Part of a flower's calyx (5)
6 Poker stake (4)
7 Minus (4)
9 Causing an emotional disturbance (9)
11 Japanese currency unit (3)
12 Shrill scream or cry (7)
14 Brownie (3)
16 Instrument that measures atmospheric pressure (9)
18 Short-tailed wild cat (4)
19 Covers for boxes, pans, etc (4)
20 Melodic subject of a musical composition (5)
21 Stretched out (4)

Down
1 Stomach (5)
2 Black and yellow stinging insect (4)
3 Consciously perceiving (8)
4 Borderline region, space or area (9)
5 Projecting ridge on a mountain (5)
8 Sudden prostration due to exposure to excessive heat (9)
10 Unceremonious and disorganised struggle (8)
13 Terminate before completion (5)
15 Having an unchanging value (5)
17 Additional (4)

628

Across
1 Made neat and orderly (6)
4 Succeed in an examination (4)
6 Aroused to impatience or anger (9)
8 Forename of golfer, Mr Woosnam (3)
10 Airstrip (6)
13 Round cheese with a red rind (4)
14 Put (pressure) on (5)
16 Coves, inlets (4)
17 Flat disc used as a seal to prevent leakage (6)
20 Muhammad ___, former champion boxer (3)
21 Uncensored or unrestricted print media (4,5)
22 Municipality smaller than a city (4)
23 One who rules during the absence of a monarch (6)

Down
1 Odd-toed ungulate of tropical America (5)
2 Supernatural being in Muslim folklore (5)
3 Soft yellow substance secreted by aural glands (6)
4 Celestial bodies (7)
5 Distressing (3)
7 Substance covering the crown of a tooth (6)
9 Foreign home help (2,4)
11 Cowboy film (7)
12 Coniferous tree (3)
15 Elongated cluster of flowers (6)
18 Careless speed (5)
19 Correct (5)
21 Adipose tissue (3)

629

Across

1 City of ancient Egypt, now part of Luxor (6)
6 Positive or favourable aspect (6)
8 Not one nor the other (7)
9 Bath powder (4)
10 Pandemonium (5)
13 Film starring Bette Davis, *All about ___* (3)
14 Devoid of practical purpose (7)
16 Type of lettuce (3)
17 Stinks (5)
19 Ensnare (4)
21 Torment (7)
22 Not so cold (6)
23 Reference point to shoot at (6)

Down

1 Loose-fitting garment (5)
2 Descent from the high-flown to the mundane (6)
3 Edible fat (4)
4 Bishop's see (7)
5 River that flows through Paris (5)
7 Message communicated to God (6)
11 Severely simple (7)
12 Upper house of the US Congress (6)
15 Area (6)
16 Ornamental jewelled headdress (5)
18 Extract (metals) by heating (5)
20 Left side of a ship (4)

630

Across

2 Voucher that is exchangeable for goods in a shop (4,5)
6 Pasted (5)
8 Devotional paintings of Christ or other holy figures (5)
11 Stuffed plaything made of fabric (3,4)
12 Military chaplain (5)
13 Firm and hearty (5)
14 Austere, bare (5)
17 Showy garden plant (5)
19 Shooting (7)
20 Hindu religious teacher (5)
21 Holy city (5)
22 Mid-morning refreshment break (9)

Down

1 Roadside direction markers (9)
2 Inedible fruit with a hard rind (5)
3 Soft creamy sweet (5)
4 Groups of three (5)
5 Small natural hill (5)
7 Tympanic membrane (7)
9 Stoppage (7)
10 Stationary, immobile (9)
15 With the mouth wide open (5)
16 Cutting instrument (5)
17 Legs or arms (5)
18 Strikes with the beak (5)

631

Across

3 Johann ___, Austrian composer of waltzes (1804–49) (7)
6 Grovel (5)
8 Acute spasmodic nerve pain (9)
10 Equipment for taking pictures (6)
11 Perforate (6)
13 Gives assistance (4)
16 Basic unit of currency in Germany (4)
18 Approached (6)
20 Lords (6)
22 Very small in scale (9)
23 Canal boat (5)
24 Written acknowledgement of payment (7)

Down

1 Tree with sharp thorns (6)
2 Manufactured, not occurring naturally (3-4)
3 Drink noisily (5)
4 Tempt (6)
5 Arachnid (6)
7 Very small (3)
9 Apparel (7)
12 Implements for eating food (7)
14 Eventually (2,4)
15 Containing salt (6)
17 Forced out (6)
19 Uncertainty (5)
21 Woman's garment (abbr) (3)

632

Across

1 Curved gateway (4)
3 Peninsula in south-western Europe (6)
6 Very dark, black (4)
7 Woven into a thread (4)
8 Greek god of darkness who dwelt in the underworld (6)
9 Give new life or energy (10)
14 Owner (10)
17 Seldom (6)
19 Pimple (4)
20 A few (4)
21 Plot of ground adjoining a house (6)
22 Single and isolated from others (4)

Down

1 Preposterous (6)
2 Follower of a major religion (5)
3 Nickname of US president Eisenhower (3)
4 English romantic poet (1788–1824) (5)
5 Harden to (5)
10 Shock physically (3)
11 Listening organ (3)
12 Shoddy or tasteless articles (3)
13 Move in a twisting or contorted motion (6)
14 Pedestrianised public square (5)
15 Heartbeat (5)
16 Display stand for a painting (5)
18 Distant but within sight (poetical) (3)

633

Across

1 Uncouth (5)
4 Legendary creature resembling a tiny old man (5)
7 Postal service for overseas (7)
8 Domestic swine (3)
9 Examine thoroughly and closely (5)
11 Oliver ___, Dickens character (5)
12 Carve (3,2)
14 Repeated theme (5)
16 Adult male swan (3)
17 Curving inwards (7)
19 Elvis Presley's middle name (5)
20 In a peculiar manner (5)

Down

1 Chafe at the bit, like a horse (5)
2 Ventilate (3)
3 Strong wooden or metal post with a point at one end (5)
4 Style of glazed earthenware or pottery (5)
5 Assign a duty to (7)
6 Conflict (5)
10 Autumn month (7)
12 Bedtime beverage (5)
13 Smooth brown oval nut (5)
14 Oval fruit with a very large seed (5)
15 Flaming (5)
18 Also (3)

634

Across

1 Make free from confusion and ambiguity (9)
8 Oil-bearing laminated rock (5)
10 Muscular strength (5)
12 Go back in (2-5)
13 Closer to the centre (5)
14 Burn with steam (5)
15 Give an improvised speech (2-3)
18 Rice and raw fish wrapped in seaweed (5)
20 Insanely irresponsible (7)
21 Rounded projections of ears (5)
22 Make up for (5)
23 Cooking (vegetables) briefly (9)

Down

2 Discover (5)
3 Shout of approval (5)
4 Financial obligations (5)
5 Head ornament (5)
6 Deserving of respect or high regard (9)
7 Without careful prior deliberation or counsel (9)
9 Movement of the sea in the same direction as the wind (3,4)
11 Recently enlisted soldier (7)
16 Defamatory writing (5)
17 Large wild ox with shaggy hair (5)
18 Secret store (5)
19 Contempt (5)

635

Across

1 State in north-eastern India, noted for the production of tea (5)
4 Brag (5)
7 Unspecified person (7)
8 Suffuse with colour (5)
10 Etch into a material or surface (8)
13 Ms Amos, songstress (4)
15 Depression in a surface (4)
17 High-tech (8)
19 Scent, smell (5)
20 Spanish painter, born in Greece (1541–1614) (2,5)
21 Computer memory units (5)
22 From that time (5)

Down

1 One who is physiologically dependent on a substance (6)
2 Fowl that frequents coastal waters (7)
3 Old Testament prophet (5)
5 Excessively devoted to a single faction (3-5)
6 Submerged (6)
9 All existing matter and space considered as a whole (8)
11 Metal container (3)
12 Member of a nomadic tribe of Arabs (7)
14 Annie ___, famous US sharpshooter (6)
16 Flourish, prosper (6)
18 Chills (5)

636

Across

1 Scene (5)
4 Large antelope (5)
7 US law enforcement agency (inits) (3)
8 Horizontal support (5)
10 Crystal of snow (5)
11 Centre of a storm (3)
12 Liberate (3,4)
13 Vehicle test (inits) (3)
15 At a great distance (3)
17 Professional entertainer (7)
20 Adult males (3)
21 Native of Basra, for example (5)
22 Put pen to paper (5)
23 Compete (3)
24 Identifying appellation (5)
25 Thin-toned (5)

Down

1 Flower jars (5)
2 Mattress cover (5)
3 Asserting that a fact is so (11)
4 Landmark located on the Champ de Mars in Paris (6,5)
5 Fear resulting from awareness of danger (5)
6 Resided (5)
9 Doglike nocturnal mammal (5)
14 Group of eight (5)
15 Lose consciousness momentarily (5)
16 Cook in an oven (5)
18 Have a cigarette (5)
19 Adversary (5)

637

Across

1. Country, capital Tokyo (5)
4. Mr Fawkes, Gunpowder Plot conspirator (3)
6. Alternative (5)
7. Garment worn on the upper half of the body (5)
9. Positive (7)
11. Made of clay (7)
13. Genuine (7)
15. Chief port and town of the Falkland Islands (7)
16. See 18 Across
17. Take in with the tongue (3,2)
18. and 16 Across Prayer to the Virgin Mary (3,5)
19. Hirsute (5)

Down

1. Opaque form of quartz (6)
2. Depression scratched into a surface (5)
3. Stir vigorously (5)
4. Constellation of Ursa Major (5,4)
5. Involuntary intake of breath through a wide open mouth (4)
8. Bad-tempered (9)
10. Suggestive of the supernatural (5)
12. Gift in a will (6)
13. Ramp (5)
14. Minor goddess of nature (5)
15. Heroic tale (4)

638

Across

1. Worked into an emotional fever (coll) (3,2)
4. Bulk (4)
7. Twin brother of Romulus (5)
8. Her (3)
10. Expression used to frighten away animals (4)
11. Method (6)
13. Inform wrongly (7)
16. Place at intervals (5)
17. Guru (7)
18. Humorously sarcastic (6)
21. Recounted (4)
23. Basque terrorists (inits) (3)
24. Primitive plant forms (5)
25. Wise man (4)
26. Mike ___, former champion boxer (5)

Down

1. Rudolf ___, WWII Nazi leader (4)
2. Golfing pegs (4)
3. Acquire for oneself before others can do so (3-4)
4. Brawny tissue (6)
5. Burned remains (3)
6. Rapier (5)
9. Greek mythological monster (5)
12. Florida city (5)
14. Blood-red (7)
15. Scrutinise accounts (5)
16. Bicycle seat (6)
17. Nocturnal winged creatures (5)
19. Famous Scottish loch (4)
20. Abel's brother (4)
22. Fall behind (3)

639

Across
1 From the Netherlands (5)
3 Floor consisting of open space at the top of a house (5)
6 Former communist country (inits) (4)
8 Becomes separated into pieces or fragments (6)
9 Woollen cap of Scottish origin (3)
11 Plays, theatre (5)
12 Machine used for printing (5)
14 Marked by refinement in taste and manners (7)
15 Area where animals graze (5)
16 Conspicuous success (5)
18 Colouring agent (3)
19 Single-celled organism (6)
20 Harvest (4)
21 Arch (5)
22 Eerie, peculiar (5)

Down
1 Celtic priest (5)
2 Firm chewy sweet (7)
3 Velocity of a plane (8)
4 Person who changes location (9)
5 Prices (5)
7 Entrance used by performers and other theatre personnel (5,4)
10 Lower jawbone (8)
13 Use again after processing (7)
15 Former French coin (5)
17 Recorded on a magnetic strip (5)

640

Across
1 Oarsman (5)
3 Exchanges for money (5)
6 Loaves of bread baked at the same time (5)
7 Add together (5)
10 Antisocial misdeed by a minor in violation of the law (11)
13 Magic word used in a spell or in conjuring (11)
15 Cubes of meat cooked on a skewer (5)
18 Combined stakes of the betters (5)
19 Walked through water (5)
20 Second planet from the Sun (5)

Down
1 Fanatical (5)
2 Mexican tortilla (9)
3 Chronic drinker (3)
4 Allow (3)
5 Denigrate, defile (5)
8 Being in force (9)
9 Having the same measure as another (5)
11 Outward flow of the tide (3)
12 Low-breed dog (3)
13 Cockeyed (5)
14 Deep chasm (5)
16 Not good (3)
17 Partially opened flower (3)

641

Across
1 Fleeced (5)
3 Farm storage buildings (5)
7 Nickname for the old sixpence (6)
9 Pale yellowish-green colour (4)
10 Young newt (3)
11 Weaving machine (4)
13 Imaginary monster or ogre (3)
15 Act of God (7)
17 Silvery metal (3)
18 Act presumptuously (4)
20 Rod Hull's famous bird (3)
21 Period of 52 weeks (4)
22 Drill used to shape or enlarge holes (6)
24 In golf, a hole played in two strokes under par (5)
25 Makes senseless or dizzy by a blow (5)

Down
1 Take up residence (6)
2 Go fast (3)
4 In total (3,4)
5 Small hard fruit (4)
6 Too soon (9)
8 Old Testament mother-in-law of Ruth (5)
12 Ore (7)
14 Provide again with weapons (2-3)
16 Scattered wreckage (6)
19 Use a keyboard (4)
23 Fitting (3)

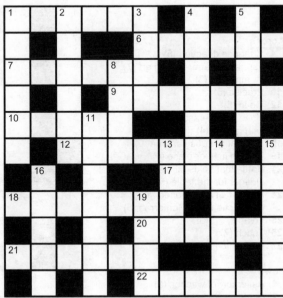

642

Across
1 Large bath for more than one person, used for recreation (3,3)
6 Incapable (6)
7 Type of monkey, macaque (6)
9 Double-barrelled firearm (7)
10 Supple (5)
12 Either end of the sail support of a square-rigged ship (7)
17 Great feast (5)
18 Spacecraft designed to transport people (7)
20 Bring into harmony with (6)
21 Thin layer of superior wood glued to a base of inferior wood (6)
22 Rests on bended legs (6)

Down
1 Barely (6)
2 Number denoting a score (6)
3 Shrub (4)
4 Catch (7)
5 Book for collecting stamps (5)
8 Exploiter (4)
11 Short-tailed burrowing rodent (7)
13 Assist in doing wrong (4)
14 Animal or plant material used to fertilise land (6)
15 Cringes with submission or fear (6)
16 Biblical tower intended to reach to heaven (5)
19 High-flying songbird (4)

643

Across

1 Country, capital Nicosia (6)
6 Floating aimlessly (6)
7 Decorative strip (6)
8 Solidified carbon dioxide, used mainly as a refrigerant (3,3)
10 Bird associated with the Tower of London (5)
13 Shrub that yields coffee beans (7)
16 First appearance (5)
18 Computer application program that uses the client's web browser to provide a user interface (6)
20 Rope or canvas headgear for a horse (6)
21 Infuriate (6)
22 Strong-scented, mat-forming wild herb (6)

Down

1 One who looks after a sick relative (5)
2 Latex from trees (6)
3 Grains on the beach (4)
4 Car used as a taxi (7)
5 Alloy of iron used as a structural material (5)
9 Sudden attack (4)
11 Bloodsucker in folklore (7)
12 Back of the neck (4)
14 Basement (6)
15 Afterwards (5)
17 Projected through the air (5)
19 People in general (4)

644

Across

4 Changes direction (5)
7 Japanese paper-folding art (7)
8 Commotion (3)
10 Precise (5)
12 Go in (5)
13 Units of force associated with gravity (4)
15 State at a particular time (9)
19 Near in time or place (4)
21 Bottle that holds oil or vinegar for the table (5)
24 Ancient city mentioned in conjunction with Gomorrah (5)
25 To and ___ (3)
26 Teach (7)
27 Pries into (5)

Down

1 Assembly of witches (5)
2 Scolding or domineering woman (6)
3 Went off in different directions (6)
4 Periodic rise and fall of sea level (4)
5 Harangue (4)
6 Clever (5)
9 Colour of the rainbow (6)
11 Container for burning incense (6)
14 ___ City, 2005 film (3)
16 Paper handkerchief (6)
17 Expression of sorrow (2,4)
18 Large body of water (5)
20 Deep yellow colour (5)
22 Vehicles from outer space (inits) (4)
23 Digits of the foot (4)

645

Across
1 Trick (5)
4 Accepted practice (5)
7 Ms Earhart, female aviator (6)
10 Walking-stick (4)
12 City in central Mali near the Niger river (8)
13 Provinces (6)
14 In case (4)
16 Highest level attainable (4)
19 Wiped out (6)
22 Scratchy (8)
23 Decapod crustacean (4)
24 Designating sound transmission from two sources (6)
25 Flour mixture stiff enough to knead (5)
26 Grows from, originates (5)

Down
1 Body of water between Kazakhstan and Uzbekistan (4,3)
2 Eighth letter of the Greek alphabet (5)
3 Noise of a bell (5)
5 Absence from work, due to illness (4,5)
6 Group containing one or more species (5)
8 Person who drops refuse in public places (9)
9 Localised sore (7)
11 Had a meal (3)
15 Tiresome (7)
17 Freight (5)
18 Qualification (inits) (3)
20 Customary practices (5)
21 Twilled woollen fabric (5)

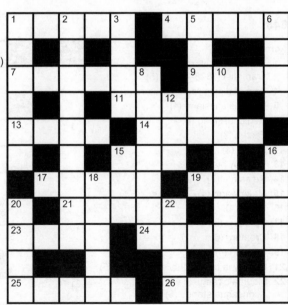

646

Across
1 Highest peak in the Alps, Mont ____ (5)
4 Second largest of the Great Lakes (5)
7 Noisy disturbance (6)
9 Sean ___, US film actor and director (4)
11 Asian pepper plant (5)
13 Drum out (4)
14 Inert gas (5)
15 Work with (a tool) steadily (3)
17 Same again (5)
19 Halo of light (4)
21 Workmanship (5)
23 Notion (4)
24 Severe shortage of food (6)
25 Country, capital Santiago (5)
26 Hinged lifting tool (5)

Down
1 Market trader's cart (6)
2 Truce (9)
3 Association (4)
5 Remove clips, as from a washing line (5)
6 Number of players in a baseball team (4)
8 Impose a blockade on (4,3)
10 Effective manner of speaking (9)
12 Have a go (3)
15 School group (inits) (3)
16 Identification tags (6)
18 Drag behind (5)
20 Bluish-white metallic element (4)
22 Sharp, acidic (4)

325

647

Across

1 Emblem of Christianity (5)
4 Drenches (5)
7 Directions for making something (7)
8 Wise bird (3)
9 Keep or accumulate for future use (5)
12 Finicky (5)
15 Dome-shaped dessert (5)
18 Part of a tree that remains after felling (5)
20 Grandmother (3)
21 Associate who works with others (7)
23 Fibre used for making rope (5)
24 Lofty nest of a bird of prey (5)

Down

1 Strikes playfully with an open hand (5)
2 Belonging to us (3)
3 Cook in a marinade (5)
4 Woollen item worn about the neck (5)
5 Minute particles of matter (5)
6 Spread open or apart (5)
10 As well (3)
11 Massage (3)
13 In the month preceding the present one (abbr) (3)
14 Uncle ___, personification of the US government (3)
15 Public announcement of a proposed marriage (5)
16 Cares about (5)
17 Throw out (5)
18 Bout, period of indulgence (5)
19 Fruit pulp (5)
22 And not (3)

648

Across

1 Henrik ___, Norwegian dramatist (1828–1906) (5)
4 Item of dining room furniture (5)
8 Indonesian island (4)
9 Regional slang (6)
10 Fasten (3)
11 Fertile (4)
13 Went by plane (4)
14 Reinstate (7)
15 Make warm (4)
16 Fiend (4)
17 Sprocket (3)
18 Creature (6)
19 Created (4)
21 County in the Republic of Ireland (5)
22 Mountain range in which Aconcagua stands (5)

Down

2 Constricting snake (3)
3 Descriptive word or phrase (7)
5 Sell illicit products such as drugs or alcohol (7)
6 In another location (9)
7 Elaborate and remarkable display on a lavish scale (9)
8 Skin blemish formed whilst in the womb (9)
12 More demented (7)
13 Underwater diver (7)
20 Directly or exactly, straight (3)

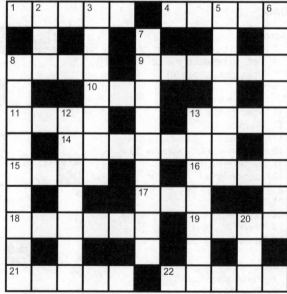

649

Across

1 Characteristic of song (5)
4 Lining of the stomach of a ruminant used as food (5)
7 Speculative undertaking (7)
8 Tolerate (5)
9 Give up work (6)
12 Hymn of mourning (5)
15 Choose by a vote (5)
17 Infuriate (6)
18 Cloak, often knitted (5)
19 Savage and excessive butchery (7)
20 Slightly sticky to the touch (5)
21 Implore (5)

Down

1 Long-bodied reptile (6)
2 Coastal area of Italy and France (7)
3 Enclosed (7)
5 The selling of goods to consumers (6)
6 Astronomical unit of distance (6)
10 Become nervous or uneasy (5,2)
11 Regress (7)
13 African antelope with ridged curved horns (6)
14 Port city of northern Poland (6)
16 Writings on Jewish law and tradition (6)

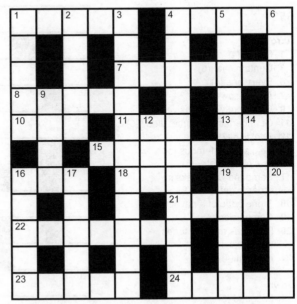

650

Across

1 Port in southern Iraq (5)
4 Becomes evident to the mind (5)
7 Savouring (7)
8 Residence of a clergyman (5)
10 Breed of dog (3)
11 Steal (3)
13 Wander from a direct course (3)
15 Finger next to the thumb (5)
16 Unattended cash machine outside a bank (inits) (3)
18 Append (3)
19 Health resort near a spring (3)
21 Urge or force to an action (5)
22 Capable of being stretched (7)
23 Make sore by rubbing (5)
24 Layers (5)

Down

1 Barrage balloon (5)
2 Injured by a nettle (5)
3 Option (11)
4 Unruly (11)
5 Dispense with, forgo (5)
6 Sweetening agent (5)
9 Female relative (4)
12 Curious (3)
14 Fully developed (4)
16 Ancient Mexican civilisation (5)
17 Miraculous food (5)
19 Talked (5)
20 False name (5)

651

Across

1 Object thrown in athletic competitions (6)
6 Not certain (6)
7 Unwanted email (4)
8 Member of a police force (7)
12 Air attack (5)
13 Sprang up (5)
14 Electrical resistance unit (3)
15 Encourage, cause to act (3,2)
18 Give qualities or abilities to (5)
19 Come down (7)
21 Foreman (4)
22 Stately court dance of the 17th century (6)
23 High-pitched cry (6)

Down

1 Invalided (8)
2 Thin slices, especially of planed wood (8)
3 Ride the waves of the sea on a board (4)
4 On the move (5)
5 Sign of the zodiac (5)
8 Toxic form of oxygen (5)
9 Widely known and esteemed (5)
10 Blister near the mouth caused by a viral infection (herpes simplex) (4,4)
11 The act of going backwards (8)
16 Freezing, glacial (5)
17 Come to pass (5)
20 Hard fruits (4)

652

Across

1 Prison (4)
3 Contaminate (5)
6 Every one (4)
7 Amount owed (4)
9 Confidently aggressive (9)
11 Of uncertain outcome, dicey (5)
12 Shellfish (7)
15 Belgian port famous for its cloth industry (5)
17 Someone who basks in order to get a tan (9)
18 Stone edge of a pavement (4)
19 Compulsion (4)
20 Produces musical tones with the voice (5)
21 Indolent (4)

Down

1 Fatigued (5)
2 Releases (4,2)
3 Painstakingly careful and accurate (8)
4 Disingenuous (9)
5 Post a short message on the internet site Twitter (5)
8 Game played with rackets and a shuttlecock (9)
10 Curriculum (8)
13 Israeli monetary unit (6)
14 Cricketing trophy (5)
16 Cat mottled with black (5)

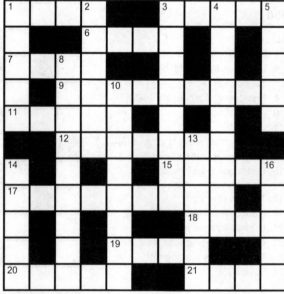

653

Across
1 Marked by hard-headed intelligence (6)
4 Makes a wager (4)
6 Authorise use of medicine (9)
8 Fatal disease of cattle (inits) (3)
10 Deviates from a course (6)
13 Smoothing tool used on clothing (4)
14 Freedom from disputes (5)
16 Cage for poultry (4)
17 Bunch of cords fastened at one end (6)
20 Large brownish-green New Zealand parrot (3)
21 Reticent (9)
22 Release after a security has been paid (4)
23 Locks of hair hanging across the forehead (6)

Down
1 Natives of Kuwait or Qatar, for example (5)
2 Thin candle (5)
3 Colour fabric after knotting it to produce an irregular pattern (3-3)
4 Small and pulpy edible fruits (7)
5 Holy ___, papal court (3)
7 Baby's knitted footwear item (6)
9 Victim of ridicule or pranks (6)
11 Attire (7)
12 Occupied a chair (3)
15 Salted roe of a sturgeon (6)
18 Coil of knitting wool (5)
19 Cavalry weapon (5)
21 Cry (3)

654

Across
1 Alloy of copper and zinc (5)
4 Area equivalent to 4840 square yards (4)
6 Magnetic metallic element, symbol Fe (4)
7 Short, sharp nail with a broad head (4)
8 Topic (5)
10 Heavenly being (5)
12 Red eruption of the skin (4)
14 Solemn promise (4)
16 Confess (3,2)
18 Reddish-brown colour (5)
20 Endorsement made in a passport (4)
21 US space-flight agency (inits) (4)
22 Remain, sit tight (4)
23 Wrinkled, creased (5)

Down
1 Product made by churning cream (6)
2 Second wife of Henry VIII, ___ Boleyn (4)
3 Alarm (5)
4 Graceful deerlike animal (8)
5 Space vehicle (6)
9 Hard, dark wood much used in furniture making (8)
11 Alcoholic spirit (3)
13 Painter or sculptor, for example (6)
15 Made warm (6)
17 Commonly encountered (5)
19 Chess piece (4)

SOLUTIONS

1

```
H E A R T A C H E . C
. L . H . O . L . H
A L I K E . V O D K A
L . V . S U E . E . L
T H E R E . R U R A L
I . . O . . M . E
M A K E R . B A S I N
E . O . A G O . T . G
T R A I N . A D O R E
E . L . G . R . V
R . A M E N D M E N T
```

2

```
C R . A D D R E S S
H E E L S . E . L
A . V . H A T C H E D
P R I C E . O . E
E . E A S I E R . P
L A W S . N . D A S H
. U . S U N S E T . A
. T . E . T R O U T
A U S T R I A . M . R
. M . T . G L I D E
I N T E N S E . C . D
```

3

```
S U R V E Y . P . F
A . A . O N E W A Y
L A T E . Y . A . R
O . H . C O S T U M E
N . E . O . A . E
S P R I N G B O A R D
. O . G . L . S . E
C R U S A D E . Y . C
. T . T . O . G L U E
R E C E S S . U . I
. R . P . S U B M I T
```

4

```
B O B B I N . D . B
A . O . E U R E K A
S M O G . W . L . B
I . O . S T R I D E
S E T T O . R . V . L
. S A N J O S E
S . H . C . T E R M S
W R I T E R . N . I
A . R . E . S A F E
M E T R E S . O . V
P . S . T H R I C E
```

5

```
T A S T E . F O C U S
R . E . L . A . E
A P S E . B A F F L E
P . O . H . W . E . D
S A U N A . L O T U S
. T . R Y E . E
A P H I D . S C R U B
N . P . S . S . I . U
G L O V E S . S A I D
U . L . L . P . G
S H E L L . B A D G E
```

6

```
B A T C H . S H E A R
E . A . K . G . O
A P A R T . I V O R Y
R . T . A . E . A
D E T R I M E N T A L
. R . I . B . T . S
C A N D L E L I G H T
H . G . R . L . O
A S P E N . S A L A D
P . A . A . T . A
S P R A Y . F E R R Y
```

7

```
S T Y L E . B E A K S
E . E . B . V . H
A L B I N O . E U R O
B . E . W O N . P
E X A M . L A S S O
D . S . P E T . A . C
. S T E E R . F L E A
J . B A H . V . R
A L S O . A L C O V E
C . N . T . O . S
K E N Y A . B O G U S
```

8

```
S P A I N . B . U P S
H . A C O R N . C
A S P I C . W . S . A
B E H . E T H E R
B A R N O W L . A
Y . C . A . C . S
. O . B R A C K E T
L O L L Y . S . L . A
A . A . L . K N E E L
C . T R A C E . L
E W E . W . W A L E S
```

9

```
B A T H E . D E B T
A . O . A C H E . A
R . G . S . C L U B
S W A S T I K A . L
. O . T . M . D I M E
. O . A B A S E . E
S L A G . G . N . M
P . E L E C T I O N
A L A S . A . C . A
R . E A R L . O . V
E D I T . M I N T Y
```

10

```
B A C K S . S O R T S
R . L . U . K . U . H
I M A G I N A T I V E
D . M . T . T . N . D
E A S E . S E N S E S
. N . Y . I . I . G
S T R E E T . B A G S
H . I . X . B . L . I
A P P L I C A T I O N
L . E . T . I . E . K
L A N D S . T E N D S
```

11

```
. R A C E H O R S E
D . M . L . N . C . R
I M A G O . S P A D E
S . S . P I E . M . T
A I S L E . T A P E R
F . I . . R . . E
F A C E T . M E C C A
E . E . W H O . H . T
C O A T I . I R A T E
T . S . C . S . O . D
. D E F E A T I S M
```

12

```
T R O O P . S C U B A
O . V . I . A . L
W . E . P A I N T E R
A G R E E . N . A
R . L . S T R E T C H
D R A B . O . S O H O
S O P R A N O . N . L
. T . U . A L I B I
V A R I O U S . G . D
. T . S . I . H . A
S E V E N . S A T A Y
```

13

```
S L I D   S C A M P I
E   E V E         R
C H O P   T A T T O O
O   O     W   V
N E T T L E S O M E
D N A   D     O R B
  A N G L O P H O B E
  M   U     Y   E
B O A T E R   P A C T
  U     A L E     L
G R E A S Y   R O B E
```

14

```
A T L A S   R O T O R
S   E   U S E   O   A
C L A S P   V   P A D
O     H E R E   I   A
T A S E R   R A C E R
  T   F   E   A
S N A R L   N Y L O N
T   M   U N T O     A
O B I O   O   I B S E N
R   N   U S A   A   N
M E A N S   L A Y B Y
```

15

```
A   Q   D   H E D G E
C R U C I F Y   I   A
U   A   S   M   S   G
T O R S O   N A C R E
E   R A W         R
  G Y M N A S I U M
O   B     U R N   C
P E T A L   D E L T A
T   A   E   D   O   M
I   K   A V E R A G E
C R E E D   N   D   L
```

16

```
T H I E F   S C O P E
R   N   U   H   L
A F T E R S   A H O Y
C   E     T I T A N
T E R R O R   T Y K E
O   E   I   E     M
R E E L   P U R S U E
  M A I Z E   A   R
B O R E   D A H L I A
  T   V   C   V   L
N E V E R   E M E N D
```

17

```
A B B E Y   B A L L S
N   A   S   M     C
T U T T U T   B E T A
I   I   O   L     N
C O M M A N D E E R
S   E   G E E   X   B
  T R E A D W A T E R
I   N   E   R     A
D A I S   A T T A I N
E     U   D   R   D
S A L E S   B Y W A Y
```

18

```
S H I F T   S M A R T
O   O   E   I   B   R
L A N T E R N   S E A
I     N   U   T   D
D U M P S   S C A L E
      E       I
S T A M P   T O N I C
H   N   U   O     R
A I D   T R A C H E A
D   E   T   S   I   Z
E A R L Y   T I P S Y
```

19

```
S H A R K   Y A C H T
  E   E   B   L   A
P R O P   R A P I D S
A     T E A   P   T
R A B I E S   M A C E
  A L L S T A R   L
L O R E   B A T T L E
Y   R   A R T     S
S E A S O N   H I S S
I   G   D   E   I
S C E N E   A W A R D
```

20

```
S T A G S   F R I A R
T   G   H   U   N
E   E   E L A N   I
P O S S E   L A M E
P     T W E E   U
E P I C   I   T O S S
  L   A U N T     E
S A L T     R I S E R
  C   N O V A   H   I
  I   I     I   O   E
A D E P T   T R E E S
```

21

```
P A N I C   C L O U T
I   N     A   R   E
Q U A F F   S I G M A
U   L E O N E   A   M
E N T R E E   O N U S
      E     W     I
B A R B   T H E S I S
E   N   P S A L M   P
A P A C E   S U S H I
N   T   S   D     C
S W E A T   B E A D Y
```

22

```
S H A F T S   E   S
O   L     A L P A C A
L I L T   M   E   O
D   C   C E L E S T A
I D L E R   O   I T S
E   E   O F F   G   B
R Y A   N   T E N S E
S O R C E R Y   P   S
  K   R   U   B O A T
G E N I U S     S   O
  L   B   E L A T E S
```

23

```
M I N E     S C U R F
I     V A L E   N   I
D O P E     T   S O L
A   E N S L A V E   L
S O N   K   S   T H Y
    P R E D I C T
G N U   T   D   L O B
I   S E C R E T E   R
D O H   H     I D E A
D   E   E A R N     I
Y A R D S     T A R N
```

24

```
C O P I E S   F E E D
A   I   N     O     I
R   A U T H O R I S E
D O N   O     E   H
S T O R M Y   S L A M
  T   O B E S E   V
C A N S   S T E R E O
  W   E     A   E R R
S A L T W A T E R   I
U   T     U   U   E
M O L E   K E N N E L
```

SOLUTIONS

25

```
S T O L I D . . G . A
I . . A . R O L L E R
B L O T T E R . A . R
Y . . I . S I E S T A
L I O N E S S . S . Y
. . C O L . O R E . .
D . A . A M N E S I A
U N R I P E . G . L .
S . I . S T A R R E D
T I N D E R . E . E .
Y . A . E I T H E R .
```

26

```
A . P O T A S S I U M
R . R . R . N . N . .
T R I B E . E J E C T
H . M . A P E . P . O
R A P I D . R A T I O
I . R . . C . T . . T
T W E E D . S T A S H
I . X . A P T . W . P
S C I O N . I R A Q I
. . L . C . L . I . C
P R E C E D E N T . K
```

27
```
I . A . A D I P O S E
S E N D S . . A . H .
L . G . T E R R I E R
A G I L E . . K . A .
N . N . R A G E . R .
D R A Y . D . D E S K
I . . A T O P . A . E
. A . W . . A I R E R
I L L N E S S . N . N
. T . E . S U E D E .
B O N D A G E . R . L
```

28

```
B E S T . A N T L E R
E . . R I D . . . R .
S K Y E . D R A G O N
I . S . . K . D . . .
D I S S O C I A T E .
E . U . U . E . R . .
. T E M P E R A N C E
R . E . S . . S . B .
H U N T E D . S A G E
C . . A X E . . L . .
B E H E A D . T H U S
```

29

```
B A C O N . S P L I T
E . A . E . T . A . I
V E R B E N A . R A M
E . . D . N . G . E .
L I S T S . D R E G S
. . T . . . L . . . .
B R A N D . A B Y S S
L . R . I . L . . E .
O F T . A B A S H E D
O . E . R . R . E . G
M E R C Y . M A N G E
```

30

```
. C A U T E R I S E .
W . N . I . E . L . T
O W N E R . S N A K E
R . E . E R E . I . L
T E X A S . T I N G E
H . . Y . . C . . P
L A S E R . B E N C H
E . C . O V A . I . O
S L A N G . S A X O N
S . R . U . E . O . E
. D E F E N D A N T .
```

31

```
T U L I P . S T O A T
A . A . O . A . G .
L V . S I X T E E N
L I A R S . T . N .
O . . E E R I E . T
W O R K S . G R O S S
V . I S S U E . . T
E . N . . A D D E R
T R O D D E N . E . E
D . L . A . L . S
B O G E Y . S O L E S
```

32

```
M E L T S . H E A L S
A . A . I . C . W
G A I N S . J . T H E
I . K . R A K E . E
C L A S S I C . D I P
. O . A S K . L
A T E . V E S S E L S
R . A X I S . E . E
R A G . N . A R G U E
O . L . G . V . M
W E E D S . G E R M S
```

33

```
R I V A L . R . P E R
E . . S O L A C E . O
T E M P O . B . R . S
A . A . S . B R I B E
I S R A E L I . M .
N . E . E . E . P
. S . A D A P T O R
B O N U S . L . E .
E . E . Y . T A R O T
E . S E E S A W . T
N I T . T . R E A D Y
```

34

```
D E B U G . S O O T
E . A . R A F T . I
A L E . E A S E L .
F A S T E N E R . T
. G A I N . T S A R S
. U . M . . H . A
C E L E B . S I N G
A . L A M P P O S T
R I V E R . O . I . A
G . S E A R . S . C
O D D S . . T R E A T
```

35

```
D E A T H . S T O O D
R . . O . O . R . U
A S S O C I A T I O N
F . T . O . P . G . C
T H R E W . S E I N E
. . E . O P T . N
M O T O R . O P A R T
E . C . K . N . T . I
A C H I E V E M E N T
N . E . R . . A . H
T U R N S . C R I M E
```

36

```
T U B B Y . S P R A T
H . I . M E R E . Y
R O U T E . C E D A R
U . E . H . V . E
M A R T I A L A R T S
. R . H . N . R . E
S C R E W D R I V E R
H . D . Y . C . U
R E B U S . F A N G S
E . A S H Y . T . T
D I R T Y . H E A V Y
```

SOLUTIONS

37

```
S A N T A   V A L I D
U     E   M   F     R
P L E A   E N T I R E
L   S T I R   E     W
L O T S   C U R L Y
Y   E     E     L   C
  A R S O N   C A V A
I   I   A T O M   R
I R E N D E R   P A L E
I   L   Y     R   E
S O B E R   C A B E R
```

38

```
S H A D O W   P   L
K   B     E R A S E R
O Y S T E R   P   A
P   O   M E M E N T O
J A R   I   R   H
E M B A R R A S S E D
  M   N   L   C R U
G E S T A P O   R   R
  T   H   A E R A T E
L E V E L S     P   S
  R   M   S W E E T S
```

39

```
B U L G E D     P   C
E     R   O A F I S H
R A V A G E S   E   A
R     N   S K I R T S
Y A R N S   F   C   E
    E Y E S O R E
B   F   L   R E S I T
L O I T E R   V     I
I   N   C A R E F U L
S W E A T S   A     E
S   D   P E L V I S
```

40

```
C   A   H   D U V E T
A G I T A T E   O   O
M   D   R   L   T   T
E L E C T R I C E Y E
O     O   H   H   M
  G A R D E N I N G
S   P   U   P     A
T O A S T M A S T E R
U   X   O   C   B   M
N   L   M A N D A T E
G E E S E   E   R   D
```

41

```
A L O N G   P A P A L
B   B   L   F   C
A R E N A S   G I R L
N   Y   S H A H   I
D I S U S E   A D D S
O   P   R   N   H
N E A R   I D I O C Y
V   I F F Y   L   N
G O N G   F I N I T E
K   H   N   V   S
B E R T H   G U E S S
```

42

```
M I L A N   B A N K S
O   L   C   L     E
R A I L   A B L A Z E
T   G E A R   O   M
A B L Y   T O W E L
R   O   H   N   M
  R O M E O   D D A Y
T   E   R A R E   S
H E A R T S   A D Z E
I   I   E   W     L
S A L T Y   A L O O F
```

43

```
M U C U S   S Y R U P
O   A   L   H   E   I
O U T D O O R   P R O
R     P   U   L   U
S H A V E   G R I T S
  N     C
P L A N T   S N A I L
R   E   U   P     O
A R M   C H A R T E R
N   I   K   T   O   R
G R A S S   E L E G Y
```

44

```
B L E E D   P E P Y S
  Y   A   P   R   A
W E A R   A S T E R N
A     S O S   C   C
I T C H   T   V E N T
S   L O A T H E D   I
T E A T   E   R E D O
C   V   N U T     N
O D I O U S   I B I S
A   E   E   G   C
T A R D Y   F O Y E R
```

45

```
C L A S S   E S S A Y
A   W   N   A     R
L   A D O R A T I O N
L A Y E R   I   U
U   D E A L S   S
S A R I   I   F E E S
  L   C O R G I   C
  L   A   R E F E R
C E N T I P E D E   I
  G   E   A   A   B
T E D D Y   T E R S E
```

46

```
S M I T H   H O I S T
E     H O M E   C   H
N E W Y E A R S E V E
N   M   S     C   F
A S S E N T   M A L T
    T   I   P
S C O T   C L O S E T
C   R   A   P     O
A N A E S T H E S I A
L   G   P E A R   D
P I E T Y   G A S S Y
```

47

```
F I B U L A   W   E
L   E     R E A L L Y
A V E N G E   D   V
U   T   R A R E B I T
T U R B O   E R A S E
I   O   T O P   S   R
S H O U T   O V E R T
T A T T O O S   L   I
  Z   T   M E D I N A
R E N E G E     N   R
  L   R   N I N E T Y
```

48

```
C O G S     C A D E T
R     O H I O   E   Y
E C R U   N   S   P
D   E L E C T R O D E
O I L   P   R   L A D
  S A T I R I C A L
S L Y   L   T   T E D
P E R S E V E R E   E
A   A   P     E D A M
C   C   S A I L     O
E N E M Y   Y A R N
```

333

49

```
G A S . C H E C K U P
L . P . H . O . . . U
O . E C O N O M I C S
S K A . P . M . . . O
S E R A P H . I N F O
. T . W Y A T T . . F
S T Y E . M U S S E L
. L . S . R . . L E O
M E M O R A B L E . G
O . M . O . . . E . O
B E N E F I T . . P E N
```

50

```
S T A R E D . . D . C
C . E . A T T A C H
A G H A S T . N . . E
R . . D . A P O G E E
F R E E S . U . L . K
. . . G R A P P L E .
B . . G . A E S O P
A C T U A L . G . . A
S . R . E L I X I R
T H I N K S . O . . T
E . P . S U N D A Y
```

51

```
. C A S S E R O L E .
O . M . L . U . A . S
T A B O O . M O U S E
H . E . P U B . R . V
E E R I E . A B A S E
R . . C . . A . . . N
W A F E R . S T O A T
I . A . E F T . B . E
S P L I T . A N E L E
E . S . C . I . . . N
. M E T H O D I S T .
```

52

```
S Q U A T . . C U S P
W . G . H A L O . . I
A . L . U . . A G E S
B L I S S F U L . . T
. O . U . O . E A S E
. B . I D L E S . . I
S E C T . I . C . . D
A . C L O S E S E T
T O G A . O . C . . A
Y . . S T O A . A . K
R A C E . . P E N N E
```

53

```
C A M P S . B I R T H
E . E . A . M . I
L I N E U P . P A N E
E . S . C O D E . E
S H A R E S . T O S S
T . . E . T . U . . O
E A R S . U L S T E R
N . T O R I . I . . C
Y O G A . E M E R G E
. D . T . I . E . . R
R E B E L . T O D A Y
```

54

```
D A T E D . S H E L F
E . X . H . N . . . A
B A S I N . O U G H T
T . C L A S P . R . A
S E R E N E . B A I L
. . U . . L . V
D U M A . M A L I G N
R . M . S A T I N . A
A W A K E . E G G O N
K . G . N . H . . . C
E L E C T . I T C H Y
```

55

```
R A D O N . M A R C H
E . R . A . T . R
S H E K E L . T S A R
T . S . . A P R O N
Y E S M A N . A L E C
L . . I . Y . C . . O
E A T S . A T T A I N
. L A T E R . S . . F
L I R A . D E S I R E
. G . K . E . A . . S
U N D E R . L I N K S
```

56

```
S P L A S H . A G E S
O . U . T . R . . . A
W . S H O W . M E A L
S A T . W . F . P . T
. . G . G A S O L I N E
C O W . W . R . C O D
A G I T A T E D . V
S . L . Y . B . L A B
S O D A . L O P E . A
I . R . . D . E . . T
S C O T . C E N S U S
```

57

```
R A V E N . H E E L S
A . . M I N E . V . I
C H A M B E R L A I N
E . E . W . . S . G
R O U T E S . F I L E
. . T . G . V
A P E X . R E H E A T
R . N . O . O . . . A
I N S T R U C T I O N
E . I . O P E L . . G
S O L I D . P Y G M Y
```

58

```
S E S A M E . S I T S
H . O . A . L . . . U
E . R E T A L I A T E
A F T . T . P . O
R U S S E T . P L U G
. R . A R O S E . P
P O N D . T A R G E T
. R . N . T . L E I
V E N E Z U E L A . M
A . S . E . Z . E
T H U S . U N L E S S
```

59

```
. P R O P R I E T Y .
S . U . A . N . E . V
T O N G S . L A N A I
A . U . T E A . S . C
T I P S Y . W H E R E
E . A . . O . O . . V
S I F T S . C Y C L E
M . O . A G O . O . R
A V A I L . M E N D S
N . L . V . E . G . A
. E S S E N T I A L .
```

60

```
M O D E M . . S A G E
I . A . A T O L L . N
L A D E . E . A B E T
D R O P S . N . . . E
. . G . . T R I G G E R
. U . R . M . . . R
H E N C O O P . . N
A . R . . R E S I N
R I L E . E . N E E
E . S P I E S . A . W
M A D E . . S I G H S
```

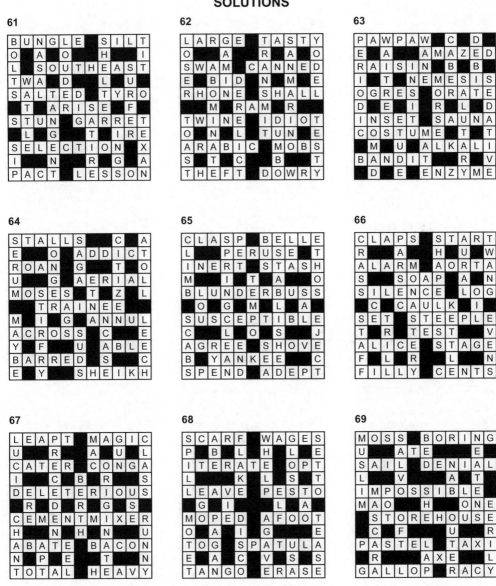

61
```
B U N G L E . S I L T
O . A . O . H . . I
L . S O U T H E A S T
T W A . D . L . U .
S A L T E D . T Y R O
. T . A R I S E . F
S T U N . G A R R E T
. L . G . T . I R E
S E L E C T I O N . X
I . N . R . G . A
P A C T . L E S S O N
```

62
```
L A R G E . T A S T Y
O . A . R . A . O
S W A M . C A N N E D
E . B I D . N . M . E
R H O N E . S H A L L
. . M . R A M . R
T W I N E . I D I O T
O . N . L . T U N . E
A R A B I C . M O B S
S . T . C . B . T
T H E F T . D O W R Y
```

63
```
P A W P A W . C . D
E . A . . A M A Z E D
R A I S I N . B . B
I . T . N E M E S I S
O G R E S . O R A T E
D . E . I . R . L . D
I N S E T . S A U N A
C O S T U M E . T . T
. M . U . A L K A L I
B A N D I T . R . V
. D . E . E N Z Y M E
```

64
```
S T A L L S . . C . A
E . . O . A D D I C T
R O A N . G . T . O
U . . G . A E R I A L
M O S E S . T . Z . L
. . T R A I N E E
M . I . G . A N N U L
A C R O S S . C . E
Y . F . U . A B L E
B A R R E D . S . C
E . Y . S H E I K H
```

65
```
C L A S P . B E L L E
L . P E R U S E . T
I N E R T . S T A S H
M . I . T . A . O
B L U N D E R B U S S
. O . G . M . L . A
S U S C E P T I B L E
C . L . O . S . J
A G R E E . S H O V E
B . Y A N K E E . C
S P E N D . A D E P T
```

66
```
C L A P S . S T A R T
R . A . H . U . W
A L A R M . A O R T A
S . S O A P . A . N
S I L E N C E . L O G
. C . C A U L K . I
S E T . S T E E P L E
T . R . T E S T . V
A L I C E . S T A G E
F . L . R . L . N
F I L L Y . C E N T S
```

67
```
L E A P T . M A G I C
U . R . A . U . L
C A T E R . C O N G A
I . C . B . R . S
D E L E T E R I O U S
. R . D . R . G . S
C E M E N T M I X E R
H . N . H . N . U
A B A T E . B A C O N
N . P . E . T . N
T O T A L . H E A V Y
```

68
```
S C A R F . W A G E S
P . B . L . H . L . E
I T E R A T E . O P T
L . . K . L . S . T
L E A V E . P E S T O
. G . I . . L . A
M O P E D . A F O O T
O . A . I . G . E
T O G . S P A T U L A
E . A . C . V . S . S
T A N G O . E R A S E
```

69
```
M O S S . B O R I N G
U . . A T E . E
S A I L . D E N I A L
L . V . . A . T
I M P O S S I B L E
M A O . H . O N E
. S T O R E H O U S E
. C . F . U . R
P A S T E L . T A X I
. R . A X E . L
G A L L O P . R A C Y
```

70
```
S T R A T A . L . E
T . A . C R A V A T
A S I A . M . S . V
R . L . M E A S L E S
T W I N E . H O I S T
E . N . L I E . T . A
R O G U E . A T E A M
S U S P E N D . R . P
. T . P . O . B A B E
R E C E S S . T . D
. R . D . E X C I T E
```

71
```
C A B B Y . A M A S S
. W . A . R . T . O
U N I T . E S T E E M
N . H A D . L . E
W I F E . U . D I E T
I . I R O N O R E . I
L E G S . D . A R U M
L . H . A B C . E
I N T E R N . H I S S
N . E . T . M . P
G I R L S . K A Y A K
```

72
```
R O B E S . U M B E R
H . U . W . E . V
E . I . A S H T R A Y
S A L A M I . R . D
U . D . I N V I T E
S C U D . C . C O D A
. O P E N E R . T . C
. R . L . R A F T E R
T O W E R E D . E . O
. N . T . A . R . S
D A T E D . R O S E S
```

SOLUTIONS

73

```
R   P I S T A C H I O
E O C   U   A
H E L L O   G E N U S
E   I   P I E   D   E
A R O S E   R E S I N
R   I     M     S
S I G N S   F U R Z E
A Y   N I L   O   L
L I B Y A   O V U L E
  E   K R   N   S
W A S T E L A N D   S
```

74

```
S P O U S E   C L U E
H   N   I   O     A
E   I N N E R M O S T
E G O   C     M   T
P E N C E   S A L O N
  N   R U E     R
B E I G E   R E S E T
  R R   V   L Y E
B A L A L A I K A   N
O   V     L   N   O
P A C E   N E U T E R
```

75

```
L Y C R A   U P S E T
U   R N A N   Q   W
C R A S S   D E U C E
R U M   W   E   A   E
E M P R E S S   D D T
  B   R   I   R
T A T   P A R E S I S
R   O   H   A   W E T
I D A H O   B L A S E
A   S   N I L   R   E
L I T H E   E I D E R
```

76

```
S N E E R   C A R R Y
Y   Y   P   B     A
R E N E G E   A N O N
I   A   N O T     K
A V I D   P R E S S
N   A   H U B   C   R
  I D E A S   C O P E
F   N T H   U   C
O N U S   E N T R E E
O   U   R   O   S
T O K E N   B O G U S
```

77

```
C A S K E T   M   R
O   C   W A I T E R
S P A R S E   N   V
T   R   H E E D F U L
A L A M O     S   E
R   B I O F U E L   A
  S   M   S T E P S
M E D I A T E   G   S
V   C   A S S U M E
B E A R D S   M   T
N   Y   K N E E L S
```

78

```
M A P S   H U S K S
I     O L I O   L   H
A R M Y   M   A   A
M   E A S T E R N E R
I   L   T   I D   K
  I O N I A N S E A
D   D   N   O R   C
A R R O G A N C E   O
Z   A   R   U R A L
E   M   A V E R   D
D I A R Y   T A P S
```

79

```
C U D G E L   T   G
O   A   A B A C U S
L A R D   M   L   A
O   K   D A N C I N G
S L A K E   O   N O R
S   G   L E T   T   I
U S E   V   E L I T E
S U S P E N D   M   V
  G   I   O   N A T O
C A P E R S     T   U
  R   D   E G R E S S
```

80

```
S P L I N T   P A I L
O   I   E   A   B   A
N   S H A P E   L   B
A L T E R   G R A Z E
R   R   R   I   Z   L
  P O S S E S S E D
D   R   A   H     C
A W A I T   P O L K A
I   T   A D I E U   V
S   O   Y   T   G   E
Y A R D   C H E E R S
```

81

```
S T A K E   L U C K Y
P   P   N   R   I
R   R   M A C B E T H
A L O H A   A   T
N   P   S T A N C E
G R O S S   M E A N S
  A S T E R N   N   E
V   A   E X T R A
T A C T I C S   A   M
  G   U   I   T   A
L E V E R   A G A I N
```

82

```
S A X O N   M A R K S
K   C   F   V     I
E A S T E R   A C I D
T   L   A   I     E
C R I T I C A L L Y
H   M   T   I   P
  E Y E W I T N E S S
C   R   O   G   A
U R G E   U N V E I L
T   C   S   A   M
S C O T T   A L I A S
```

83

```
S   R E P U G N A N T
P   O   U   N
A N G E R   S P I N S
R   E   G O T   S   P
T E R S E   O B E S E
A   E     O   A
C A S T S   T O W E R
U   C   T I E   A   H
S A U N A   A R G U E
  D   R   S   E   A
T A S T E L E S S   D
```

84

```
B   D   T   B O O T S
R O E D E E R   P   L
E   T   P   E V E   E
W R O T E   D A N C E
S   U R E A   L   P
  P R O S C R I B E
E   W   E A S E   F
G R I E G   P E N N E
Y   A L I   T   G   V
P   M   B R O C A D E
T A B L E   R   L   R
```

SOLUTIONS

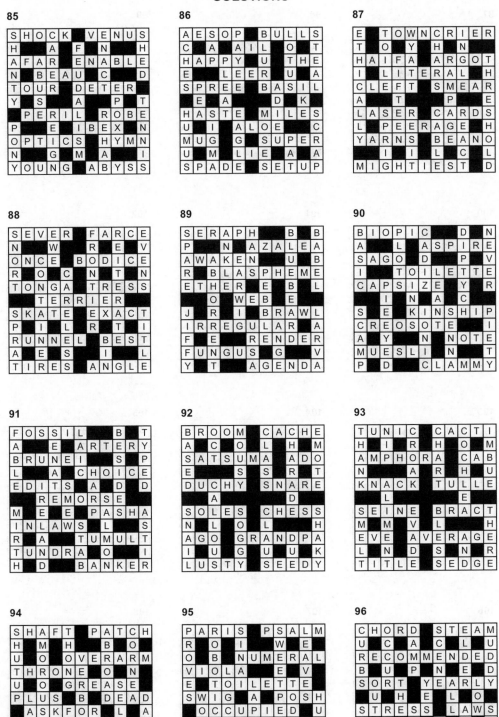

SOLUTIONS

97

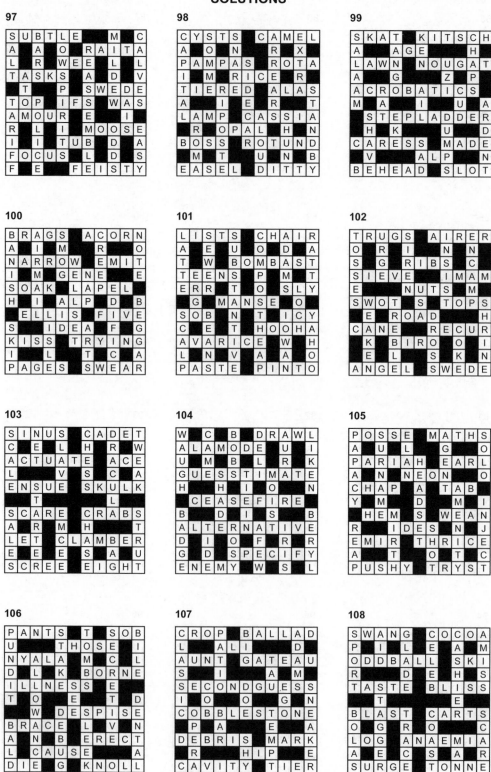

```
S U B T L E   M   C
A   A   O   R A I T A
L   R   W E E   L   L
T A S K S   A   D   V
    T   P   S W E D E
T O P   I F S   W A S
A M O U R   E   I
R   L   I   M O O S E
I   I   T U B   D   A
F O C U S   L   D   S
F   E   F E I S T Y
```

98

```
C Y S T S   C A M E L
A   O   N   R   X
P A M P A S   R O T A
I   M   R I C E   R
T I E R E D   A L A S
A   I   E   R   T
L A M P   C A S S I A
  R   O P A L   H   N
B O S S   R O T U N D
  M   T   U   N   B
E A S E L   D I T T Y
```

99

```
S K A T   K I T S C H
A   A G E   H
L A W N   N O U G A T
A   G   Z   P
A C R O B A T I C S   A
M   A   I   U   A
  S T E P L A D D E R
  H   K   U   D
C A R E S S   M A D E
  V   A L P   N
B E H E A D   S L O T
```

100

```
B R A G S   A C O R N
A   I   M   R   O
N A R R O W   E M I T
I   M   G E N E   E
S O A K   L A P E L
H   I   A L P   D   B
  E L L I S   F I V E
S   I D E A   F   G
K I S S   T R Y I N G
I   L   T   C   A
P A G E S   S W E A R
```

101

```
L I S T S   C H A I R
A   E   U   O   D   A
T   W   B O M B A S T
T E E N S   P   M   T
E R R   T   O   S L Y
  G   M A N S E   O
S O B   N   T   I C Y
C   E T   H O O H A
A V A R I C E   W   H
L   N   V   A   A   O
P A S T E   P I N T O
```

102

```
T R U G S   A I R E R
O   R   I   N   N
S   G   R I B S   C
S I E V E   I M A M
E   N U T S   M
S W O T   S   T O P S
  E   R O A D   H
C A N E   R E C U R
  K   B I R O   O   I
  E   L   S   K   N
A N G E L   S W E D E
```

103

```
S I N U S   C A D E T
C   E   L   H   R   W
A C T U A T E   A C E
L   V   S   C   A
E N S U E   S K U L K
  T   L
S C A R E   C R A B S
A   R   M   H   T
L E T   C L A M B E R
E   E   E   S   A   U
S C R E E   E I G H T
```

104

```
W   C   B   D R A W L
A L A M O D E   U   I
U   M   B   L   R   K
G U E S S T I M A T E
H   H   I   O   N
  C E A S E F I R E
B   D   I   S   B
A L T E R N A T I V E
D   I   O   F   R   R
G   D   S P E C I F Y
E N E M Y   W   S   L
```

105

```
P O S S E   M A T H S
A   U   L   G   O
P A R I A H   E A R L
A   N   N E O N   O
C H A P   A   T A B
Y   M   D   M   I
  H E M   S   W E A N
R   I D E S   N   J
E M I R   T H R I C E
A   T   O   T   C
P U S H Y   T R Y S T
```

106

```
P A N T S   T   S O B
U   T H O S E   I
N Y A L A   M   C   L
D   L   K   B O R N E
I L L N E S S   E
T   O   E   T   D
  W   D E S P I S E
B R A C E   L   V   N
A   N   B   E R E C T
L   C A U S E   A
D I E   G   K N O L L
```

107

```
C R O P   B A L L A D
L   A L I   D
A U N T   G A T E A U
S   I   A   M
S E C O N D G U E S S
I   O   O   G   N
C O B B L E S T O N E
  P   A   E   A
D E B R I S   M A R K
  R   H I P   E
C A V I T Y   T I E R
```

108

```
S W A N G   C O C O A
P I L E   A   M
O D D B A L L   S K I
R   D   E   H   S
T A S T E   B L I S S
  T   E
B L A S T   C A R T S
O   G   R O   C
L O G   A N A E M I A
A   E   C   S   A   R
S U R G E   T O N N E
```

SOLUTIONS

109

110

111

112

113

114

115

116

117

118

119

120

121

```
G R E E N   N I G E R
A   B M   N       I
M U M B A I     S I G N
B   I   S K I     G
L E N S   E   D E W
E   C A R R I E R   C
  P E R   A   R A T A
L   D A B   T   C
A N T I   L O G O U T
S   N   E   I   U
T O W E L   A N G U S
```

122

```
T R U C E   L I N E D
  A   H T     E   I
A N T E   R A B I E S
R   E T A     T   M
T H A T   N   R H E A
E   B A N S H E E   N
F I S H   P   B R U T
A   C   O W E     L
C R I S I S   C O M E
T   S   E   C   O
S C E N E   L A M B S
```

123

```
S   E   A C H I E V E
T U R K S     N   E
U   S   P A S T U R E
P R A T E     E   S
D A Z E   O   N E S T
  F   S E T T E R   A
  F   H   R E R U N
B A R I S T A   O   D
  I   R   S E R G E
B R I T I S H   S   M
```

124

```
C R A M S   O B E Y S
H   X   A   R   T
O   I G N O R A N C E
P E S E T A   I   W
  L   R A R E N E S S
  B M   L   W   C
M A N I T O B A   A
U   C   C O V E R S
S P R I N K L E D   I
I   D   T   E   N
C H E E R   S E N D S
```

125

```
B A L E R   N A S T Y
E   I   A   C   I
S   F O R E F R O N T
T H E S E   O   N
O   C R U M B   E
W A D I   P   A I D S
  M   L I S Z T   A
  P   L   O I L E D
D E C A D E N C E   D
R   T   A   A   L
S E V E N   L A N C E
```

126

```
T R U N K   M A C A W
E   E   C O L A   O
S L U S H   P L U M B
T   T   N   T   B
M U E S L I   M I L L
A   X   G   O   E
T A P E   H O B N O B
C   A   T   R   O
H E N R Y   L A M I A
E   S E E N   V   R
S E E D S   B O R E D
```

127

```
G   P   P R O T E S T
H Y E N A   H   L
E   E   S I D E C A R
T O L L S   I   C
T   E   E V E R   K
O D D S   I   S A S H
  A   A J A R   N   A
  S   L   I N T E R
C H E V R O N   H   D
  E   E   S I E G E
T R I R E M E   M   N
```

128

```
P A P A L   R A I N
E   I   U R S A   A
G   L   R   A V E R T
S P A C E A G E   A
  O U R S   E N R O L
  M   E   O   V
S P R E E   R U D E
E   P L E A S I N G
P I N E S   L   X   O
A   R E A L   I   L
L O S S   Y I E L D
```

129

```
M A R C H   G   R O B
I   O X E Y E   I
S T A I R   T   F   N
S   N   D R A W E R S
E N T R E A T   R
D   I   Y   E   B
    P   R O M A N C E
S T A M I N A   C   T
O   S   S   S H E E R
R   T O K Y O   A
T W O   S   N E R V Y
```

130

```
S I L I C A   B   W
E   E   C O U P O N
P I A F   M   F   R
T   V   S E L F I S H
E R E   A   A   T
T E S T M A T C H E S
  C   B   H   A D O
C O M P A S S   Z   L
  V   O   L   B A R E
D E V O T E   R   M
  R   R   D E A D E N
```

131

```
G U A V A   M U M M Y
R   E   R   N   A
E   R   S P A R I N G
E D I T O R   E   T
N   A   N O D E   I
S I L T   F   L A S S
  N   O N U S   S   H
  J   N   S T A P L E
J U G G L E R   I   A
R   U   I   R
Y E M E N   P R E S S
```

132

```
H O T   R O S E B U D
A   U   E   A   U
V   B E D S P R E A D
O D E   S   T   L
C A R P E T   H O B O
  H   R A I S E   E
S L O E   P E N C I L
  I   C   C   E T A
C A F E T E R I A   Y
A   P   E   S   B
P O R T E N T   E L Y
```

133

```
S C A M . . E L F I N
U . . E N D S . R . I
N I B S . . C . E V E
U . A S S U A G E . C
P E R . U . P . V I E
. R E P L A C E . . .
P T A . P . D . R I D
I . C A R P E T S . I
C R U . E . . B E E R
O . D . S K U A . G .
T E A M S . . R I P E
```

134

```
S H A R I F . B . F .
T . E . . L E E W A Y
U N R I P E . C . R .
N . A . R E G A T T A
T O T . O . M . H . .
S P E E D O M E T E R
. T . L . E . E R E N
D I L E M M A . N . M
. M . V . A L K A L I
D U R E S S . N . . S
. M . N . S L A T E S
```

135

```
. S T A T E M E N T .
A . R . I . E . E . A
S W A R M . L A W N S
S . M . E C O . E . C
U P P E R . N E R V E
R . D . . . A . . N .
A B H O R . M U M P S
N . A . O B I . E . I
C H I N A . D I E G O
E . K . S . S . T . N
. M U L T I T A S K .
```

136

```
S E R I E S . P . . B
A . E . . H O R R O R
R I N K . O . E . . A
I . T . S E C T I I O N
. D A T A . Z . . . C
C . L A C Q U E R . H
A . B . . S L E W . .
R E C L U S E . M . D
T . O . A . B O D Y .
E D G I N G . . T . E
L . D . A C C E S S .
```

137

```
G U C C I . P A S S .
E . A . D A D O . H .
Y . F L Y . . S L A P
S T E E L . T . D . .
E . A L I V E . E . .
R A G S . N . R A S P
. N . E N N U I . A .
. Y . H . . M O W E R
C O C O . . B R A . K
. N . L E A R . D . E
F E E D . . A H E A D
```

138

```
C Y N I C A L . F . A
A . U . O . A M E N D
F A N C Y . C U T . D
E . C O O P E R A T E
S A I N T . . D . . R
. . O V E R S E E . .
A . E . . A R U B A .
R E T R I E V E R . R
M . A G O . A R O M A
E G R E T . G . P . B
D . E . A G E L E S S
```

139

```
T I L E S . C U P I D
U . E . W . O . R . O
R E U N I O N . O D D
F . . N . I . R . G .
S P A C E . C R A Z E
. . N . . . . T . . .
A W A R D . B E A R S
I . T . U . L . . . H
D U O . S O A N D S O
E . M . K . R . O . W
D R Y L Y . E N T R Y
```

140

```
B . P R O G N O S I S
O V A . B . E . L . C
G . N . O R E G A N O
E G G H E A D . V . N
Y . . A . P . M E R E
. . S T U T T E R . .
F A C E . U . T . . H
R . H . F R E E S I A
A N I S E E D . W . Z
N . S . A . A . A P E
C A M E R A M A N . L
```

141

```
S . T . S U N B E A M
T E E T H . . U . T .
U . D E A T H R A T E
C H I E F . . I . U .
C . O . T U R E E N .
O P U S . R . S L E W
. A S C E N D . E . A
. R . U . . R A C K S
N E G L I G E N T . H
. N . P . . S T O K E
S T A T U E S . R . R
```

142

```
A N V I L . S H U N T
L . N . U . R . U . U
P R I S M . M A N O R
H . P . A . P . N . N
A R M E D F O R C E S
. U . C . T . I . A .
B E S T S E L L E R S
E . . O . R . F . . W
A P A R T . B O M B E
D . C . I . O . . . E
S H E E N . A L E R T
```

143

```
S M A C K . S T A C K
. A . R I M . H . N .
F I N A L E . R O P E
. L . C O C K E R E L
B O O K . H . W E P T
. R . . . A . . P . .
A D E N . N . E V E N
T E M E R I T Y . R .
T . . . . . C A R B O N
R U E . . . S K I . N
C A U S E . . E E R I E
```

144

```
I N D E X . D E S K S
N . R . E . E . E . T
D E L A Y . C . W H O
I . S . M A L E . R .
A L T E R E D . D R Y
. A . A T E . . . A .
D Y E . P A S S I N G
O . N A I L . T . . A
M A D . D . B O X E S
E . E . L . N . . . E
S A D L Y . H E A R S
```

145

```
C H A S M ■ C L A S H
U ■ G ■ I R A ■ R ■ I
F L O S S ■ P E A R L
F ■ R ■ T E E ■ B ■ L
S H A D Y ■ R I S K Y
■ U ■ E ■ ■ ■ R ■ I
H E N N A ■ D E L T A
I ■ U ■ L E E ■ U ■ G
V E R S O ■ M A N I A
E ■ S ■ F R O ■ A ■ P
S L E P T ■ B E R N E
```

146

```
B L A D E ■ C H A F E
■ A ■ E ■ S ■ P ■ S
A X I L ■ A R M P I T
C ■ I N N ■ A ■ R
Q U E B E C ■ A R I A
U ■ R E D T A P E ■ N
I D E S ■ U N P L U G
E ■ M ■ A Y E ■ E
S A I L O R ■ A U L D
C ■ T ■ Y ■ S ■ I
E J E C T ■ J E W E L
```

147

```
■ C O N S T R I C T ■
A ■ W ■ P ■ E ■ H ■ C
N O I S E ■ C L O N E
A ■ N ■ E R A ■ K ■ L
R I G I D ■ P I E C E
C ■ C ■ ■ ■ K ■ ■ S
H I K E R ■ B E S E T
I ■ R ■ A D O ■ A ■ I
S P I T Z ■ S E L M A
M ■ L ■ O ■ S ■ S ■ L
■ C L E R G Y M A N ■
```

148

```
S T R I D E ■ T I E S
H ■ O ■ O ■ A ■ ■ U
E ■ O D D J O B M A N
A C T ■ G ■ L ■ I
F A S T E N ■ E Z R A
■ S ■ O M E G A ■ M
B U R R ■ B R U T A L
■ A ■ R ■ O ■ O N E
B L U E P E T E R ■ M
U ■ N ■ T ■ C ■ U
D U S T ■ M O T H E R
```

149

```
I ■ P ■ T E X T U R E
N O R T H ■ R ■ A ■
D ■ O ■ R O Y A L T Y
O U T D O ■ I ■ H ■
O ■ E ■ W R I N G E R
R E S T ■ O ■ S E R E
S A T I E T Y ■ T ■ P
■ G ■ P ■ O N A I R
P L A T E A U ■ W ■ E
E ■ O ■ R E A D S
A S S E N T S ■ Y ■ S
```

150

```
R I D E R ■ A R O M A
I ■ E ■ E ■ E ■ A
C ■ F ■ L A U N D R Y
K H A K I ■ T ■ K
E ■ C ■ C R E E P E R
T I T O ■ Y ■ D U D E
S C O O T E R ■ R ■ I
■ E ■ D ■ U N I T S
G A S L A M P ■ T ■ S
X ■ E ■ E ■ A ■ U
B E A S T ■ E R N I E
```

151

```
S H E D S ■ V O M I T
T ■ E ■ A ■ E ■ O
E R I C A ■ T O N G A
V ■ E ■ H ■ R ■ D
E F F I C A C I O U S
■ O ■ T ■ V ■ G ■ R
S E L F R E L I A N T
W ■ U ■ N ■ N ■ E
A I S L E ■ B A R N S
N ■ O ■ L ■ T ■ T
G R U F F ■ R E P A Y
```

152

```
A ■ D ■ R O M A N C E
B U R S A ■ N ■ O
Y ■ E ■ D I A G R A M
S W A M I ■ E ■ T
M ■ D ■ I D Y L L I C
A ■ E ■ I ■ A ■ A
L O D G I N G ■ N ■ N
■ P ■ E ■ O U G H T
W A L T Z E R ■ U ■ E
R ■ U ■ G R I P E
S T I P P L E ■ D ■ N
```

153

```
S P E A K ■ S P I C E
E ■ G ■ C ■ Y ■ V
A C E R ■ A F L A M E
M ■ C E N T ■ O ■ N
A B L E ■ A N N E X
N ■ A ■ L ■ G ■ H
■ S T E L E ■ B R I E
B ■ R ■ P U R E ■ R
A N N A L S ■ A T O M
N ■ S ■ Y ■ V ■ I
D A T E D ■ P O I N T
```

154

```
P A S T Y ■ R E C A P
■ Y ■ E ■ H ■ A ■ E
H E L M ■ E X E T E R
I ■ P E A ■ W ■ M
G R A T E R ■ R A K E
H ■ C E N T R A L ■ A
L O R D ■ L O C K E T
I ■ E ■ E T C ■ E
G L A N D S ■ O A R S
H ■ G ■ S ■ O ■ O
T W E E T ■ K N O W N
```

155

```
■ B L A C K B E L T ■
W ■ E ■ A ■ L ■ U ■ R
I N P U T ■ U N C L E
T ■ E ■ T O R ■ I ■ V
T A R R Y ■ B A D G E
I ■ U ■ ■ ■ L ■ ■ R
C A R E T ■ P L E A T
I ■ I ■ U R I ■ N ■ I
S C O W L ■ S I T I N
M ■ J ■ L ■ T ■ E ■ G
■ T A K E H E A R T ■
```

156

```
A D O B E ■ S T O O P
M ■ O ■ C ■ R ■ A
O D E S ■ R E A S O N
E ■ A U T O ■ I ■ S
B U R N ■ S A L T Y
A ■ N ■ S ■ H ■ E
■ A S K E W ■ L I O N
L ■ N ■ I D L E ■ E
O P T I C S ■ A F A R
O ■ F ■ E ■ M ■ G
P A C E D ■ B A D L Y
```

SOLUTIONS

157

158

159

160

161

162

163

164

165

166

167

168

SOLUTIONS

169

```
E K I N G   A L I A S
X   U   A   E     E
C A N N O N   A X L E
E   A   T   D     D
P R O C L I V I T Y
T   M A Y   A N Y   C
  F I R E E N G I N E
P   T   D     N   L
U N D O   G U R G L E
M   O   Y   U     R
P R U N E   A B B E Y
```

170

```
S C A B S   W A I V E
  O   L   E   C   N
I D L E   S P R E A D
N     S E P T   D   U
C A P S   A   S T I R
E   R E S T A T E   A
S H E D   I   E A R N
S   M   B A L E     C
A N I M A L   P I K E
N   E   S     L   I
T U R N S   T E N T H
```

171

```
B L I M P   F   S O P
A     U R B A N E   O
D I N G O   I   C   P
G   O   B   N E R V E
E A R N E S T   E
R   T   A     T   N
    H   C Y A N I D E
O M E G A   C   V   T
V   A   B   T E E T H
A   S P I G O T     E
L O T   N   R A C E R
```

172

```
C U F F S   S P O R E
L   A   H   T   C   V
A C T U A T E   A X E
M     P   A   R     N
P E A C E   D R I F T
    V         N
S W I L L   C H A P S
N   A   I   L     T
O P T   T R A I L E R
R   O   H   S   E   I
T E R S E   P U T U P
```

173

```
S E R I E S   P   M
A   E     C A R R O T
L A N D   A   E   N
U   A   A N O T H E R
T A M E R   Z   Y
E   E X C I T E D   Z
  R   P   A L I K E
S A P L I N G   S   R
  V   O   O   A M M O
B E H I N D     A   E
  N   T   E C C L E S
```

174

```
C U R I O   R O D S
A   I   P O R E   T
V G U   U   A I D A
A S S E S S O R   L
  O   F   N   W A D E
  R   F R E Y A   A
B E A U   E   R   W
E   S T R I D E N T
T A X I   D   U   U
E   V A N E   R   N
L I M E   S H O V E
```

175

```
S E A M S   D R A W S
I   O   C     I   H
N U C L E A R F R E E
K   A   N   F   L
S A C R E D   B A I L
    U   I   R
C A R R   D E S E R T
A   R   A E     W
B R E A S T P L A T E
A   N   E   M   A
L A T C H   B A T I K
```

176

```
B L A N D   R E C U R
A   C   I C E   L   U
S O I L S   P R A N G
E N D   T   O   M   B
D I S M I S S   P A Y
  C   N   S   W
P E A   C H E E T A H
L   L   T   S   E R A
A L I B I   S I R E N
T   E   V I E   R   D
O U N C E   D I A R Y
```

177

```
N   C H R Y S A L I S
E   O   E   H   A
W A Y N E   R A I D S
L   P   L E E   T   U
Y O U R S   D R Y E R
W   O       A     P
E L E C T   S P O O R
D   I   E F T   L   I
S E D A N   A R I E S
    E   S   T   V   E
P E R S E V E R E   S
```

178

```
C A L F   R H I N E
O   R O L E   L   L
P U P A   G   L   V
R   R U S T I C A T E
A L E   L   O   T   R
  S C I E N C E
E   C   P   A   A I M
A C R O P O L I S   E
T   I   E   D E A R
U   B   R O S E     G
P I E T Y   S U R E
```

179

```
T   B   C   S C U R F
E M U L A T E   G   R
D   Y   G   N   L   I
D E S S E R T W I N E
Y   T   A   H   D
  P R E T T I E S T
W   E   I   A     L
I N O P P O R T U N E
V   L   A   A   N   V
E   I   T E N S I L E
S N O R E   D   T   E
```

180

```
S H R U B   N O M A D
C   A   O W E   E   I
O F F A L   X   C A N
R   G U R U   C   G
E L V I S   S H A K Y
  I   L     A   E
P E T E R   B L U N T
A   O   O B O E     E
T I P   O   R Y D E R
C   E   T E E   N   S
H E R B S   D R A P E
```

SOLUTIONS

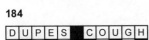

181

S	O	F	I	A	■	■	C	H	A	R
H	■	O	■	M	I	T	R	E	■	H
U	F	O	■	N	■	■	E	R	G	O
N	U	T	M	E	G	■	E	■	■	N
■	T	■	■	S	U	P	P	O	S	E
■	O	■	I	T	A	L	Y	■	O	■
A	N	O	D	Y	N	E	■	■	U	■
V	■	I	■	O	A	F	I	S	H	
A	U	T	O	■	■	T	■	R	A	Y
S	■	A	C	U	T	E	■	A	■	P
T	R	O	Y	■	■	D	E	N	S	E

182

A	T	L	A	S	■	P	■	M	A	C
F	■	■	■	U	T	U	B	E	■	A
F	E	V	E	R	■	L	■	D	■	F
R	■	I	■	L	■	S	H	A	M	E
A	C	O	L	Y	T	E	■	L	■	■
Y	■	L	■	E	■	L	L		V	
■	I	■	C	A	P	T	I	V	E	■
B	I	N	G	O	■	A	■	O	■	R
O	■	I	■	L	■	L	U	N	G	S
M	■	S	P	O	T	S	■	■	■	U
B	I	T	■	N	■	Y	E	A	T	S

183

S	■	A	■	I	■	T	U	R	K	S
C	A	L	U	M	N	Y	■	A	■	T
R	■	L	■	P	■	R	A	G	■	E
A	D	I	E	U	■	O	B	E	S	E
M	■	E	D	G	E	■	L	■	L	
■	I	S	I	N	G	L	A	S	S	■
S	■	B	■	O	U	Z	O	■	P	
W	H	A	L	E	■	M	E	D	I	A
E	■	W	E	N	■	B	■	D	■	U
L	■	A	■	V	I	E	W	E	R	S
L	A	Y	B	Y	■	R	■	N	■	E

184

D	U	P	E	S	■	C	O	U	G	H
A	■	U	■	W	■	N	■	E		
R	■	T	R	I	B	U	T	A	R	Y
I	N	T	E	R	■	H	■	M		
N	■	C	L	O	V	E	■	A		
G	A	T	E	■	B	■	S	A	N	D
■	T	■	P	R	I	M	P	■	A	
■	T	■	T	■	I	O	W	A	N	
C	A	L	I	B	R	A	T	E	■	C
■	C	■	V	■	O	■	E	■	E	
C	H	E	E	K	■	W	A	D	E	R

185

S	O	L	U	B	L	E	■	P	■	C
U	■	A	■	L	■	L	A	U	G	H
I	■	W	■	U	S	E	■	L	■	A
T	E	N	O	N	■	P	U	P	■	I
■	V	■	D	■	H	■	■	R		
M	A	T	H	E	M	A	T	I	C	S
A	■	■	R	■	N	■	■	O		
D	■	J	O	B	■	T	A	R	O	T
D	I	■	U	Z	I	■	A	■	A	
E	L	V	E	S	■	N	■	G	R	
N	■	E	■	S	T	E	P	S	O	N

186

F	A	C	E	S	■	S	C	O	F	F
U	■	A	■	E	■	O	■	E		
N	R	■	W	I	N	N	I	N	G	
G	L	A	C	E	■	T	■	D		
U	■	W	A	R	H	O	R	S	E	
S	P	A	S	■	O	■	A	C	R	E
■	H	Y	S	T	E	R	I	A	■	N
■	O	■	E	■	A	L	T	E	R	
A	B	S	T	A	I	N	■	T	■	A
I	■	T	■	■	C	■	E	■	P	
C	A	M	E	L	■	H	U	R	S	T

187

S	A	T	Y	R	■	D	O	W	E	R
T	■	I	■	E	■	C	■	L		
A	R	M	A	D	A	■	T	S	A	R
R	■	E	■	C	R	O	A	T		
T	A	S	T	E	R	■	B	E	E	F
E	■	E	■	O	■	E	■	O		
R	A	T	E	■	B	U	R	S	A	R
■	M	A	N	N	A	■	A	■	C	
P	A	P	A	■	T	R	I	F	L	E
■	Z	■	G	■	O	■	E	■	P	
L	E	V	E	R	■	W	O	R	K	S

188

A	T	O	L	L	■	B	L	A	C	K
K	■	O	■	B	■	O	■	■	E	
I	M	P	A	L	E	■	T	I	M	E
M	O	O	N	■	N	■	T	■	N	
B	O	I	S	T	E	R	O	U	S	■
O	■	S	■	F	■	M	■	R		
■	D	E	S	P	I	C	A	B	L	E
S	■	L	■	T	■	R	E	E	L	
P	O	L	O	■	E	M	E	R	G	E
R	■	■	P	■	D	■	N	■	N	
Y	E	M	E	N	■	F	A	U	L	T

189

P	A	P	A	Y	A	■	D	■	S	
A	■	R	■	C	R	E	C	H	E	
C	H	E	F	■	M	■	G	■	E	
I	■	M	■	C	E	R	A	M	I	C
F	A	I	R	Y	■	O	S	A	K	A
I	■	S	■	C	A	P	■	C	■	T
S	T	E	A	L	■	E	L	A	T	E
M	I	S	L	E	A	D	■	R	■	R
■	G	■	L	■	C	■	G	O	B	I
R	E	T	O	R	T	■	■	N	■	N
■	R	■	W	■	S	A	V	I	N	G

190

S	U	C	K	S	■	■	S	A	C	S
W	■	H	■	H	I	N	T	■	P	
A	■	E	■	E	■	A	R	O	S	E
P	R	E	S	E	R	V	E	■	N	
■	U	P	O	N	■	E	A	S	E	D
■	H	■	L	■	M	■	P			
B	R	A	I	N	■	S	E	M	I	
R	■	T	A	M	A	R	A	C	K	
A	T	E	A	M	■	V	■	L	■	Y
N	■	R	E	N	O	■	T	■	A	
D	A	V	Y	■	■	Y	E	A	S	T

191

H	U	S	S	A	R	■	C	■	O	
E	■	U	■	A	R	A	B	L	E	
I	M	P	A	I	R	■	V	■	D	
R	■	P	■	N	E	M	E	S	I	S
L	O	R	D	S	■	I	S	L	E	T
O	■	E	■	I	■	S	■	O	■	A
O	N	S	E	T	■	T	O	W	E	R
M	I	S	R	U	L	E	■	D	■	D
■	N	■	R	■	O	R	M	O	L	U
E	N	T	O	M	B	■	■	W	■	S
■	Y	■	R	■	S	I	G	N	E	T

192

B	E	A	R	D	■	T	A	B	L	E
E	■	R	■	I	■	T	■	E		
L	■	T	■	V	E	R	T	I	G	O
U	N	I	T	E	■	L	■	A		
G	■	C	■	R	E	P	E	A	T	
A	T	L	A	S	■	R	E	F	E	R
■	H	E	R	E	T	O	■	F	■	A
O	■	C	■	■	C	H	E	F	S	
A	R	M	H	O	L	E	■	C	■	H
■	A	■	E	■	■	S	■	T	■	L
O	X	I	D	E	■	S	I	S	S	Y

SOLUTIONS

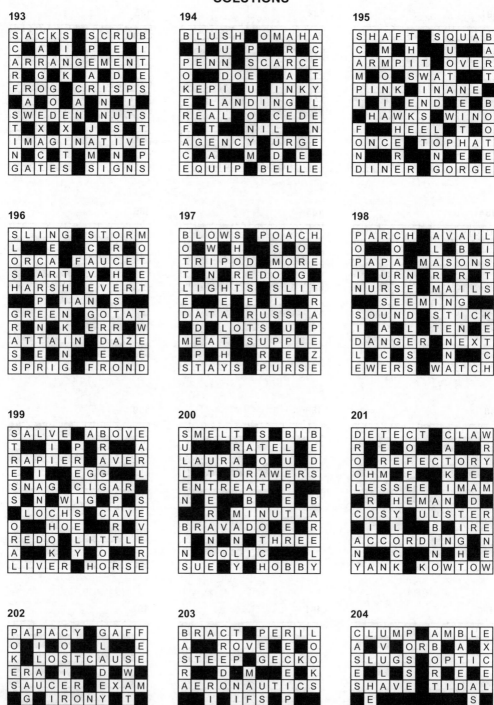

205

```
D A T E S   B A T H S
O   O   E   D       K
C A R I E S   D E L I
T   P   R U N E     D
O B E Y   C A R O B
R   D   A C T   P   D
  C O P S E   W I R E
W     A P S E   N   B
E R O S   S E N I O R
L     S     L   O   I
L O N E R   S E N D S
```

206

```
B A S I C   S H O R E
O   P   R   U   E
L   H   O P E N I N G
S T E W S   G     T
T   R   S L E E P E R
E V E R   O   R O D E
R O S E B U D   R   P
  O   G     O T T E R
A D O R I N G   R   E
  O   E     M   A   S
M O N T H   A B Y S S
```

207

```
B E N D S   C L A S S
R   E   H   H   M   L
A V O C A D O   P E A
W     L   P   H   V
L A T T E   S T O V E
      I           R
T A M P A   S W A R M
U   P   W   E       I
B R A   F O R W A R D
E   N   U   V   R   S
S T I L L   E X E R T
```

208

```
M E L B A   A S H E S
E   L   O G E E     T
M E D A L   M A I N E
O     N O D   N   T
R E S C U E   N O A H
A   O   D U B   U   O
B R A N   C A S S I S
I   N   E L Y     C
L O D E S   I N T R O
I   S O L O   O   P
A G O N Y   A D O R E
```

209

```
M A S S   A B R O A D
E   W A G       R
D O S E   A S T R A L
I   D     A   B
U N D E R P A N T S
M   I   A   E   D
  R E S I S T A N C E
A   H     D   S
D I V E R S   D U K E
T     O D E   R
B A L L A D   R O U T
```

210

```
C I D E R   R E P L Y
O   R   E   G   O
H O O T E D   O R G Y
A   O   F E A T   I
B Y P A S S   I N C H
I   U   S   S   E
T A P S   E S T A T E
  R   T E R N   G   D
D O M E   T I P O F F
  M   R   P   R   U
B A B E L   S M A L L
```

211

```
S O L E S   S T R U T
K   A   H   W   U   H
I M P L O R E   F A R
E     W   E   F   U
R I S K Y   P R I S M
  H         A
A B Y S S   T O N I C
R   N   N   E     L
R U E   A M N E S I A
O   S   R   E   I   W
W A S T E   T O N G S
```

212

```
D I M S     A T S E A
R     O D I N   Q   D
E B O N   G   U   A
A   F A S T E N I N G
M U F T I   L   G   E
    C A C H I N G
A   H   K   C E L L O
B R A I N W A V E   V
U   N   E   A S I A
T   C   S H O D   T
S T E P S   A N N E
```

213

```
S K I R T   M A N I A
L     E   F U M E   N
E G E S T   D O D G E
E     P   B   N   L
P O L I C E S T A T E
  U   R   A   I   H
S T E A M R O L L E R
T   T   D   L   A
A V A I L   N A T A L
M   H O O F   D   L
P R A N G   B O B B Y
```

214

```
A M A S S   S M O C K
C   M   A   A   O
A   O   L A U N D R Y
C A R E S   U   N
I   O   A B R A D E
A Q U A   E   L E A P
  U S E N E T   C   L
E   R   A N I S E
O B T A I N S   B   N
  E   T   K   E   T
A C T E D   S I L L Y
```

215

```
B O W I N G   L   T
L   A     U N I S O N
E D I T O R   M   P
S   T   S U R P A S S
S T R U T   E   S   K
Y   E   L A C   S   I
O   S   E   I N E P T
U N S T R A P   S   T
  E   O   W E A S E L
C A R E E R   O   E
  P   D   Y E A R N S
```

216

```
  S T R A N G L E R
B   I   C   R   N   R
R O T O R   O U N C E
I   L   I   S   U   P
E M E N D   S L I D E
F     O       O     A
C R A W L   C U B I T
A   N   I   E   O   I
S O D O M   L I N E N
E   R   I   L   E   G
  P E N T H O U S E
```

SOLUTIONS

217
```
H A I L ■ S A I L O R
O ■ ■ O W E ■ ■ ■ I ■
B L E D ■ T A N G L E
N ■ G ■ ■ ■ I ■ W ■ ■
O S T E N S I B L E ■
B O A ■ ■ K ■ ■ A L B
■ P R O F I T A B L E
■ R ■ N ■ ■ ■ N ■ E ■
C A V O R T ■ G O A T
■ N ■ ■ W O E ■ ■ L ■
T O M A T O ■ R A C E
```

218
```
R E T O R T ■ G A S P
A ■ E ■ A I R Y ■ L ■
I ■ A C T S ■ P A R A
L E K ■ I ■ D ■ V ■ T
■ L ■ F O R E B O D E
B A D ■ N ■ L ■ N H S
A N I M A T E D ■ A ■
R ■ G ■ L ■ G ■ A L A
M O S T ■ T A L C ■ S
A ■ A ■ A B U T ■ R I
N U M B ■ G E N E V A
```

219
```
F A N C Y ■ S I G H T
O ■ R ■ E ■ R ■ R ■ R
L O V E D ■ V ■ A G O
K ■ S ■ V E T S ■ O ■
S T A T I O N ■ P O P
■ H ■ N U T ■ ■ W ■ ■
Y E A ■ S C H O O L S
A ■ B A T H ■ D ■ I ■
W H O ■ A ■ C O U L D
N ■ V ■ N ■ U ■ U ■ E
S W E A T ■ B R O W S
```

220
```
F A M O U S ■ ■ M ■ L
O ■ N ■ M I M O S A ■
A N X I O U S ■ M ■ T
M ■ ■ O ■ G O B B L E
S C A N S ■ M ■ A ■ X
■ U S E L E S S ■ ■ ■
U ■ D ■ T ■ R O A S T
S K I R T S ■ C ■ ■ H
U ■ T ■ L E G I B L E
R I O T E R ■ A ■ ■ I
Y ■ R ■ ■ F A L T E R
```

221
```
S ■ D ■ T H I M B L E
T R I B E ■ A ■ I ■ ■
R ■ S A X O P H O N E
E X T R A ■ L ■ D ■ ■
E ■ U ■ S E R E N E ■
T O R T ■ A ■ R E N T
■ A B S O R B ■ E ■ I
K ■ H ■ ■ L E D G E ■
P L A I N T I F F ■ D
■ E ■ R ■ S T U D Y ■
M Y S T I C S ■ L ■ E
```

222
```
O ■ P ■ M ■ M U L C H
V O L C A N O ■ I ■ A
U ■ A ■ D ■ S ■ E ■ I
L U N A R ■ S Q U A T
E ■ A B A ■ U ■ ■ I ■
■ B R A S S B A N D ■
B ■ T ■ ■ E Y E ■ O ■
E X P E L ■ I S A A C
A ■ A ■ I ■ R ■ R ■ T
R ■ C ■ E Q U A B L E
S T E R N ■ T ■ Y ■ T
```

223
```
C A U S E ■ B O R E S
A ■ K ■ C ■ D ■ ■ L ■
S A L I V A ■ D I V A
I ■ A ■ T O M ■ ■ M ■
N O R M ■ A ■ E R G ■
O ■ V A C C I N E ■ A
■ S A C ■ L ■ T A N S
A ■ ■ H A Y ■ ■ C ■ S
R O B E ■ S T A T U E
C ■ ■ T ■ M ■ G ■ ■ T
H I K E R ■ B E A T S
```

224
```
S H I P ■ ■ S T R A P
T ■ ■ E R I E ■ I ■ O
O A F S ■ ■ N ■ V I P
I ■ R O S E T T E ■ P
C H I ■ P ■ I ■ R A Y
■ C O Y N E S S ■ ■ ■
S E A ■ G ■ N ■ I M F
L ■ S A L U T E D ■ A
A S S ■ A ■ ■ S E C T
N ■ E ■ S U M P ■ ■ A
T R E E S ■ ■ Y E L L
```

225
```
M O T ■ U R U G U A Y
U ■ A ■ P ■ ■ E ■ ■ E
R ■ N A K E D N E S S
A R K ■ E ■ ■ T ■ K ■
L E S S E R ■ E D A M
■ G ■ A P P L E ■ T ■
T A L L ■ M I L L E T
■ L ■ I ■ A ■ I R A ■
R E B E L L I O N ■ L
A ■ ■ N ■ S ■ E ■ ■ O
P A R T A K E ■ S U N
```

226
```
C O C O A ■ F O C U S
R ■ A ■ W ■ A ■ A ■ E
E X T R A C T ■ N E T
P ■ ■ ■ I ■ E ■ T ■ I
T A C I T ■ D R A I N
■ R ■ ■ ■ ■ T ■ ■ ■ ■
S T O M P ■ S H A C K
W ■ A ■ I ■ ■ T ■ N ■
O C T ■ E D U C A T E
O ■ ■ I ■ C ■ M ■ N E
P L A C E ■ P E N A L
```

227
```
J ■ S ■ R A T C H E T
O C H R E ■ ■ L ■ N ■
Y ■ R ■ H E D O N I C
O P E R A ■ ■ S ■ G ■
U ■ W O B B L E ■ M ■
S O D A ■ A ■ S L A P
■ T ■ D E G R E E ■ O
■ T ■ S ■ ■ A T T A R
D A V I N C I ■ H ■ T
■ W ■ D ■ ■ S P A D E
P A L E T T E ■ ■ L R
```

228
```
M E T E R ■ B L E A K
■ T ■ N ■ T ■ P ■ ■ I
G A N G ■ E N S I G N
A ■ ■ A I R ■ ■ T ■ S
S W I G ■ R ■ D H O W
T ■ D E V O T E E ■ O
R O O D ■ R ■ S T E M
O ■ L ■ ■ I M P ■ ■ A
P L I E R S ■ I R O N
O ■ S ■ ■ T ■ S ■ F ■
D R E A D ■ D E I F Y
```

229

```
R A P I D S . L A S H
O . L . . O V A . . I
B L A M E S . D U S T
E . Z . Y O R E . W .
S T A K E . A N T O N
. A . L I P . . . R .
S I N G E . T A S E R
. N . O T T O . O . E
S T I R . O R D A I N
O . . S O Y . . . V A
W I S E . S Q U E A L
```

230

```
F A S C I A . F . F .
E . O . I N D O O R .
A M U S E D . R . E .
R . T . S T E E R S .
S H E A F . A . L . H
. . T R A I P S E . .
L . E . U . E I G H T
A I R I N G . M . U .
T . N . A L M O N D .
E N A M E L . E . O .
R . L . L A R D E R .
```

231

```
P R O U D . C R I M E
L . P . I . E . U . .
A E . S A M P L E R .
S E N S E . O . S . .
M . T A P E R . L . .
A R I A S . A T E I N
. E . M E T R E . I .
. T . P . P R A W N .
M I N E R A L . S . E
N . D . U . A . T . .
M A K E R . G Y P S Y
```

232

```
M A L I . M A G N E T
I . C R A B . X . . .
S H O O . P O D I U M
U . N . U . D . . . .
S U B S T I T U T E .
E . O . O . W . P . .
. B A K I N G S O D A
. E . D . O . R . . .
R E D S E A . B A R S
. C . A D Z E . O . .
S H I E L D . R A I N
```

233

```
S E L E C T . B . P .
U . A . O P A Q U E .
B A D E G G . Y . C .
T . I . O S T R I C H
L E E . N . U . I . .
E A S T G E R M A N Y
. R . O . E . R I O .
V A N I L L A . O . U
. C . L . A M O U N T
C H E E R S . S . H .
. E . T . S I R E N S
```

234

```
C U P P A . A A R O N
R . R W A N D A . A .
A R I E L . T O N E D
S . D . B . L . I . .
S P E E D O M E T E R
. E . C . A . S . L .
M A D E I R A C A K E
I . A . D . E . P . .
G L A S S . G N O M E
H . M E T R I C . E .
T I P S Y . N E W T S
```

235

```
A R O M A S . R . C .
N . . O . A P P E A R
T A I L . G . M . I .
I . T . O D I O U S .
C R E E K . E . V . P
. E N N O B L E . . .
A . L . O . T A S T E
S O W E T O . M . L .
I . O . U . B A U D .
D A R K E R . D . E .
E . M . S L A V E R .
```

236

```
L A C E S . P A P E R
O . A . C . O . A . O
C U R I O U S . D A Y
A . . U . E . D . C .
L E A S T . R H Y M E
. D . I . U . A . . .
S O R R Y . D E M O N
C . U . O . E . I . .
R A M . U M B R A G E
U . B . R . I . P . C
B E A N S . T I T L E
```

237

```
M O W E R . H I V E S
I . X . E . O . U . .
M O R P H . N E W E L
I . L . M . X . K . .
C E R E M O N I O U S
. R . T . D . S . S .
R E S I D E N T I A L
E . V . L . E . A . .
L I B E L . U N I O N
I . Y . I . C . C . .
C H E S T . V E N U E
```

238

```
C L E R K S . G . C .
A . A . C R A V A T .
T A R E . O . Z . B .
A . N . S T E A M E R
C H I L L . R . U R I
O . N . A . N . T . N
M E G . K . I C I N G
B E S I E G E . L . T
. R . T . U . D A D O
C I R C U S . T . N .
. E . H . T H I E V E
```

239

```
. M A H A R A J A H .
H . L . P . W . D . D
A M O U R . A W A K E
V . F . I T S . M . T
E X T O L . H A S T E
R . A . . L . S . S .
S W A R D . S P E N T
A . L . A C E . X . I
C A B I N . P L A I N
K . U . C . A . M . G
. E M B E L L I S H .
```

240

```
N I G H . B A T H S .
A . . E R N E . A . W
U S S R . R . X . I .
R . C O L L I S I O N
U G H . Y . B . D U E
. R E P R I E V E S .
H I M . I . R . R E T
A N A R C H I S M . U
I . T . I . . H Y M N
R . I . S A R I . I .
Y A C H T . A M O S .
```

241

```
S E E O F F . U . S
T . N . . R A N D O M
R E V O K E . T . U
A . I . I T E R A T E
T H E R E . . I . H
A . D E V O T E D . B
. B . E . . E D U C E
M O C K U P S . R . H
. W . I . A T T I R E
T E N N I S . . N . S
. L . G . T A U G H T
```

242

```
A . S P E C T A C L E
M . P . L . R . H
B O O Z E . U P E N D
E . I . G E T . E . E
R E L A Y . H A R E M
G . . R . . L . E
R O W E L . F L O R A
I . H . A X E . L . N
S H A R P . A M I G O
. R . S . S . V . U
O F F C E N T R E . R
```

243

```
C . R E L E V A N C E
O . E . O . I . A
L E A R N . O P I N E
O . R E G U L A R . T
N E S T S . A P A C E
I . R . . . R . R
S A F E S . B I S O N
E . O A T C A K E . A
D U E T O . N A V A L
. . H . N . D . E . L
H A N G E R S O N . Y
```

244

```
. O C C U P A N C Y
E . A . N . D . O . A
M E D I C . L I N E D
A . G . A L I . G . V
C H E A P . B L A D E
I . I . . E . . R
A W A R D . M E A N T
T . L . R Y E . P . I
E D I F Y . T E R M S
D . C . L . A . O . E
. R E C Y C L I N G
```

245

```
R O Y A L . C O S T A
E . F . E . T . V
B E E T . R E M O V E
U . R E A R M . M . R
S T A R S . E X A L T
. D . S A T . C
T R I C E . I C H O R
A . C . N A C R E . I
B O A S T S . A R T S
O . T . P . Z . E
R E E V E . B E G I N
```

246

```
C E R I S E . B . N
A . U . . A V E N U E
N I N E . S . A . R
V . N . S T U D I E D
A T E . N . N . Y
S E L F A S S U R E D
. R . K . E . A V E
P R O T E S T . R . A
. I . B . O . B E L L
N E P A L I . . L . E
. R . R . L A W Y E R
```

247

```
H A D E S . S H U N T
E . A . . O . P . H
F I R S T . M I S E R
T . T Y K E . U . E
Y E S . R . T . R O E
. . T R A D I N G .
T W A . N . M . E S P
H . T . N O E L . E
R H I N O . S A I N T
O . O . U . . M . T
B O N D S . D A F F Y
```

248

```
L O U G H . V I S T A
O . R . . I . C . R
S T E I N . N O O S E
E . L E A S E . U . T
S H A G G Y . A N T E
. . B . . L . D .
R O O D . P L U R A L
E . R . P H A S E . E
I M A G E . Y A L T A
N . T . N . G . . F
S L E E T . H E A V Y
```

249

```
B I S H O P . . W . N
A . E . A R N I C A
S H A R E S . . D . V
I . M . S T R O D E
L O V E R . R . W . L
. . I S O L A T E
F . T . S . M O R A L
A R R O Y O . U . . E
N . I . D E C I D E
G R O U N D . H . R
S . L . S L E A Z Y
```

250

```
C A U C U S . . M . D
A . A . O C T A V O
R E A D . F . G . L
E . C E L A N D I N E
D I T T O . O . . E
. S . O . N . C
. L . N . E V O K E
D E C R Y P T E D . N
A . O . O . E D G E
S L A C K S . R . M
H . X . E A S I L Y
```

251

```
. O T O L O G I S T
B . I . I . E . T . C
U N M A N . C A I R O
L . E . E L K . F . A
L I S T S . O F F A L
F . O . . R . M
I D I O M . C O A T I
N . N . I D O . T . N
C L A U S . V A L U E
H . N . E . E . A . R
. T E R R O R I S T
```

252

```
S A G G Y . C A R G O
T . R . T . T . . K
A L C O V E . T U N A
G A L A . A . I . Y
E C O N O M I C A L
D . U . M . M . M
. S T A L A G M I T E
C . W . T . A G A R
A L T O . E N C O D E
S . K . S . R . . L
T O N E R . B O B B Y
```

253

```
. W O R K H O U S E .
W . M . E . N . E . A
I N E R T . S L E E T
T . G . C U E . M . T
T E A C H . T A S T E
I . . A . . . R . . N
C O S T S . S C O L D
I . H . T O M . N . A
S C A L Y . A L I E N
M . V . L . R . O . T
. D E F E A T I N G .
```

254

```
C H O K E . C R A M P
H . V . S I R . G . A
A M A S S . E . R A N
O . C A T S . E . T .
S C A R Y . T E E N S
. A . U . . S . O . .
A D O B E . S H O R E
Z . U . B R A E . M .
T U T . O . D R A M A
E . E . N I L . D . I
C A R R Y . Y O D E L
```

255

```
S T R U T . S . A R M
E . E . E A T E R . A
E S S E N . O . R . T
S . E . O . O V A L S
A D R E N A L I N E .
W A V E . N . O G E E
. T A L E N T L E S S
P A T S Y . O . M . T
A . I . R . T E E T H
I . O V I N E . N . E
N U N . E . S I T A R
```

256

```
M E D A L . W . E V E
E . . L I G H T S . A
A R A B S . I . S . S
G . S . T E M P E S T
R A S H E R . N . . .
E . O . N E W . T . T
. . C . . C A S I N O
T H I R S T Y . A . U
O . A . P . L I L A C
A . T A R M A C . . A
D U E . Y . Y E A R N
```

257

```
S T R E S S . L . T .
C . N . A L C O V E .
A C T I O N . C . P .
R . G . D E F A M E .
F L A M E . V . T . E
. M A L A I S E . . .
M . A . B . L A D L E
A F L O A T . L . L .
P . G . R E M I N D .
L E A N T O . O . E .
E . M . D A N C E R .
```

258

```
C A C T U S . . P . A
R . E . T R Y I N G .
A V E N U E . R . R .
M . U . M A N A G E .
S T I R S . F . T . E
. . M E T H A N E . .
M . A . U . R A S E D
A N G I N A . T . . A
Y . I . L O I T E R .
B A N G L E . O . . E
E . E . C A N V A S .
```

259

```
C R O C U S . F . P .
O . U . A B R O A D .
O N T O . T . E . R .
K . L . S E V E N T Y
I M A G O . Z . Y . .
E . W I D O W E R . U
. B . N . A S H E N .
T A R G E T S . E . L
. B . H . E . I S L E
P E D A L S . U . S .
. L . M . T R U S T S
```

260

```
C O M E T . J U L E P
A . I . H . E . I . I
B . L O O S E E N D S
E N D U S E R . E . T
R . . R E A S S U R E
. . D . L . . P . . .
M E R M A I D S . . R
O . Y . G O R I L L A
T E R M I N A T E . T
E . O . L . F . A . I
L A T H E . T A N G O
```

261

```
C R U S H . R E E D S
. A . T . O . R . L .
D Y K E . A D M I R E
I . L A M E . T . E .
S A I L . M . D R I P
R . C A L O R I E . L
E W E R . N . L A T E
P . C . B I L E . . S
U T O P I A . M A R S
T . L . R . M . U . .
E N D E D . M A L T A
```

262

```
M O G U L . M O N T H
A . L . I . R . R . .
S . U . S E M I N A R
S H E E T . E . D . .
E . I N S T A N C E .
S A N E . O . T Y R O
. A G R A R I A N . L
. C . V . B L I N D .
S H E A V E S . C . M
. E . T . E . A . A .
K N E E S . N Y L O N
```

263

```
S E R I A L . S M U T
U . E . M E M O . . I
R . S E E D . T W I N
F A T . N . C . H . N
. L . C A M O M I L E
E G G . B . U . P O D
R A I L L E R Y . R .
A . B . E . T . S E W
S U E T . S I L O . A
E . . O B O E . L . I
D U S T . B R I D A L
```

264

```
R A I S E S . . U . B
E . . U . T W E N T Y
B E E F T E A . R . R
U . F . M I C A . O .
S E P I A . T . V A N
. . E X C R E T E . .
D I N . C . R E L I C
I . D O O R . A . . R
Z . I . S U B S I D E
Z E N I T H . E . . E
Y . G . R O T U N D .
```

SOLUTIONS

265

```
B E F A L L . . F E W
U . B . E M I R . E
R E M O R S E . E L L
K . A V A S T . E . L
I N N E R . E A R E D
N . G . E G O . A . R
A G A I N . R I N S E
F . N . E K I N G . S
A B E . S O C K E T S
S . S A S H . E . E
O D E . . L O D G E D
```

266

```
A N G L E . S U L K S
C . U . V . K . I . E
R U M M A G E . M E N
I . . . D . W E B . S
D R O N E . S C O N E
. U . O . . H . I
K N E A D . C O R P S
N . C H I . R . . T
I L L . A N A R C H Y
F . A . R . S A . E
E N T R Y . S I N U S
```

267

```
G L A S S . G E N U S
U . F . C O O . O . N
A D I E U . U L T R A
R . R . L E G . E . K
D W E L L . E N D U E
. O . O . . . E . S
T O U G H . B E G A N
I . N . A L E . A . E
L O T U S . G I V E R
T . I . T W O . E . V
H O L L Y . T U L L E
```

268

```
B A T C H . S W A R M
O . A . E . D . A . A
N A S T Y . A T O L L
U . H . U . R . . E
S W E E P S T A K E S
. E . D . U . N . K
S T A R C R O S S E D
P . A . P . P . . I
A I S L E . D O U B T
S . I . L . . S . T
M I N I M . J E L L Y
```

269

```
S H A F T . E D I T H
E . I . H . A . E
L . R . I C E R I N K
D O M I N O . N . D
O . A . G R I E V E
M A I M . T . D A R T
. P L A N E T . N . R
. L . L . G E M I N I
C O N I F E R . L . V
. M . C . . S . L . E
A B B E Y . E X A L T
```

270

```
D E S T R U C T I O N
I . P . E . L . N . O
S C A M S . E L F I N
C . C O T E R I E . P
O M E N S . K A R M A
U . K . . . I . . R
R E S E T . A S S E T
A . E Y E B R O W . I
G O O S E . G N A T S
E . U . M . U . P . A
S A L E S P E R S O N
```

271

```
S T A G . . G I F T S
E . . H A I R . R . I
R I P E . . A . E . X
V . R E C O N N E C T
E G O . O . U . W . Y
. . S Q U E L C H
O . T . N . E . E B B
F O R E T A S T E . A
T . A . E . . A L A S
E . T . S O W S . . I
N E E D S . . K E E N
```

272

```
P E T T Y . E P O C H
A . A . O . . A F R O
N . N . K N I T T E D
A N K L E . T . A
M . E . L O W E R S
A C R E . A . R E E D
. O S S I F Y . Q . R
. R . C . U V U L A
A N T O N Y M . I . G
N E A R . . M . E . O
D A N T E . Y E M E N
```

273

```
A Z T E C . . C A R L
X . O . H U M A N . O
I C Y . E . . L A I R
S Y S T E M . L . . R
. C . T E N A N C Y
. L . S A L E S . U
N E I T H E R . . R
A . R . E V O L V E
D E L I . O . E E L
I . A D I E U . G . S
R A G E . . S W O R E
```

274

```
B E L T S . F L O S S
U . I . H . I . . T
R A N S O M . C A M E
I . S . W I N K . W
A C E R . L A S T S
L . E . S K Y . W . A
. I D E A S . B O W S
P . . P L O T . T . S
A U T O . P O L I C E
I . C . . N . M . N
R I G H T . S H E E T
```

275

```
S C O U T . W A G E S
P . C . H . M . . L
I T A L I C . O K R A
N . R . S H I N . T
A C I D . A L G A E
L . N . A S K . I . R
. B A S I S . U R G E
P . . A R I D . F . C
O P A L . S A F A R I
S . A . . D . R . P
Y A R D S . O B E S E
```

276

```
G L O S S . C R E P T
R . A . P . A . N . H
E N T R E A T . T O E
E . . N . E . H . R
T R A C T . R O U T E
. N . . . . . S
S L I N G . C H E S S
T . S . L . A . . C
A Y E . A C R E A G E
I . E . Z . E . X . N
N U D G E . T H E F T
```

SOLUTIONS

277

278

279

280

281

282

283

284

285

286

287

288

SOLUTIONS

289

```
E M B A R R A S S E D
M   R   I   P   H   U
E   O   O N E R O U S
R O O S T   X   O P T
Y   K E E L       T O Y
  B   C R E E L     N
C O S       E X A M   H
O R C   B   C H A F E
M E A S U R E   M   A
I   N   S   S   B   V
C A S E H I S T O R Y
```

290

```
W I L D E   C L A S S
    C   O   A   P   W
D E A N   R I P P L E
O     J A B   A   E
U R D U   I   F R E T
B   O A K T R E E   P
L E O N   R   S L O E
E   R   A C T     A
B O W L E R   I R I S
E   A   Y   V   R
D O Y E N   L E P E R
```

291

```
B E T A   H O T D O G
I     B O O     V
S L A Y   T I C K E T
E   S     O   R
C O N S O L I D A T E
T   I   E   R   N
S E L F E V I D E N T
  X   U     E   R
F A B R I C   A N N E
  M     A I L     A
A S C E N D   T A C T
```

292

```
C A L F     A L I G N
O   L U L U   N   A
L A N E   G   F   K
I   E X C L U S I V E
C O C O A   S   R   D
    E R R A T U M
A   S   N   U N A R Y
D I S P E N S E R   A
H   A   G   A Y A H
O   R   I N N S     O
C L Y D E     Y O Y O
```

293

```
R I G I D   S A C K S
O   R   I M P   E   U
T S A R S   E L L I S
O W N   H   E   L   H
R E T R E A D   O B I
  E   V   C   R
N T H   E L A S T I C
O   A   L   M   O A R
S W I R L   E X T R A
E   R   E A R   E   Z
D O S E D   A D D L E
```

294

```
F L A T S   T I M E S
R   R O B E   A   I
U B O A T   A C R E S
M   P   A   T   S
P O S S I B I L I T Y
    H   F A R   N
P A I N S T A K I N G
R   N   E   N   R
O U I J A   B O N G O
O   E   G L O W   P
F O R G O   A N K L E
```

295

```
S U C R E   A S T O R
O   A   M   O   F
L A P D O G   M E T E
I   R E T R I E V E
C R I M E A   T A N K
I   I   N   H   E
T A R T   U N I S O N
  H E A D L I N E   N
B E D S   E N G I N E
  A   S   O   Z   D
U D D E R   N E E D Y
```

296

```
R O W A N   A W A I T
U   O   U   D   V   H
M O N G R E L   A X E
B     S   I   R   S
A B A T E   B R I D E
    D         C
C H A P S   S H E E P
O   P   P   I     A
N O T   R E B O U N D
C   O   A   Y   S   R
H U R R Y   L I E G E
```

297

```
B O S N I A   I   B
I   U   L A N D A U
T I N G L E   S   B
C   L   A C C U S E R
H A I K U   R   L
Y   T O D D L E R   W
  B   N   A R E N A
R O S T R U M   C   S
  G   I   L A V I S H
R E C K O N   P   E
  Y   I   A C C E S S
```

298

```
M   L   O   S T E E P
E L O N G A T E D   E
C   N   R   O N E   P
C A D R E   P A N S Y
A L O E     C   S
  I N C O G N I T O
S   R     T O N E
W I D E N   P Y L O N
O   E A U   A   E   T
O   A T T A I N D E R
P I L E S   D   O   Y
```

299

```
C   P   C R Y B A B Y
A B H O R   A   O
N   A D U L A T O R Y
C O R D S   T   S
E   A   T H R E S H
R I O T   U   R A T E
  S H O W E R   L   S
L   P   A D I O S
P A L E S T I N E   A
  N   K   N A N N Y
I D E A L L Y   T   S
```

300

```
V I S T A   P L A I D
I   A   O   T   R
G A G S   W O R T H Y
I   U T T E R   E   E
L I N E R   D O N O R
    P   A G E   D
S W O R N   A P A R T
P   W   C O L O N   O
R U D D E R   S T O W
I   E   B   E   E
G O R S E   I D L E R
```

SOLUTIONS

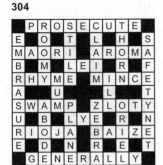

301

```
M O S C O W ░ ░ ░ E ░ D
E ░ ░ H ░ A V E N G E
D E F A C T O ░ S ░ L
I ░ ░ O ░ E Y E L E T
C L O S U R E ░ A ░ A
░ ░ A ░ P ░ U ░ V ░ ░
E ░ R ░ S O R C E R Y
M U S L I M ░ A ░ A ░
P ░ M ░ D I V I D E R
T E A S E T ░ R ░ D ░
Y ░ N ░ ░ S H O R T S
```

302

```
C I T Y ░ ░ E R A T O
O ░ ░ E A S T ░ L ░ W
M E S A ░ H ░ T ░ N
M ░ P R E C I P I C E
A C E ░ X ░ O ░ M A D
░ R E D P E P P E R ░
B U D ░ L ░ I ░ T E N
E X T R I C A T E ░ A
A ░ R ░ C ░ ░ I R I S
R ░ A ░ I D O L ░ T
D E P O T ░ ░ L A D Y
```

303

```
A ░ R ░ G E N T I A N
C R E E L ░ ░ H ░ S
A ░ C ░ O P P R E S S
C O I L S ░ ░ I ░ I
I ░ P A S T E L ░ S
░ E ░ D E C R E E ░ O
░ F ░ M ░ ░ E D G A R
C E D I L L A ░ E ░ S
░ C ░ N ░ ░ C H A S E
S T R E T C H ░ N ░ T
```

304

```
░ P R O S E C U T E ░
E ░ O ░ T ░ L ░ H ░ S
M A O R I ░ A R O M A
B ░ M ░ L E I ░ R ░ F
R H Y M E ░ M I N C E
A ░ U ░ ░ L ░ T ░ ░
S W A M P ░ Z L O T Y
U ░ B ░ L Y E ░ R ░ N
R I O J A ░ B A I Z E
E ░ D ░ N ░ R ░ E ░ T
░ G E N E R A L L Y ░
```

305

```
E I G H T ░ S T E A M
N ░ U ░ U ░ U ░ ░ A
C O S M O S ░ L A W S
A ░ C ░ H ░ I ░ ░ H
G R I M R E A P E R ░
E ░ F ░ U R I ░ P ░ Y
░ D I S B E L I E V E
N ░ A ░ T ░ E ░ ░ A
E D G Y ░ T E A S E R
A ░ S ░ S ░ E ░ R ░ L
T H R O W ░ M C C O Y
```

306

```
R O O M ░ ░ D R A M A
I ░ ░ ░ I D L E ░ D ░ M
D I S C ░ ░ T ░ V I A
G ░ P A S S A G E ░ Z
E W E ░ C ░ I ░ R O E
░ ░ E N A B L E S ░
B A D ░ V ░ E ░ A U K
R ░ B R E E D E R ░ N
E G O ░ N ░ ░ S Y N E
A ░ A ░ G R I P ░ ░ E
M E T R E ░ ░ Y A W L
```

307

```
R A P I D ░ U S H E R
E ░ N ░ F ░ T ░ ░ U
L O A F ░ R A I S I N
I ░ H E R E ░ N ░ ░ S
V E E R ░ E I G H T ░
E ░ A ░ P ░ ░ O ░ P
░ A D D E R ░ S O F A
P ░ R ░ E A C H ░ T
A N T I C S ░ O A T H
S ░ F ░ S ░ O ░ ░ O
S M I T H ░ S P U D S
```

308

```
C L O C K ░ W A S P S
H ░ O ░ ░ O ░ A ░ P ░ E
I N A N E ░ S T A L E
E ░ C ░ T ░ E ░ ░ R
F L U I D O U N C E S
░ I ░ E ░ K ░ T ░ K
P E A R L Y G A T E S
A ░ G ░ O ░ T ░ ░ H
R O G E R ░ L I B Y A
E ░ A ░ A ░ V ░ D
D O P E Y ░ B E L L Y
```

309

```
S T A L L S ░ T ░ B
C ░ C ░ O N E W A Y
R A T E ░ L ░ N ░ G
I ░ U ░ P O I N T E D
B O A ░ A ░ ░ I ░ L
E ░ L A W L E S S ░ J
░ G ░ T ░ L ░ A P E
B A P T I S M ░ L ░ R
░ V ░ A ░ T ░ F A N S
D E S I R E ░ ░ M ░ E
░ L ░ N ░ W A R I L Y
```

310

```
D R O L L ░ S O R T S
O ░ ░ I ░ I ░ H ░ E
R O O T S ░ R O O S T
I ░ T U B E ░ M ░ U
C A V E M A N ░ B O P
░ G ░ R ░ N ░ K ░ A
P A L ░ C A V A L R Y
O ░ I ░ O L I O ░ E
R U M B A ░ P L A Z A
E ░ I ░ C ░ I ░ S
D I T C H ░ U N L I T
```

311

```
D A U N T ░ I M A G E
E ░ A ░ M ░ U ░ ░ Y
F E E T ░ A S S U R E
E ░ Y A W S ░ I ░ S
C U R L ░ O S C A R
T ░ I ░ C ░ L ░ U
░ D E P T H ░ S P A N
A ░ R ░ I N C H ░ R
G E N I U S ░ O A H U
R ░ M ░ M ░ N ░ L
A B B E Y ░ J E T T Y
```

312

```
S T A R T ░ A ░ R ░ I
R ░ ░ H A N S A R D
P A G E A N T ░ W ░ L
I ░ F I N I S H ░ E
C L E F ░ O ░ P I E R
░ E V E R Y B O D Y ░
F R E T ░ A ░ R E E D
R ░ R E N N E T ░ L
U ░ E ░ A C R Y L I C
I N S U R E S ░ ░ D
T ░ T ░ K ░ T U L S A
```

313

```
V E I N ■ S T R I P E
I ■ A N T ■ ■ ■ ■ L ■
C H I C ■ Y E O M A N
T ■ H ■ ■ R ■ Y ■ ■
I M P O S S I B L E ■
M A R ■ ■ A ■ ■ E R E
■ L O N E L I N E S S
■ A ■ U ■ ■ O ■ ■ T
V I E N N A ■ T R U E
■ S ■ ■ S H E ■ ■ E ■
K E E P U P ■ D R U M
```

314

```
T O X I C ■ B E F O G
■ B ■ C ■ R ■ I ■ U
R I L E ■ S E S A M E
E ■ ■ B E N D ■ N ■ R
P E S O ■ O ■ S C A R
U ■ C A P R I C E ■ I
T R O T ■ K ■ H E A L
A ■ U ■ M E M O ■ L
B U R I A L ■ L A V A
L ■ G ■ N ■ A ■ I
E L E G Y ■ G R E E T
```

315

```
F L O C K ■ B U S E S
■ I ■ H ■ W ■ ■ P ■ O
C E D E ■ A N K A R A
A ■ ■ D O T ■ N ■ P
R A I D ■ E ■ S I L O
B ■ N A R R A T E ■ P
U S S R ■ P ■ A L O E
N ■ U ■ O H M ■ ■ R
C A R N A L ■ I D E A
L ■ E ■ O ■ N ■ B
E A R L Y ■ L A M B S
```

316

```
A M P L E ■ B R A C E
N ■ I ■ B ■ U ■ O
N ■ E O R B S ■ L
A R S O N ■ ■ S H O E
L ■ ■ Y O K E ■ U
S C O T ■ U ■ T O R E
■ H ■ A I R S ■ ■ N
M O A T ■ ■ L I V I D
O ■ T O F U ■ I ■ U
S ■ L ■ ■ S ■ E ■ R
J E R E Z ■ H A W S E
```

317

```
C A C H O U ■ B ■ D
O ■ O ■ ■ S W E D E N
S C R A P E ■ S ■ L
M ■ P ■ A R B I T E R
I ■ S ■ D ■ D ■ T
C H E S S ■ B E S E T
■ E ■ P ■ E ■ A ■ I
V A L A N C E ■ L ■ M
■ D ■ R ■ U N R I P E
B O W S E R ■ N ■ L
■ N ■ E ■ B R E E Z Y
```

318

```
S P R A Y ■ E D I C T
T ■ C ■ I ■ E ■ ■ I
R O T T E N ■ N A V E
O ■ I ■ T I E ■ ■ R
L A N D ■ E L B O W
L ■ G ■ I N K ■ V ■ B
■ D E S K S ■ F E T A
G ■ L E I ■ ■ R ■ K
N A Z I ■ V I R T U E
A ■ C ■ E ■ O ■ R
W A D E D ■ E D I F Y
```

319

```
B E H A L F ■ G A I T
A ■ I ■ I O T A ■ ■ I
B ■ L Y N X ■ S L O T
A P T ■ G ■ L ■ E ■ L
■ L ■ R E L I A N C E
S O N ■ R ■ K ■ S O D
E Y E L I N E R ■ D
P ■ E ■ E ■ W ■ S A N
S O D A ■ P I C A ■ E
I ■ ■ L I E S ■ T ■ W
S W A B ■ R E C E S S
```

320

```
M O O N S ■ O X B O W
E ■ O ■ ■ P ■ I ■ E
S T O O D ■ T R O T S
O ■ ■ S U D S ■ M ■ T
P ■ G E A R ■ M A R C
O ■ O ■ L A G ■ S ■ O
T A U T ■ M E S S ■ U
A ■ L ■ S A N E ■ N
M E A N T ■ E R E C T
I ■ S ■ U ■ U ■ R
A S H E N ■ I M P L Y
```

321

```
H O B B Y ■ C H E E K
A ■ L ■ A ■ C ■ N
I N D I A ■ S T O K E
T ■ A N G L E ■ N ■ A
I N L I E U ■ L O U D
■ ■ A ■ ■ N ■ M
T H I N ■ G A R I S H
H ■ L ■ A S P I C ■ E
O P A L S ■ T Y S O N
N ■ M ■ H ■ ■ A ■ R
G R A V Y ■ P L I N Y
```

322

```
S T A I N ■ L A S E R
A ■ N ■ D E E P ■ E
L A T H E ■ K O A L A
V ■ E ■ U ■ L ■ D
O P P R O B R I O U S
■ I ■ I ■ O ■ A ■ R
R E S T R A I N I N G
O ■ A ■ T ■ H ■ ■ R
U P E N D ■ P A N D A
T ■ A C I D ■ R ■ V
E R R E D ■ S P U M E
```

323

```
B R A S S ■ H E D G E
E ■ M ■ A G O ■ I ■ L
A P P A L ■ M ■ S E E
S ■ R E N O ■ D ■ C
T I C K S ■ S H A F T
■ ■ O ■ P ■ A ■ I
A B A S E ■ P A N E L
N ■ L ■ R A I N ■ Y
N U T ■ S ■ E N N U I
U ■ I ■ O W N ■ O ■ N
L A T I N ■ S P R I G
```

324

```
S ■ T ■ B ■ S P O U T
P I A N O L A ■ G ■ O
A ■ X ■ W ■ S ■ R ■ W
S W I S S C H E E S E
M ■ ■ ■ A ■ ■ S ■ R
■ W E A R I N E S S ■
A ■ N ■ ■ R ■ ■ ■ S
G O L D E N S Y R U P
A ■ A ■ X ■ A ■ A ■ O
P ■ C ■ I N C I S O R
E R E C T ■ K ■ H ■ E
```

SOLUTIONS

325

```
B L O W S . P A U S E
I . V . K . U . . H
A . E D I T O R I A L
S I N . . A . E . L
E . . M A N G O . . O
D U N E . K . L U M P
. N . S P A R E . . A
. T . S . R . . Z I P
G R E A T D A N E . A
. U . G . . P . R . C
N E V E R . E P O X Y
```

326
```
P . B . R U B B I S H
A G I L E . . O . H
N . L . C A N N E R Y
G U I T A R . D . E
A . O . P R E S I D E
E . U . . A . M . G
A B S C O N D . A . O
. E . L . G A D G E T
B R O A D E N . E . I
. T . W . . C A R D S
T H I S T L E . Y . M
```

327
```
C A M P U S . . L . R
U . . O . O N L I N E
R A N S O M . . G . A
V . . E . E T C H E D
E X T R A . O . T . Y
. . E S P O U S E . .
A . A . E . T A N G O
D E L U X E . H . . V
A . E . . L E A G U E
G R A H A M . R . . N
E . F . S T A T U S
```

328

```
G E N I U S . G . H
R . C . A N Y O N E
A L L Y . F . N . N
S . Y . V E S P E R S
S I E G E . A . A
. D . N I B . . C
. L . U . L O W E R
S E C R E T E . O . E
C . A . O . S O U L
O D I O U S . U . A
T . N . S I M P L Y
```

329
```
L U C I D . S T O C K
A . H . R . E . A
T R A G I C . T A N S
H . I . P U M A . N
E G R E S S . N E A T
R . T . T . U . E
S A M E . O Y S T E R
. R . R E D O . A . S
S I G N . Y U P P I E
. S . A . R . E . L
D E A L S . S U R L Y
```

330

```
F L O S S . P L A I N
O . A . W . A . P . U
A R T L E S S . O R T
L . . P . T . S . T
S I G H T . E N T R Y
. . A . . . L
C U B I C . S P E N D
A . R . H . E . . U
S R I . O T T O M A N
K . E . K . U . A . C
S O L V E . P R O B E
```

331

```
P E R C H . P A S T E
R . A . O . E . T . N
I N D E P E N D E N T
C . A . E . C . E . R
E A R S . B E T R A Y
. S . E . E . E . S
P H R A S E . A S K S
L . I . H . A . P . T
A P P R O X I M A T E
N . E . E . M . I . M
K I N D S . S I N G S
```

332

```
W R A T H . S E P I A
H . R O P E . L . N
I N S I D E T R A C K
L . L . R . . T . L
E X I L E S . M E T E
. M . E . A
D E A D . C A S U A L
O . G . U . E . . O
S P I R I T L E V E L
E . N . R E E K . . L
S L E E K . U S U R Y
```

333

```
M O T L E Y . D U M P
I . A . R . E . . O
N A R R O W . I R A N
U . A . S E D G E . D
T A N K . L A N C E
E . T . P L Y . T . A
. M U C U S . C A N S
B . L A B E L . N . P
E L A N . T O N G U E
A . O . . A . L . C
D E A N . I N S E C T
```

334
```
S A I N T . R . P U G
O . L . I R A T E . L
V O L G A . L . N . U
I . U . R . L O U S E
E C S T A S Y . L
T . I . A . . T . S
. O . V E S T I G E
B O N G O . P . M . N
A . I . I . A L A M O
C . S A L A D . T . R
H A T . E . E N E M A
```

335
```
S E L D O M . . N . F
P . O . A C C E D E
A L B U M S . . S . A
D . S . K N I T . S
E M B E D . E . E A T
. I . O V A . G
H U T . O . R I G H T
A . T U R K . N . A
R . E . H U N T E R
S E R B I A . E . D
H . N . N O R W A Y
```

336

```
C O M P E L . . E . E
O . . A . A M U S E S
Y E O M A N . . C . S
P . P . D E F A C E
U P S E T . O . P . X
. . T R O U N C E
B . E . G . S L E E P
A V A T A R . A . . A
D . L . . A D R O I T
L I T M U S . E . . E
Y . H . P O T I O N
```

SOLUTIONS

337

338

339

340

341

342

343

344

345

346

347

348

SOLUTIONS

349

```
P R I S E . N E W E R
I . T . E . A . U
L O G O . C A C T U S
L . L O W . R . E . T
S C A L E . M A R R Y
. . D . A L I . F
S L I N K . S T O N Y
H . A . N . S A W . A
O U T L E T . S L U R
O . O . S . . T . N
T Y R E S . P E E R S
```

350

```
D E B U T . W I D O W
A . A . E . H . I . O
R E T R A C E . G A B
E . . S . L . U . B
S U I T E . P A P A L
S . . A . . S . . E
A D A P T . T H R O B
L . P . E . O . . O
A G A . A M N E S I A
R . R . C . I . E . R
M A T C H . C R E E D
```

351

```
O K A P I . D O U B T
R . . . B O O . P . E
C O R G I . S . P U P
. . N . S H A D E . E
K I L N . . . G O R S E
. O . O G L E S . H
K N A V E . . S N A P
E . R A N C H . . P
R A G . I . A S P E N
B . U . A Y R . . I
S W E L L . E N R O L
```

352

```
S . H A P H A Z A R D
W . O . I . L . C
E X U D E . A B O U T
E . S . C U R . R . E
T H E S E . M I N U S
P . . U . . C . . T
E T H E R . H Y E N A
A . O . A X E . D . M
S P U R N . A L I V E
. . R . G . V . T . N
T A S T E L E S S . T
```

353

```
G U A R D . C H A M P
L . F . R . H . B . I
E X T R E M E . A R E
A . . A . A L . C
M O D E M . P R O N E
. . R . . . N
V Y I N G . B L E A K
E . F . A . L . . N
N E T . M A E S T R O
O . E . U . N . O . W
M E R I T . D E M O N
```

354

```
P O P P Y . P L U M B
A . R . . A . Z . O
N A T O . T R Y I N G
T . V . I . A . . I
S A V I N G G R A C E
. I . D . H . D . A
A D V E R T I S I N G
C . N . E . T . . E
C O T T O N . I C O N
R . O . U . . C . R
A B O R T . S K I V E
```

355

```
M . W H E T S T O N E
E . I . A . E . V
L A N D S . L O A D S
O . C . E E L . R . P
D W E L L . S T Y L E
R . E . . . O . . A
A N V I L . L O W E R
M . A . I R A . R . H
A T L A S . S P A T E
. U . L . S . C . A
P I E C E W O R K . D
```

356

```
A S S . Z A M B E Z I
D . A . A . E . . C
H . L E G I S L A T E
O D E . R . C . U
C O S S E T . H A R D
. T . O B E S E . E
W A L L . A N S W E R
. R . V . I . A N I
A D H E S I V E S . S
I . N . E . T . K
M E N T H O L . E L Y
```

357

```
D I S U S E . T . G
A . Y . . C R A V A T
M U L L A H . X . Z
A . L . L O G I C A L
S T A R K . O . O . O
C . B . A . A . E . O
U . U . L . T A R T S
S U B S I D E . C . E
. F . T . R E G I M E
B O D I C E . . O . N
. S . R . W A R N E D
```

358

```
S P L I T . A F I R E
T . E . R . . A C H E
A . T . U M P T E E N
N O T E S . . T . A
D . E . T O K E N . D
B I R D . U . N A P E
Y . S O R R Y . M . A
. Z . T . . O R I O N
L O C A T E D . B . E
S N A G . . E . I . R
D E T E R . L O A M Y
```

359

```
F I E L D . C A R A T
E . C . I . L . A . A
D I O R A M A . M O B
U . . N . S . P . B
P A S T A . S O A P Y
. . . T . . . G
P L A I T . D R E G S
U . M . R . A . . O
P S I . A N T O N Y M
I . N . I . E . E . M
L E A N T . D O D G E
```

360

```
G I V E U P . A F R O
R . O . N . . F . N
I . T H E R E F O R E
E V E . V . A . A . A
G A R D E N . I F F Y
. L . E N T E R . F
B O S S . H A S S L E
. U . C . . G . Y E T
I R R E G U L A R . U
V . N . . E . I . D
Y U R T . E S C A P E
```

361

```
A L E R T ■ P U R S E
Z ■ S ■ R ■ R ■ E ■ L
T E Q U I L A ■ P R O
E ■ ■ P ■ W ■ L ■ P ■
C E A S E ■ N A I V E
■ B ■ ■ ■ ■ ■ C ■ ■ ■
C R A P S ■ B R A S S
O ■ N ■ T ■ E ■ ■ H ■
C U D ■ A C A D E M Y
K ■ O ■ T ■ C ■ S ■ L
S I N G E ■ H A P P Y
```

362

```
S H R U B ■ B I D E T
H ■ E ■ E A U ■ U ■ O
E ■ A ■ N ■ E ■ M A N
I M P R E G N A B L E
K ■ S ■ F ■ O ■ O E R
■ S ■ K I O S K ■ S ■
O W E ■ C ■ A ■ D ■ G
P O N T I F I C A T E
E T A ■ A ■ R ■ C ■ N
R ■ C ■ R Y E ■ C ■ I
A P T L Y ■ S N A K E
```

363

```
F I A S C O ■ ■ B ■ B
L ■ ■ H ■ P A G O D A
I M B I B E ■ ■ N ■ B
E ■ E N U N C I A T E
S T A Y S ■ L ■ P ■ L
■ ■ ■ N ■ T A U ■ A ■
V ■ S ■ L ■ M I R T H
O N T H E S P O T ■ O
C ■ A ■ ■ A S W E L L
A I L I N G ■ A ■ ■ E
L ■ K ■ A R N O L D
```

364

```
L A C K S ■ S ■ S E W
A ■ A ■ N E H R U ■ A
B U R M A ■ E ■ E ■ R
E ■ U ■ I ■ D I Z Z Y
L I S T L E S S ■ I ■
S T O A ■ K ■ L U N G
■ E ■ C R E D E N C E
S M O K E ■ O ■ W ■ Y
H ■ I ■ P ■ W A R D S
O ■ L E A V E ■ A ■ E
W H Y ■ Y ■ L E P E R
```

365

```
P E C A N ■ P R E S S
S ■ ■ S ■ R ■ L ■ O
A C E S ■ F A C I A L
L ■ V ■ W ■ C ■ M ■ I
M I A M I ■ T H I R D
■ ■ P O R T I O N ■ ■
G R O P E ■ S P A R K
L ■ R ■ L ■ E ■ T ■ R
A B A T E S ■ L E V I
R ■ T ■ S ■ I ■ I ■ L
E V E N S ■ I D Y L L
```

366

```
T A K E N ■ S M I T H
U ■ ■ N ■ W ■ N ■ A
N E S T ■ B A N N E R
E ■ E R A ■ S ■ O ■ M
R A N E E ■ T I C K S
■ ■ S A R D I N E ■ ■
D U E T O ■ K E N Y A
R ■ L ■ B ■ A R C ■ G
A L E X I S ■ T E A R
W ■ S ■ C ■ I ■ ■ E
L A S T S ■ H A L V E
```

367

```
D R A G S ■ G O A L S
E ■ R I P E ■ I ■ Y
A L L I N ■ M U R A L
T ■ T ■ P ■ S ■ P
H O R S E R A D I S H
■ ■ H ■ L A Y ■ C ■
S T I F F N E C K E D
T ■ Z ■ K ■ H ■ U
E P O C H ■ C O I N S
M ■ M ■ O N U S ■ T
S C E N T ■ B E R R Y
```

368

```
U ■ C O R K S C R E W
N ■ H ■ U ■ P ■ U
S T E M S ■ A D M I T
C ■ W ■ T A N ■ B ■ R
A S S A Y ■ K H A K I
T ■ D ■ ■ ■ I ■ M
H A V O C ■ S T A T E
E ■ E ■ O F T ■ L ■ S
D J I N N ■ O W L E T
■ N ■ G ■ R ■ E ■ E
D I S C O V E R Y ■ R
```

369

```
S T O R Y ■ S Y R U P
■ E ■ E ■ A ■ I ■ A
S E N T ■ P U R S E R
I ■ ■ R A P ■ O ■ C
C A P E ■ L ■ I T C H
K ■ R A D I A N T ■ M
L O O T ■ A ■ S O L E
E ■ P ■ N U T ■ ■ N
A T O M I C ■ A B E T
V ■ S ■ E ■ L ■ V
E J E C T ■ B L E A T
```

370

```
A T T I C ■ C R U E T
S ■ I ■ A ■ E ■ C
I ■ N ■ P I T F A L L
M O N K S ■ L ■ A
O ■ E ■ I S L E ■ I
V A D U Z ■ E X T R A
■ G ■ M E L T ■ I ■ B
■ E ■ P ■ D E M U R
I N V I T R O ■ I ■ U
■ D ■ R ■ W ■ N ■ P
C A M E L ■ N I G H T
```

371

```
M A S S E S ■ C ■ V
A ■ U ■ P I R A T E
G U L F W A R ■ T ■ R
I ■ F ■ M O D E R N
C A N E D ■ N ■ R ■ E
■ O R I F I C E ■ ■
J ■ S ■ S ■ C U R I O
E Y E F U L ■ P ■ M
L ■ G ■ S E G O V I A
L E A V E S ■ L ■ N
Y ■ Y ■ S C A M P I
```

372

```
B I S H O P ■ K ■ F
O ■ O ■ I C I C L E
T H U D ■ T ■ N ■ A
T ■ N ■ N A U G H T Y
O D D ■ A ■ L ■ T
M O S Q U I T O N E T
■ L ■ R ■ R ■ E R R
S P A T U L A ■ G ■ A
■ H ■ Y ■ I ■ W A R D
M I R R O R ■ ■ T ■ E
■ N ■ E ■ A P P E A R
```

SOLUTIONS

373
```
S T U M P . D E F E R
C . A . A . O . . A .
O I L S . V A L U E D
F . E A G E R . R . O
F R A I L . R E S I N
. F . A L E . C . . .
H E M I N . S T O O P
O . O . C A T E R . I
A B U S E R . M E A T
R . L . K . P . . . H
D A D D Y . L O B B Y
```

374
```
G U S T A V . B . F .
A . U . . E M E T I C
S T R I C T . L . N .
P . M . H O S T E S S
E C O L I . I . S . E
D . U . L A M . C . A
A . N . L . P R O O F
L A T R I N E . R . A
. L . U . O R A T O R
P E A N U T . E . E .
. E . S . E V A D E R
```

375
```
S H A C K S . H . S .
Y . I . . A N I M A L
L A R D . G . F . R .
L . L . S O L I C I T
A D I E U . U . O . H
B . N . S A P . I . I
U . E . H . I O N I C
S E S S I O N . C . K
. D . C . V . W I N S
M A N A N A . D . E .
. M . B . L O W E S T
```

376
```
A F O O T . B U R N S
R . N . S . N . . . T
M . W E S T . M A Z E
A S H . . A . A . . P
D . E S T R A N G E .
A . R . G . U . . . K
. M E S S A G E S . I
M . I . Z . H E R . S
A R I D . E A S Y . S
S . L . R . K . . . C
S N E E R . M Y R R H
```

377
```
. A B I L I T I E S .
N . R . I . R . A . I
U S I N G . A T T I C
I . D . H E M . E . E
S L E P T . P A N I C
A . A . I . L . R . R
N E S T S . G L O V E
C . T . T R Y . N . A
E R A S E . P R I S M
S . G . L . S . O . S
. R E M E D Y I N G .
```

378
```
S I C K P A Y . C . C
U . R . A . A T O L L
G A U N T . R . M . O
A . M . O D D M E N T
R A B B I . E . . . H
. S U S P E N D . . .
C . . L . . . N U R S E
U S E L E S S . Y . G
R . S . D . I C I E R
I R A Q I . G . N . E
E . U . T O N I G H T
```

379
```
C H E C K . A N G E L
O . H . P . H . . . O
M O R A L . P . O F F
I . I . T O Y S . T .
C H I N A . I . T R Y
. O . D E N . U . . .
S P Y . V . T H I N G
C . I D E A . E . A .
E Y E . R . B A C K S
N . L . B . . L . E .
T I D E S . A S H E S
```

380
```
L A S S . . S C A R E
E . . I N C H . A . .
T H U S . A Y E A Y E
T . A . V . . O . . .
E V A L U A T I O N .
R . W . L . R . N . N
. B L U E C H E E S E
. R . . A . L . . . T
V A R I E D . B U S T
V . . . N E R O . . L
P O U N D . . W A G E
```

381
```
C R E A M . O V O I D
O . M . O A F . I . I
M A C R O . F E L O N
E . E . R U E . E . A
T R E S S . R I D E R
. Y . O . . . O . A .
D E B U G . A N G R Y
R . U . R O W . R . E
A O R T A . A G O R A
F . M . P H I . A . T
T R A C E . T U N E S
```

382
```
C H A R M . S C U R F
A . N . U . R . A . A
L . N . S C R A W N Y
L A U R E L . Z . G .
U . L . S E C E D E .
P I A F . A . D A R E
. G R E E N S . R . I
. U . T . S C U L P T
P A R T N E R . I . H
. N . E . E . N . E .
B A R R Y . E D G A R
```

383
```
M I T E S . I G L O O
O . S . U . R . . . G
R O U G E . R E C U R
T . N . T R E E . . E
A F A R . A N N E X .
R . M . A I D . M . E
. T I L L S . H O O T
B . O M E N . T . H .
R O A D S . A L I B I
A . G . I . O . C .
N A K E D . L I N K S
```

384
```
. P O S S E S S E D .
M . A . T . . M . F .
A R R A I G N . B E E
R . . F . . U . R . U
S E R I F . P L A I D
U . E . . . . . C . A
P A G E R . S H E L L
I . R . E . I . . . I
A T E . N E M E S I S
L . S . A . O . I . M
. E S P L A N A D E .
```

SOLUTIONS

385

386

387

388

389

390

391

392

393

394

395

396

SOLUTIONS

397

```
L I N K S . . A M P S
E . E . A P E S . . T
G . R . I . . B E A R
S H O E L A C E . . U
. E . M . R . S M U T
. R . P A I N T . G .
L O C H . E . O . L .
E . . A S S A S S I N
T E E S . . J . O . A
U . . I O W A . N . M
P L U S . . R O G U E
```

398

```
P L A N T . T R A D E
E . C . H . O . E . .
E I T H E R . S I C K
L . O . M A D E . A .
S T R E E T . H E M P
W . Y . T . I . P . .
C O L E . R E P O S E
. S . S W A N . F . W
T O G O . P E S T L E
. M . R . . M . E . R
S E W E D . Y A N K S
```

399

```
L A C T I C . D . H .
E . O . . O C E L O T
G O B A C K . N . R .
A . W . O E D I P U S
C R E A M . . Z . S .
Y . B R A C K E T . A
. G . A . . I N O F F
A I M L E S S . M . F
. V . S . P S Y C H O
P E S E T A . . A . R
. N . A . R E S T E D
```

400

```
S O U P . O R D E A L
I . . A L P . . . U .
M A L I . T A K I N G
I . N . . . O . T .
L O W S P I R I T S
E . E . M . . E . W
. G E T U P A N D G O
. R . O . . Y . R
B I C E P S . L A S S
M . . . A D O . . E
B E H E A D . N O O N
```

401

```
S U S A N . D A R T S
H . I . O . R . H
R . L I B R A R I A N
A T O N E . O . N
N . S L I N G . K
K I W I . N . A L S O
. N . N I N O N . W
. D . C . O C E A N
L I F E S I Z E D . E
. G . R . E . G . R
J O K E R . D E E D S
```

402

```
B I O P S Y . D . M
A . . O . A S H O R E
L E E K . W . V . E
S P U R T . U . U
. U . B Y E . M
. R . A . D E P O T
T E D D Y B E A R . R
O . E . L . T Y P E
N E E D L E . E . A
S . M . W A N T E D
```

403

```
O R A N G E . S A I D
A . I . R . U . . O
T . S T E R I L I S E
H A L . A . P . H
S I E S T A . H O R N
. R . M . I . U . I
A B L E . M A R I N A
. A . A . G . N E W
A G G R E G A T E . A
D . E . . I . P . R
D Y E D . U N I T E D
```

404

```
K E N N E L . R . S
E . E . I M M U N E
B E T A . M . S . V
A . R . B O T T L E
B R I E F . R . L . N
. C R E M A T E
R . E . E . L A R C H
A C R O S S . I . I
L . I . H . L O A N
P O N C H O . O . G
H . K . P U R P L E
```

405

```
D I S A P P E A R . P
. . T . U . R . E . R
S C E N T . U N I T E
U . M . T A P . N . S
R U S T Y . T A S T E
P . H . . G . N
R E S E T . F E A S T
I . E . A D O . R . L
S L E D S . R U G B Y
E . K . E . G . U
D . S E R I O U S L Y
```

406

```
M U S S E L . C . T
A . . T . A P I A R Y
M O J O . K . P . P
B . E L S E W H E R E
A Z T E C . R . V . D
. S . R H O . E
P . T . E . T A R O T
A R R O W H E A D . E
N . E . . E . R E A R
D I A D E M . O . S
A . M . S U N D A E
```

407

```
. D E P O S I T E D
C . N . C . M . G . F
L A D L E . P A G E R
O . U . A Y E . O . E
S K E I N . L A N C E
E . N . . G . . V
C R E S S . H E N C E
A . V . T E A . A . R
L E A K Y . B O O K S
L . N . L . I . M . E
. A S C E R T A I N
```

408

```
F A N O U T . . E . L
R . . N . H E R N I A
A R R I V E . . C . Y
U . E C O M M E R C E
D U V E T . Y . Y . R
. . O . E . O . P
L . L . R . P E T A L
I N T E S T I N E . O
M . I . . W A R D E R
B O N S A I . O . R
S . G . G U L L E Y
```

SOLUTIONS

409

```
B A I T . S A C H E T
O . . A N T I . . V .
S C A B . Y O N D E R
N . L . . L . . N .
I M P E R V I O U S .
A . I . I . R . C .
. P E R C E P T I V E
. L . R . A . N .
C A L V E S . P A S S
. Z . P A R E . . U .
H A T R E D . R A Y S
```

410

```
S W I F T . B O A R D
T . L . . E . I . I
A L L A H . G A M M A
M . T . A . V . Z .
P L U T O C R A C Y .
. A . E . T . L . O
. C O R I O L A N U S
B . E . R . N . . P
A V E R T . O C C U R
R . N . E . H . . A
N U D G E . D E R B Y
```

411

```
B L I S S . B A S E D
L . . . . C A S E . U . E
A B R A C A D A B R A
N . . N . N . . J . L
D O T T E D . K E P T
. . U . . S . . C .
S A R K . T I L T E D
C . M . . O . O . . A
A B O M I N A T I O N
L . I . R E N T . . D
D E L T A . D O L L Y
```

412

```
. E S S E N T I A L .
M . C . A . R . N . S
A M O N G . I N G O T
T . L . E . A . L . R
E L D E R . D R O V E
R . . . . . . . . . S
N E C K S . J E S U S
I . O . I . U . A . I
T W A N G . N Y L O N
Y . T . M . T . V . G
. E S C A L A T O R .
```

413

```
A . B . A B A S H E D
B L E S S . P . M .
B . H . S C A R L E T
E X I L E . E . R .
S . N . T U N A . G
S I D E . P . D I E T
. T . A L S O . N . U
. H . R . U D D E R
F A S T I N G . I . K
. C . H . H E A V E
B A B Y S A T . N . Y
```

414

```
S A S S Y . Q U O I T
E . L . E . N . . R
T R I B A L . D Y K E
T . C A R E F R E E .
L I K I N G . E N D S
E . N . A . S . . C
R O A M . T U S S L E
. P L A T E L E T . N
J E E R . E N D I V E
N . I . A . N . R
A S S E S . R A T T Y
```

415

```
D R O N E . . A V O N
I . X . T A M P . E
G E C . . R U D E . D
S U N S H I N E . .
. G . A . N . S U D S
. L . S N U B S . O
S I G H . R . K . V
C . . C O N F I N E D
O U Z O . E . O . U
U . R A C E . V . K
R A I D . . S P A D E
```

416

```
B . J . C . O D I U M
U N A D O R N E D . A
L . G . P . U S E . N
L O U S Y . S C A R S
S L A T . . R . . E
. D R A I N P I P E .
O . G . . . B A R N
B A L E R . M E L E E
E . U S A . A . I . V
Y . D E F E R E N C E
S C O T T . E . G . R
```

417

```
C O V E R . J E A N S
O . X . S . M . . W
R E S T . T R A U M A
D . N O N E . I . M
O P A L . A L L E Y .
N . I . D . . T . O
. A L O O F . C H E F
D . B . A L O E . F
A T H E N S . B R A E
M . S . T . R . N
P U R E E . D A V I D
```

418

```
M U M P S . P I T T A
O . R O T E . U . S
U N I O N . W O R T H
L . M . A . N . E
D I S S O L U T I O N
. E . A . P .
S T A R C R O S S E D
C . L . M . K . I
A X I O M . P A U L A
L . O . A B E T . R
P E N N Y . N E E D Y
```

419

```
M E C C A . D O Z E N
A . O . P . V . L
N D . P O P E Y E D
T H E S E . R . V
E . T A M E D . E
L A G O S . N O U N S
N . C E N T S . E
Y . K . H E N N A
V O Y A G E R . A . A
N D . A . A . I
N E W E L . L I N E R
```

420

```
P R O N G . S P O R T
R . P . R E . A . O
E N T R A N T . T I N
S . P . U . M . N
S A B L E . P I E C E
. E . . . . . A
C H E S S . S A L E S
O . F . A . C . P
M E T . B O A R D E R
I . E . R . L . N . E
C E A S E . E R A S E
```

SOLUTIONS

421

```
T R A P S . I V O R Y
A . N . I . E . . E
R E I G N S . L A S T
T . S . S H E D . I
A B E D . U L T R A .
R . E . A T M . E . A
. A D A P T . C A M P
S . . I T E M . L . I
A G A R . R E F I N E
G . E . . A . S . C
A B O D E . L A T H E
```

422

```
S P O I L S . C . D
L . N . A L P A C A
A K I N . R . V . M
M . D E S I C C A T E
S P O R T . O . . O
. Y . . A I R . W .
. R . B . G L A N D
S E C E S S I O N . E
T . A . O . C Y A N
E G R E S S . A . S
T . D . O B L I G E
```

423

```
S E A R S . P H O T O
E . S . L . . E W E R
X . K . A L M A N A C
T W A I N . P . S
E . N . G R I E V E
T A C T . Y . D E L I
. L E A V E S . R . D
. P . L . U K A S E
L A T E R A L . N . A
I C O N . L . D . L
T A T T Y . Y E A R S
```

424

```
S C O O P . T E A C H
T . A . H . R . O
E U R A S I A . C R U
E . . S . N . H . S
D R A K E . K N I F E
. D . . . V
D U M P S . B R E W S
O . I . A . R . L
W A R . G R A N D M A
N . E . G . S . A . T
S T R A Y . H E D G E
```

425

```
F A I R . F A R O F F
I . A L I . L
S O O T . B A Z A A R
C . I . . O . T
A U T O N O M O U S
L . I . H . G . F
. S T E P M O T H E R
. H . W . E . I
C A M E R A . M A C E
V . . R I P . N
S E L D O M . T E N D
```

426

```
T R A M P . S P E L L
W . C . E . A . I
E X T E N D . P A N E
L . O . C I T Y . K
F O R C E S . R A S P
T . . O . H . U . I
H E A L . R A S C A L
. Q . L E A D . H . S
N U D E . G O V E R N
. A . G . P . A . E
U L C E R . T U T O R
```

427

```
S T O O L . W A F E R
H . F . L . O . E
A U N T I E . R I S E
B . A . M A T . D
B A S E . O K A P I
Y . A . R N A . I . A
. C L A U S . B O S S
B . L E O . U . S
O N T O . L A S S I E
A . N . E . P . S
T A L E S . B A R E S
```

428

```
. C A R T R I D G E
C . E . H . S . L . O
R O G E R . S H A F T
I . I . E M U . S . H
T A S T E . E N S U E
I . . O . . E . R
C O S T S . S T R E W
I . P . C O W . A . I
S P A C E . I N D U S
M . W . N . F . I . E
. I N F E C T I O N
```

429

```
T E A M S . J A D E D
U . O . U . O . U
S N A R L . S E L L S
K . P O S T . L . T
S A S H I M I . S P Y
. S N I F F
S H E . C L I E N T S
A . M . L E E R . U
T A B O O . D R A W N
I . E . T . E . N
N O R T H . I T C H Y
```

430

```
S H R U G . S H O O T
C . A . E . T . C . A
O R G A N Z A . A R T
U . U . N . R . T
T A R T S . D A I R Y
. U . . N
A L I A S . S H A W L
L . N . H . M . U
L E O . A D A P T O R
O . U . K . S . A . I
W A S T E . H U M I D
```

431

```
C H A R D . D U M B O
. I . A . P . O . V
S P E W . R E V I S E
Y . D U O . S . R
N O S E . L . A T O P
T . C A R O U S E . O
H A I L . N . S N O W
E . E . G N U . E
S E N A T E . A F A R
I . C . D . G . S
S M E L L . G E C K O
```

432

```
C R I S P . S P R E E
O . H . W . E . A
A I D E . B A K I N G
T . A . B . N . M . L
I G L O O . S A B L E
. A . N E O . U
C H I D E . N E R V E
A . L . L . G . S . P
R E A P E R . P E R E
E . M . S . . E . E
T R A P S . B A I L S
```

433

```
I D I O T . B O G U S
D . . N . A . O . E
A U G E R . S E N S E
H . R . I T S . D . D
O R A N G E . P O N Y
. V . . P . L . .
G H E E . I O D I N E
L . Y . O D D . E . T
A B A C K . E A R T H
S . R . A . G . . O
S A D L Y . C A G E S
```

434
```
C E A S E . P O R C H
O . L . M . Y . O
W . C . B E R S E R K
S T A T E . T . T
L . Z . D R Y E Y E D
I M A M . Y . R A Z E
P A R A P E T . O . S
N . N . . H A U N T
B A P T I S E . N . I
N . L . M . D . N
L A Y E R . E L E G Y
```

435

```
S A L T . B U S B Y
C . . I S L E . T . O
U S S R . L . A . K
B . P E S T I C I D E
A C E . P . T . R . L
. C H A O T I C .
S . I . C . L . A I L
A W A R E N E S S . A
L . L . M . H E I R
A . L . E C H O . G
D O Y E N . T A K E
```

436

```
K I T T Y . S C A M P
A . O . T . S . U
P A V E . B A N T E R
O . E C U . R . R . G
K O R A N . S C O N E
. S P E C I A L .
L H A S A . G N A R L
I . T . R . N A B . O
S K I N N Y . S E L F
T . L . E . T . T
S P E E D . D A I L Y
```

437

```
F O R E S T . B . S
A . N . U R G E N T
N A I R O B I . T . U
G . A . A C E T I C
S N A G S . H . I . K
. B E T W E E N .
M . Y . A . S U G A R
A B S U R D . R . U
R . M . V E T E R A N
G O A T E E . K . I
E . L . D E A C O N
```

438

```
C O S H . S A F E T Y
O . . U Z I . . H
P A L M . P A T R O N
Y . . U . A . R
C O N S I D E R I N G
A . O . R . N . O
T I D D L Y W I N K S
. D . E . N . L
K I D N A P . L E V I N
. O . . E V E . N
A M A Z O N . T A N G
```

439
```
S H A D E S . W . C
O . R . A B A C U S
L A C E . S . I . M
U . H . C H A S S I S
T R I A L . S T U N T
I . V . I F S . I . A
O C E A N . A L T A R
N O S E G A Y . C . T
. L . S . F . B A K E
D E V O U R . S . R
. Y . P . O B S E S S
```

440
```
B . S U P E R H E R O
R U E . I . X . H
O . R . T A P I O C A
T H E A T R E . C . R
H . V E T . E . E
. P R E D I C A T E
C . A . S E T . B
H . N . C A D E N Z A
A F G H A N I . O . B
T . E . N . N . R Y E
S T R A T A G E M . L
```

441
```
S I X T H . B A K E S
E . H . P . B . T
R E C A L L . B I L E
A V O W . U . O . P
P E R S E C U T O R
H . G . K . N . P
. D I S M I S S I V E
P . I . E . T O I L
R O P E . S P I N A L
O . G . T . L . E
P I P E R . A L E R T
```

442

```
S M E L T . B L O G S
P . O . B . E . L
L I T T E R . A R I A
A . I . O A T . Y
S I L D . A . H O D
H . D E A D S E A . S
. C E P . C . R S V P
H . L E A . I . O
A B L E . S E A S O N
R . T . T . S . G
T O W E L . S H A R E
```

443
```
F A R M S T E A D . B
. A . E . X . E . A
A M B E R . I D L E R
E . B . G A S . F . T
R A I S E . T I T H E
O . O . . K . R
S T A L L . V E R D I
P . B . A L I . O . N
A S Y E T . S T U N G
C . S . I . O . N
E . M A N F R I D A Y
```

444

```
B A N A L . B A S I L
E . . G . A . A . O
S I T E S . N A D I R
T . N U T . . N . D
S I S T E R . F E E S
E . U . T A D . S . P
L A R D . C E N S O R
L . G . . T E E . A
E V E R Y . R I S K Y
R . O . E . . G . E
S I N E W . C H A I R
```

SOLUTIONS

445

```
G A S P . B I C E P S
R . . L E E . . . . R
A L G A . T R A V E L
P . N . . X . C . . .
P A R T Y P I E C E .
A L E . . A . . A D D
. A D M I N I S T E R
. M . E . N . . . . E
B O T T L E . A B E D
D . . . A R C . . . G
B E A K E R . K A L E
```

446

```
H . S E A S O N I N G
A . E . T . R . N . .
R E T R O . B R A I D
V . T E N S I O N . I
E L O P E . T E E N S
S . . L . . D . . H .
T A L E S . R E C T O
E . A T E L I E R . N
D O P E D . D R A P E
. E . G . G . N . S .
G O L D E N E Y E . T
```

447

```
L E G O . . A D U L T
A . . B A R N . N . A
P U R L . . G . F . N
U . E A S T E R E G G
P E S T O . L . I . Y
. . . T E L L I N G .
A . R . V . C O N I C
S T A L E M A T E . L
T . I . N . . I D L Y
I . N . C H I C . . D
R E T R Y . . E A S E
```

448

```
C O M E T . V I R U S
O . S . I . R . . E .
R I B S . R O A D I E
R . R A N I . T . K .
A W A Y . S W E E T .
L . V . H . G . R . .
. N E G U S . O G L E
H . L . T Y P E . L .
A R C A D E . E D D Y
L . D . W . R . O . .
T A X E D . S A L O N
```

449

```
H A V O C . B A T H E
I . E . A . F . A . .
J . N . S C U F F L E
A N T E S . I . V . .
C . U . A V E R S E .
K I R O V . A M I S S
. R E P A I R . D . P
. R . E . S H E E R .
B U R N I S H . C . I
. P . E . O . A . T .
S T A R E . T O R T E
```

450

```
S I G H T . B A T C H
E . R . I . B . U . .
T R O O P S . A C R E
F . W . C A N O E . .
R E S I Z E . D O S S
E . N . N . O . E . .
E L S E . T U N D R A
. E E R I E . R . L .
P A N T . D E B A S E
. P . I . V . M . G .
U S U A L . A M A S S
```

451

```
S E T O F F . C . H .
M . U . U L T I M O .
A M E N D S . T . N .
L . C . S C R I B E .
L I V E S . O . Z . Y
. A S A R U L E . . .
F . G . K . P A N T S
A M U S E D . Z . L .
C . E . I G U A N A .
E C L A I R . L . I .
T . Y . T A I W A N .
```

452

```
G R A T E . S P I L T
I . R . H . N . I . .
R I T E . L A N C E T
T . A S P . M . O . A
H A R S H . B E G A N
. P . A I L . N . . .
F L A I R . E D I C T
L . U . M . S E T . R
O I L C A N . L O B E
S . I . C . T . A . .
S O N N Y . P A I N T
```

453

```
T H R E W . L I S Z T
U . L . P . T . O . .
F U S E . I N V E R T
T . E M O T E . V . A
S T R I P . S H E L L
. . E . P A T . D . .
T A N G O . L O O S E
U . G . S M E A R . N
B R E W E R . T E N T
E . T . S . H . E . .
R U I N S . A S T E R
```

454

```
B O A S T . C A R D S
. R . U . Y . E . T .
D E A R . B A F F L E
E . . R O A N . E . A
C I T E . S . P R I M
K . O A K T R E E . I
C U R L . I . R E A R
H . N . B O G S . O .
A M A Z O N . O M E N
I . D . B . . N . V .
R O O T S . E A G E R
```

455

```
G . A . M O R T I S E
R O M E O . O . T . .
O . O . S O L I C I T
C H U T E . L . G . .
E . N E S T L E . M .
R A T E . A . T S A R
. B . S E N T R Y . E
. R . H . E Y R I E .
H A L I F A X . I . K
. D . R . A B A S E .
L E T T E R S . N . D
```

456

```
M A G I C . U . R O B
U . . A M P L E . I .
S E E M S . S . C . R
T . S . T R E M O L O
E N T R E A T . N . .
R . I . B . . C . G .
. . M . M I D W I F E
B R A V A D O . L . N
I . B . R . G U E S T
D . L O C U M . . L .
S E E . H . A R G U E
```

457

```
P A R T Y . M A U L S
. N . R . C . S . . I
Z E R O . U . S A I L
. M . P A P U A . . K
C O C O . B . S P A Y
. N . S H O W S . C .
S E E P . A . I R A N
H . . H E R O N . D .
I D L E . D . A F E W
R . R . S . T . M . .
T A X E S . L E P E R
```

458
```
S Q U E A K . . C . L
E . D . I M P A L A . A
R U B I E S . . N . S
U . T . S L U D G E . R
M A S O N . A . I . R
. . C R E V I C E . .
P . O . O . R A D A R
A N O I N T . R . . A
P . T . H E A R T Y . O
A G E N D A . F . . O
L . R . . T I E S I N
```

459

```
J A C O B I . C H I N
A . O . O . O . . . O
M . M A R E S N E S T
E B B . N . Q . H . .
S Y S T E M . U N I T
. . G . S O U S E . N
B O T H . M A R V E L
. N . I . L . . O R E
T E R R I F I E D . A
A . . T . . N . K . V
B A T S . D E C A D E
```

460

```
A . B . P . S W E E P
D E R V I S H . M . O
E . I . A . U . I . L
P R E E N . T A R D Y
T . F R O . . L . . P
. I S O S C E L E S .
B . . D . . N O R . E
O F F E R . S T A I D
M . L . I . U . S . I
B . U . F O R F E I T
E L E C T . . E . R H
```

461

```
G A R . B R I T I S H
L . A . A . R . . . A
O . F O R E L I M B S
O T T . R . R . . R .
M A S T E R . E B O N
. . S . O D I U M . N
E S A U . B R E A C H
E . . R . S . . R O Y
P L A I N T I V E . E
U . . S . . N . A . N
S C U T T L E . S E A
```

462

```
T I G H T . . T R O D
O . U . A L T O . . R
P . A . C . A R E N A
S E N S I B L E . . I
. B O O T . C A P O N
. O . L . . D . W .
K N E E S . C O V E .
A . . C O L O R A D O
P A T I O . R . G . U
U . . S N A P . U . S
T E A M . . S H E E T
```

463

```
S T A F F . C O C O A
H . L . L E A . O . L
A S I D E . T R A W L
R U G . X . E . T . A
P A N N I E R . S A Y
. V . B . P . . L . .
L E G . I D I O T I C
A . U . L . L . O V A
K H A K I . L I K E N
E . V . T E A . E . D
S C A R Y . R U N N Y
```

464

```
S U B M I T . L . K .
P . R . . R E A S O N
O B O E . I . I . R .
R . O . S P E C I E S
A N K L E . D . R A P
D . L . R A G . R . E
I V Y . V . E L I D E
C O N F E S S . T . D
. C . U . O . G A P S
C A N N E D . . T . U
. L . D . A S L E E P
```

465
```
F E T I D . C H A F E
U . O . R U E . L . W
T E M P O . L . P O E
O . . A P S E . H . R
N E E D S . B E A N S
. K . R . . V . E . .
B E S E T . B A G E L
O . O . A C I D . . A
R A N . L . L E A R N
E . I . L A G . D . K
D E C A Y . E B O N Y
```

466
```
S U B U R B . A B L Y
H . L . E . N . . E .
O . I N V E R N E S S
O W N . I . U . T . .
K A I S E R . I B E X
. I . T W I S T . R .
A L G A . G E Y S E R
. E . T . C . I O U .
A D V E N T U R E . N
L . L . R . V . G .
L A C Y . R E C E S S
```

467
```
B A L S A M . F . L .
A . . O . E R R A T A
N U L L . S . R . B .
N . V . S E T T E E .
S E V E R . P . H . L
. . A S I N I N E . .
B . G . O . C A R A T
A E R A T E . U . I .
S . A . A . S P I T .
T E N N I S . E . L .
E . T . T R A N C E .
```

468

```
A B O U T . S A U C E
M . K . I R O N . . W
I . R A C E H O R S E
S T A B . T . M . . R
. I . A I R W A V E S
. L . T . L . L . R .
A L T E R E G O . . O
N . M . V . U R S A .
V I C E V E R S A . L
I . N I S I . K . A
L A T T E . D R E G S
```

SOLUTIONS

469

```
H A P P Y ■ B I P E D
■ D ■ A ■ D ■ A ■ ■ I
P O O R ■ R A B I E S
O ■ ■ A G O ■ S ■ ■ I
S A P S ■ M ■ C L A N
T ■ F O R E S E E ■ F
N O E L ■ D ■ L Y R E
A ■ N ■ ■ A C E ■ ■ C
T A N K E R ■ S P A T
A ■ I ■ Y ■ T ■ F ■ ■
L E G A L ■ P A S T A
```

470

```
C A T C H ■ Y ■ P O D
O ■ R ■ A L O H A ■ A
B R E W S ■ Y ■ T ■ I
W ■ S ■ T ■ O R R I S
E X P R E S S I O N ■
B R A E ■ U ■ O N T O
■ A S S U M P T I O N
C Y S T S ■ O ■ S ■ W
A ■ E ■ U ■ O U I J A
S ■ R U R A L ■ N ■ R
H I S ■ P ■ E D G E D
```

471

```
B L E E P ■ B ■ B A R
A ■ ■ L A C U N A ■ A
T E R M S ■ D ■ L ■ G
H ■ E ■ T ■ G R A C E
E M A N A T E ■ C ■ ■
R ■ R ■ ■ R ■ U ■ L ■
■ ■ R ■ U N A W A R E
S P A I N ■ L ■ V ■ ■
O ■ N ■ F ■ T R A Y S
L ■ G U I N E A ■ ■ ■
D Y E ■ T ■ R Y D E R
```

472

```
J ■ S ■ P ■ S W A M P
O B T R U D E ■ M ■ E
U ■ R ■ R ■ A P E ■ P
S P O D E ■ M O N E Y
T ■ B E E P ■ S ■ ■ S
■ C E A S E L E S S ■
B ■ ■ D ■ P O U T ■ B
A R M E D ■ O R A T E
B ■ O N E ■ S ■ V ■ R
E ■ D ■ C L E M E N T
S P E C K ■ N ■ S ■ H
```

473

```
S N O O P ■ C A M E O
W ■ P ■ A ■ O ■ A ■ D
A N T E N N A ■ S A D
T ■ ■ S ■ S ■ C ■ L ■
H U S K Y ■ T O A D Y
■ ■ H ■ ■ ■ ■ R ■ ■ ■
B L A D E ■ C L A P S
O ■ R ■ V ■ H ■ ■ E ■
N I P ■ O R I G A M I
U ■ E ■ K ■ P ■ N ■ Z
S I N G E ■ S T A G E
```

474

```
S O R R Y ■ F A T A L
P ■ A ■ E ■ L ■ W ■ U
E X P L A N A T I O N
A ■ I ■ R ■ M ■ S ■ G
R I D E ■ D E P T H S
■ C ■ Y ■ A ■ I ■ A ■
M E R E L Y ■ E A T S
E ■ I ■ O ■ W ■ W ■ H
A P P R O X I M A T E
N ■ E ■ P ■ N ■ R ■ D
T U N E S ■ S I D E S
```

475

```
M U S K E T ■ B ■ V ■
U ■ T ■ H A R R O W
S K O P J E ■ A ■ T ■
C ■ P ■ E N D U S E R
U R G E S ■ A N O D E
L ■ A ■ T A N ■ C ■ H
A P P L E ■ C H I L E
R E S E R V E ■ A ■ A
■ T ■ N ■ I S O B A R
A E R I A L ■ ■ L ■ S
■ R ■ N ■ E F F E T E
```

476

```
C A B L E ■ D E M O B
H ■ E ■ Y ■ A ■ E ■ ■
R U G G E D ■ G A L A
O ■ O ■ S E A L ■ K ■
M A N E ■ P R E Y S ■
E ■ I ■ G O T ■ A ■ P
■ G A P E S ■ B O D Y
A ■ A M I D ■ U ■ T ■
J O E Y ■ T R E N C H
A ■ E ■ A ■ D ■ O ■ ■
R O D E O ■ G L E A N
```

477

```
B I B L E ■ K E B A B
A ■ I ■ ■ O ■ A ■ ■ I
T ■ A I R P I S T O L
H I S S ■ O ■ P ■ ■ L
■ N ■ T I R E L E S S
■ C ■ H ■ T ■ I ■ O ■
C H A M P I O N ■ Y ■
L ■ U ■ C ■ T R A Y ■
A L M S H O U S E ■ A
W ■ A ■ A ■ ■ ■ L ■ L
S C R I M ■ T H Y M E
```

478

```
S P I R A L ■ U ■ C ■
A ■ ■ A ■ E A R N E R
C O N I F E R ■ A ■ U
K ■ S ■ S T A R ■ U M
S E P I A ■ E ■ M O B
■ E N D O R S E ■ ■ ■
B E L ■ V ■ Y O D E L
O ■ I R I S ■ N ■ ■ I
G ■ C ■ S U R N A M E
E L A T E D ■ E ■ ■ G
Y ■ N ■ S A T I R E ■
```

479

```
S C R I P T ■ B ■ F ■
U ■ I ■ ■ H I A T U S
C U B E ■ O ■ I ■ R ■
K ■ B ■ Q U A L I T Y
E D O ■ U ■ D ■ H ■ ■
R A N G E F I N D E R
■ Y ■ U ■ O ■ I R E ■
A B S C E S S ■ W ■ V
■ O ■ H ■ T ■ D A R E
D O N A T E ■ L ■ R ■
■ K ■ R ■ M A L I C E
```

480

```
D E S I S T ■ S E W S
O ■ U ■ C A S K ■ ■ O
N ■ C L E G ■ Y A W L
E L K ■ N ■ D ■ N ■ V
■ E ■ T A K E N O T E
W A S ■ R ■ L ■ N O D
O N E S I D E D ■ ■ M
M ■ A ■ O ■ G ■ L E D
B E T A ■ H A L O ■ E
A ■ L O O T ■ S ■ A ■
T A M P ■ T E A S E L
```

SOLUTIONS

481

```
B O W I E . P A L M S
R . T . L . A . T . .
A C R E S . E . T O E
N . M . V A S E . A .
D A I S I E S . R A M
. X . . T I E . . I .
S E W . A N S W E R S
T . O W L S . E . I .
O U R . I . C A N A L
R . S . C . V . K . .
M A T H S . B E A D S
```

482

```
S I N U S . I C I L Y
H . O . P . A . O . .
R . T . A R T D E C O
E N E M Y . U . K . .
D . P A S T I C H E .
S W A N . E . E A R L
. A D D E N D U M . U
. P . O . E S S E X .
P I L L I O N . T . U
. T . I . I . E . R .
F I E N D . M E R C Y
```

483

```
S E A M S . M . M E N
H . . . T R I T E . E
A G O R A . N . D . A
M . U . R . T R A C T
A R T L E S S . L . .
N . E . E . E . L . R
. . R . E X A M I N E
D E M U R . M . O . S
R . O . E . I O N I C
A . S A C K S . . . U
G O T . T . S E I N E
```

484

```
S P L I T . Y U C C A
T . S . O . I . R . U
R E D T A P E . A I D
U . . S . L . B . I .
M E R I T . D I S C O
. G . C . . D . O . .
M O S E S . S O G G Y
E . W . C . K . . A .
A B E . R O I S T E R
N . A . E . L . A . D
S U R G E . L O T U S
```

485

```
D A C H A . W O M A N
W . H . D . M . L . .
A C I D I C . I B I S
R . M . E A R N . B .
V A P O U R . O M I T
E . B . D . U . A . .
S O W S . I N S T E P
. U . C I A O . I . E
K N E E . C R A T E R
. C . N . T . A . E .
R E B E L . H O N E D
```

486

```
H A V A N A . T O G A
B . I . U . R . W . .
O . C A R T H O R S E
M O A . S . U . I . .
B O R D E R . B A L D
. D . I D E A L . I .
A L M S . P I E R C E
E . S . R . I A N . .
A S P E R S I O N . D
W . N . L . S . O . .
L U S T . W Y V E R N
```

487

```
T I B I A . A L D E R
I . A . B . E . . T .
N . R . Y A W S . H .
P O S T S . . S A I D
O . . S A F E . C . .
T A P S . W . N E S T
. V . I N N S . . H .
M A L L . . A I S L E
. T . A D A M . . N .
A . G . B . N . C . .
G R U E L . A D D L E
```

488

```
. C O M M I T T E E .
P . U . O . R . J . E
R E T R O . O V E R S
O . D . R . T . C . T
S H O E S . S A T Y R
E . . . . . . . . . A
C O C O A . P L A I N
U . A . S . I . P . G
T O R A H . T H R E E
E . G . E . C . I . D
. H O U S E H O L D .
```

489

```
S T E P S . C R E A M
C . A . A . E . A . A
O . T . F . M . R O D
P R E C E D E N T . A
E . N . D . N . H A M
. . . T E N T H . . .
H E M . P . M . P . B
E . A B O M I N A T E
I M P . S . X . N . A
S . L . I . E . T . D
T R E A T . R U S T Y
```

490

```
P A T I N A . L . M .
I . E . C L I Q U E .
C H A P . N . M . L .
K . C . D E C I D E D
I N U R E . . T . I .
N . P A N A C E A . R
G . G . . A D A G E .
S T E W A R D . C . C
. E . E . U . C H A T
C A R E S S . . E . L
. R . K . T R E N D Y
```

491

```
E M B R Y O . F . G .
C . U . . V I A B L E
H A R A R E . B . A .
O . E . I N T R U D E
E T A . C . . I . D .
S O U P K I T C H E N
. I . A . E . E N E .
E L U S I V E . L . L
. I . T . A N I M U S
E N T E R S . . E . O
. G . L . T A R T A N
```

492

```
S . D . F U L S O M E
E C O L I . M . I . .
C . W . R A V I O L I
O V A L S . L . I . .
N . G . T Y P E S E T
D R E W . O . S L U R
S E R I O U S . O . U
. N . N . . T R E K S
B E D T I M E . G . T
. G . E . A B I D E .
F E A R F U L . N . E
```

SOLUTIONS

493

```
C O B W E B ■ ■ S ■ E ■
H ■ R ■ ■ R E H E A T
A P O G E E ■ E ■ V ■
R ■ W ■ S W E A T E R
C Y N I C ■ A R I S E ■
O ■ I ■ U ■ S ■ M ■ P
A H E A D ■ T H E T A
L I S S O M E ■ B ■ I
■ T ■ P ■ A R D O U R
A C C E S S ■ ■ M ■ E
■ H ■ N ■ T U R B I D
```

494

```
C O P S E ■ G U S T O
U ■ A ■ L ■ R ■ T ■ A
R E P L I C A ■ A S S
L ■ T ■ S ■ P ■ I
S P A R E ■ S O L E S
■ I ■ ■ E
C U R B S ■ C U R D S
A ■ L ■ I ■ H ■ H
D I E ■ S C A M P E R
R ■ S ■ A ■ O ■ E
E A S E L ■ S T R A W
```

495

```
O ■ C ■ A F F A B L E
F I L M S ■ ■ S ■ A
F ■ O P P O R T U N E
S U S H I ■ ■ H ■ D
E ■ E ■ C R I M E A
T H U S ■ E ■ A G U E
■ A P H I D S ■ O ■ N
■ I ■ I ■ H O T E L
G R E N A D I E R ■ I
■ D ■ E ■ F R I E S
B O R S C H T ■ P ■ T
```

496

```
B R A C E S ■ T ■ L
I ■ F ■ A L W A Y S
S T R U C K ■ O ■ R
T ■ E ■ A I R S H I P
R I S E R ■ T ■ C
O ■ H A T C H E T ■ S
■ B ■ R ■ O P I U M
T A C T I C S ■ T ■ A
■ S ■ H ■ H E A T E R
F R I E Z E ■ E ■ T
■ A ■ N ■ W A L R U S
```

497

```
P O M P O M ■ F ■ B
R ■ A ■ A Y E A Y E
O U T R A G E ■ T ■ A
D ■ S ■ M A N I A C
S I D E C A R ■ G ■ H
■ E C O ■ L E U
U ■ V ■ H O Y D E N S
P R I V E T ■ I ■ I
P ■ A ■ R H U B A R B
E N T R E E ■ L ■ Y
R ■ E ■ R U E F U L
```

498

```
G U L A G ■ P L U S
R ■ U ■ A X I L ■ A
E M S ■ Z ■ I D O L
Y A H W E H ■ E ■ L
■ I ■ T E R R I F Y
■ Z ■ A T L A S ■ O
S E A W E E D ■ ■ R
I ■ H ■ N I M B U S
L E V I ■ A ■ I M P
O ■ L I S T ■ E ■ A
S K Y E ■ E R R O R
```

499

```
C U R I O ■ S P A S M
E ■ A ■ B O P ■ B ■ E
L I F T S ■ E ■ S A T
L ■ O O Z E ■ E ■ R
S W I R L ■ D I N G O
■ M ■ E ■ C ■ C
C O I N S ■ A G E N T
R ■ T ■ C O M E ■ H
A B A ■ E ■ E L A T E
V ■ T ■ N O R ■ R ■ I
E V E R T ■ A L T A R
```

500

```
R U I N G ■ S A R I S
E ■ N ■ O A K ■ I ■ P
L E T G O ■ I N F E R
I ■ R ■ D A M ■ L ■ A
C R O S S ■ P L E A T
■ O ■ I ■ E ■ B
A D O R N ■ C A T C H
M ■ N ■ A S H ■ I ■ O
B R A Y S ■ A N G E L
I ■ I ■ T O R ■ E ■ L
T E R R Y ■ M A R R Y
```

501

```
B A S I S ■ E M E R Y
O ■ H ■ T ■ I ■ E
B ■ E ■ A L L T O L D
C O L L I E ■ R ■ I
A ■ T ■ R A C E M E
T E E M ■ K ■ D A F T
■ F R A C A S ■ R ■ H
■ F ■ N ■ G H E T T O
F I A N C E E ■ I ■ R
■ G ■ E ■ E ■ N ■ N
M Y R R H ■ P A I N S
```

502

```
P O L K A ■ S A M O A
U ■ Y ■ M O W ■ A ■ M
R ■ I ■ B ■ E ■ L O B
S E N T I M E N T A L
E ■ G ■ V ■ P ■ A T E
■ N ■ B A L S A ■ H
C O B ■ L ■ T ■ B ■ B
I N O P E R A T I V E
R O W ■ N ■ K ■ K ■ R
C ■ E ■ C U E ■ E ■ N
A E R I E ■ S U R G E
```

503

```
G A B L E ■ P O P U P
U ■ I N J U R E ■ I
E M B E D ■ S C R A P
S ■ D ■ A ■ H ■ E
S I D E E F F E C T S
■ T ■ T ■ T S
I N T E R E S T I N G
N ■ C ■ R ■ R ■ O
C O A T S ■ L A G E R
A ■ N O U G A T ■ G
S C A R E ■ D E L V E
```

504

```
B L E E D ■ B E A S T
I ■ A ■ E ■ L ■ R
S A L T E D ■ V A N E
E ■ I ■ E ■ E ■ E
C O N V A L E S C E
T ■ G ■ C W T ■ A ■ B
■ M O N T E C A R L O
B ■ O ■ I ■ V ■ W
L I M O ■ S T R E S S
O ■ N ■ S ■ O ■ E
C A R E Y ■ C E D A R
```

SOLUTIONS

505

```
H A S T E N . . I . S
I . A . E T H N I C
J E R I C H O . H . U
A . C . R I B A L D
B A S H F U L . L . S
. A I L . E W E .
A . V . E N T H R A L
G O A T E E . I . E
N . G . C A R N A G E
E X E T E R . G . R
S . D . S E E M L Y
```

506

```
R U S T Y . L I F T S
A . W . A . L . H
P L A I T . N . A G O
I . S . I T E M . R
D A Y T I M E . E A T
. G . C A R . P .
H A M . I G N O R E D
A . O N C E . D . I
B A R . L . R O B O T
I . A . E . U . C
T A L E S . F R E S H
```

507

```
B L I M P . B O A T S
A . M . R U E . L . P
S A B L E . A W O K E
I . U . S U N . N . C
C H E S S . S P E A K
. U . E . . O . K .
F E I N T . A T T A R
A . M . E G G . H . E
T A P E R . O R R I S
E . E . S I N . U . I
D E L V E . Y E M E N
```

508

```
A T T I C . S . S O B
C . . A C U T E . A
C L A S S . N . C . H
O . R . T A N G E N T
S U R G E R Y . S . .
T . O . E . S . U
. W . U T O P I A N
N O H O P E R . O . L
E . E . S . D A N C E
W . A N E L E . . S
S A D . T . R E B U S
```

509

```
B . S . K . V O D K A
A C Q U I R E . R . D
L . U . S . R . U D
S O A R S . A R G U E
A . S H E . A . R
. P H Y S I C I A N .
M . M . O T T . W
A S K E W . P A T C H
N . I . I . P . E
G . L . S P E C I A L
O U N C E . R . N . K
```

510

```
B E R T H . A D A M S
. T . R . G . N . W
S A G A . R E S I D E
C . I C E . S . E
L I O N . A . T E N T
E . F E A T U R E . P
R I F E . D . A D Z E
O . E . A R C . A
S U N K E N . H U E S
I . C . E . E . B
S C E N E . T A B B Y
```

511

```
B A L S A M . W . S
O . C . A N G I N A
A V I A R Y . D . T
R . T R E A C H E R Y
D E I S M . L . A . R
. N . I K E . W
L . E . S . R O A S T
Y A R D S T I C K . H
N . A . A C C E D E
C I R C U S . U . S
H . Y . K A R A T E
```

512

```
J U D O . P I C O T
E . P U R R . O . E
A P S E . U . M E N
N . U N S T R A P . E
S A C . U . I . O F T
. C Y P R E S S . .
N E E . P . N . U R I
O . S C O O T E R . N
H A S . S . W E A N
O . O . E R N E . E
W O R L D . R E A R
```

513

```
B A C K U P . P . M
R . O . U P R O A R
E G R E S S . I . G
Z . R . C H A S S I S
H Y E N A . R E T C H
N . C . M . C . R . A
E S T O P . H E I S T
V E S T I G E . D . T
. V . H . A D V I C E
Y E M E N I . N . R
N . R . N U D G E S
```

514

```
O U S T E D . P . M
N . I . A N Y O N E
S I G N . M . P . A
E . M E A N S T E S T
T O T A L . P . A
. K . A D O . I
R . R . O P A L S
C A T A M A R A N . C
O . Y . R . R I C E
A T R I U M . C . N
L . E . S P H E R E
```

515

```
P . P . T A N T R U M
A W A S H . R . N
S . R . U N C I V I L
T O T E M . B . T
E . N . B L O A T E D
U S E R . E . L O D E
P A R A P E T . D . S
. V . P . W E D G E
C A P T I V E . L . R
. G . O . E X E R T
B E A R D E D . R . S
```

516

```
P I T A . E C Z E M A
A . . D A S H . O
T O G O . P O G R O M
O . R . P . S
I N D E C I S I V E
S . I . D . I . C
. A S T R O N O M E R
L . O . R . I
L I N E U P . B I N S
V . T A X I . I
S E A B E D . T H U S
```

SOLUTIONS

517

```
B R A W L ■ ■ ■ P O S T
U ■ R ■ U S S R ■ ■ ■ O
S ■ R ■ C ■ N O M A D ■ A
K N O C K O U T ■ ■ ■ ■ A
■ A W A Y ■ ■ B O B B Y ■
■ I ■ R ■ ■ ■ C ■ O ■
B L U E S ■ ■ H O L Y ■
A ■ ■ L O Y A L I S T
S K I E S ■ U ■ N ■ H
I ■ ■ S O O N ■ E ■ A
L O S S ■ ■ ■ T H R O W
```

518
```
S T R E A K ■ A G E S
A ■ A ■ U ■ B R E ■ W
L ■ V A L V E ■ E W ■
T R E N D ■ S W E D E
Y ■ ■ T ■ E ■ N ■ R
■ S C I E N T I S T ■
D ■ R ■ S ■ N ■ ■ F
A M A S S ■ S C R E E
N ■ Y ■ A L O H A ■ R
E ■ O ■ Y ■ F ■ I ■ R
S A N G ■ H A R D L Y
```

519
```
K L E I N ■ M E E T S
O ■ N ■ ■ I ■ X ■ T
R I G S ■ K N O T T Y
A ■ R U B ■ U ■ R ■ L
N A I R A ■ T R A C E
■ ■ ■ S E R R I E D ■
O U T D O ■ A G I N G
U ■ M ■ N ■ E A T ■ O
T R I V E T ■ T E N D
E ■ L ■ S ■ T ■ ■ L
R O L E S ■ B A D L Y
```

520

```
A B D U C T ■ G ■ H
Z ■ A ■ R E O R D E R
A L W A Y S ■ O ■ A
L ■ N ■ T ■ C U R T
E ■ B O M B E ■ T
A Q U A ■ A ■ R I S E
■ U ■ S A T A Y ■ F
H A N S ■ C ■ S ■ F
■ V ■ O ■ H U R T L E
B E C O M E S ■ A ■ C
■ R ■ N ■ S E C R E T
```

521

```
B R U T A L ■ R ■ M
I ■ I ■ E N C O R E
D A M P E N ■ E ■ L
E ■ T ■ S M U D G E
T A B O O ■ A ■ E ■ E
■ R E V E R S E ■
P ■ I ■ I ■ C A R E T
A M E N D S ■ T ■ O
N ■ F ■ P A I N E D
D E L P H I ■ R ■ D
A ■ Y ■ T H E O R Y
```

522
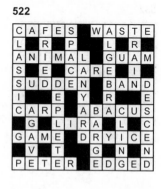
```
C A F E S ■ W A S T E
L ■ R ■ P ■ L ■ R
A N I M A L ■ G U A M
S ■ E ■ C A R E ■ I
S U D D E N ■ B A N D
I ■ E ■ Y ■ R ■ E
C A R P ■ A B A C U S
■ G ■ L I R A ■ L ■ C
G A M E ■ D R Y I C E
■ V ■ T ■ G ■ N ■ N
P E T E R ■ E D G E D
```

523

```
C H A M P ■ U M B R A
O ■ A ■ R ■ A ■ G
A S C O T ■ G O R S E
T ■ A R O S E ■ R ■ N
S C R I P T ■ D I E T
■ N ■ A ■ S ■
B E A D ■ S T I T C H
E ■ T ■ S H I R E ■ U
F R I L L ■ C A R O M
I ■ O ■ A ■ T ■ U
T A N G Y ■ D E B T S
```

524

```
M E D I C ■ C L O V E
O ■ I ■ E ■ R ■ A ■ Y
A D O ■ A D A P T O R
N ■ R ■ S ■ B ■ ■ I
S C A R E ■ S C A L E
■ ■ M ■ ■ P ■
C R A F T ■ B O O Z E
H ■ H ■ U ■ S ■ L
A B S C E S S ■ T I E
N ■ T ■ R ■ E ■ L ■ C
T H Y M E ■ S W E P T
```

525
```
O X B O W ■ U S H E R
R ■ E ■ H ■ E ■ L
T ■ A ■ A L M A N A C
E N T I R E ■ M ■ T
G ■ L ■ F A C A D E
A C E S ■ K ■ N O D E
■ I S O B A R ■ O ■ A
■ C ■ C ■ G E N D E R
R A N C H E R ■ L ■ T
■ D ■ E ■ U ■ E ■ H
C A D R E ■ N A S T Y
```

526
```
D O C K S ■ S C R A P
U ■ O ■ E ■ H ■ A ■ E
C O M P A R A T I V E
K ■ M ■ L ■ R ■ N ■ L
S C A R ■ M E S S E S
■ O ■ A ■ A ■ Y
S T A T E D ■ T I E S
H ■ G ■ X ■ D ■ R ■ I
E X A M I N A T I O N
L ■ I ■ T ■ T ■ S ■ K
F I N D S ■ A S H E S
```

527

```
A ■ B ■ D ■ H A V O C
R E L E A S E ■ A ■ A
E ■ E ■ M ■ A ■ L ■ B
N E W Y E A R S E V E
A ■ ■ E ■ G ■ M ■ R
■ C O A L I T I O N ■
Y ■ S ■ L ■ T ■ A
O F F T H E S H E L F
U ■ A ■ I ■ O ■ D ■ T
N ■ C ■ S E A S I D E
G U E S S ■ ■ K ■ T ■ R
```

528

```
S T A R E ■ B U S E S
■ I ■ E ■ O ■ ■ E ■ H
U N I T ■ P E S T L E
M ■ R A P ■ F ■ L
B R I E ■ R ■ O R A L
I ■ G A Z E L L E ■ F
L E N T ■ S ■ D E L I
I ■ O ■ S E T ■ ■ S
C A R A F E ■ I T C H
U ■ E ■ D ■ M ■ U
S A D L Y ■ R E V E L
```

SOLUTIONS

529

```
M A K E R ■ S E O U L
U ■ L ■ N A A N ■ A ■
C H E E R ■ G R E A T
U ■ C ■ D ■ T ■ ■ H ■
S L O T M A C H I N E
■ E ■ I ■ N ■ E ■ E ■
S U B O R D I N A T E
T ■ ■ N ■ Y ■ W ■ B ■
E A S E S ■ P A T I O
M ■ P E E L ■ R ■ N ■
S M A R T ■ D E C O Y
```

530

```
E ■ G O G G L E B O X
X ■ U ■ I ■ A ■ E ■ ■
T R I E D ■ S T A R S
R ■ L A D D E R S ■ H
E N T R Y ■ R A T I O
M ■ L ■ ■ M ■ ■ ■ R ■
I N G O T ■ S M E L T
T ■ A B A S H E D ■ E
Y E M E N ■ A L I G N
■ U ■ G ■ D ■ C ■ E ■
I N T R O V E R T ■ D
```

531

```
S E E D Y ■ A S S A M
C ■ U ■ R ■ H ■ ■ E ■
A R A B L E ■ A R I A
N ■ B ■ V ■ N ■ ■ N ■
T E A R J E R K E R ■
Y ■ S ■ O R E ■ X ■ A
■ W H I T E D W A R F
Z ■ ■ D ■ N ■ ■ C ■ R
E D G Y ■ C A S T L E
T ■ L ■ E ■ O ■ ■ S ■
A M B L E ■ A W A S H
```

532

```
S U D O K U ■ ■ A ■ T
L ■ C ■ S U P P L Y ■
E N D U R E S ■ P ■ P
D ■ L ■ D E L E T E ■
S Q U A T ■ N ■ A ■ S
■ ■ P R O C E S S ■ ■
S ■ S ■ D ■ T E E N S
P A W P A W ■ C ■ L ■
A ■ I ■ T A R T A R E
S O N N E T ■ O ■ P ■
M ■ G ■ T Y R A N T
```

533

```
S N A C K ■ U S U R P
K ■ A ■ H ■ M ■ ■ A ■
E N A B L E ■ E A R N
W ■ L ■ A I L ■ ■ E ■
E R O S ■ R ■ T W O ■
R ■ F E A T H E R ■ A
■ E T C ■ L ■ R A I L
D ■ ■ R U E ■ C ■ L ■
E A S E ■ S U C K L E
B ■ T ■ S ■ O ■ ■ G ■
T I M E S ■ L Y C E E
```

534

```
S H R E D ■ ■ A B E T
H ■ O ■ O P T S ■ ■ I
O ■ U ■ S ■ ■ S P A T
D R E S S A G E ■ ■ L
■ O ■ O ■ S ■ S I R E
■ S ■ M A K E S ■ U ■
C A G E ■ E ■ O ■ T ■
O ■ ■ R E D C R O S S
A L P S ■ ■ O ■ U ■ P
S ■ E D E N ■ Z ■ O ■
T A C T ■ ■ S N O R T
```

535

```
T A K E S ■ C R A M S
U ■ O ■ W A R ■ B ■ P
B R I B E ■ U ■ B O O
E ■ ■ E L S E ■ E ■ R
S M E L L ■ T R Y S T
■ E ■ L ■ ■ O ■ H ■ ■
I N S E T ■ B O W E R
M ■ U ■ A R U M ■ ■ I
A Y E ■ U ■ D Y I N G
G ■ D ■ P I G ■ M ■ E
O X E Y E ■ E X P E L
```

536

```
S H I R T ■ E N T E R
N ■ O U S T ■ U ■ A ■
O N I O N ■ A P R I L
O ■ ■ T ■ A ■ N ■ L ■
P O S S I B I L I T Y
■ U ■ N I T ■ N ■ ■ ■
S E C O N D S I G H T
T ■ T ■ E ■ V ■ W ■ ■
O R I E L ■ G O U D A
O ■ O ■ S O A R ■ N ■
L I N E D ■ L Y I N G
```

537

```
S T E P S ■ D E P T H
■ A ■ E ■ S ■ L ■ I ■
A R E A ■ U P T U R N
R ■ ■ S I R ■ N ■ D ■
B A Z A A R ■ A G A R
I ■ E N N O B L E ■ A
T E A T ■ G O L D E N
R ■ L ■ A W E ■ ■ C ■
A M O U N T ■ G I B E
T ■ U ■ E ■ R ■ S ■ ■
E S S E X ■ D O W E L
```

538

```
S U S A N ■ M ■ B A D
A ■ T ■ E N E M A ■ E
D R O P S ■ N ■ R ■ F
I ■ N ■ T ■ D I R T Y
S T E P S I S T E R ■
M I C A ■ L ■ C L I O
■ L I V E L I H O O D
B E R E T ■ N ■ R ■ E
E ■ C ■ U ■ S I G H S
T ■ L A D L E ■ A ■ S
A Y E ■ E ■ T O N G A
```

539

```
B R A C E D ■ L ■ M ■
R ■ U ■ U N E V E N ■
I R R U P T ■ S ■ R ■
E ■ O ■ E Y E S O R E
F I R ■ A ■ E ■ I ■ ■
S M A L L M I N D E D
■ M ■ E ■ D ■ E R E ■
M O R T I S E ■ C ■ P
R ■ H ■ W A P I T I ■
B A N A N A ■ D ■ C ■
■ L ■ L ■ P A R E N T
```

540

```
D R A P E ■ A W A I T
U ■ R ■ ■ I ■ R ■ E ■
B O R E D ■ D E M U R
A ■ C ■ A ■ X ■ ■ M ■
I M P E C U N I O U S
■ A ■ D ■ G ■ S ■ R ■
I N T E R E S T I N G
S ■ N ■ R ■ E ■ ■ ■ ■
S K A T E ■ I N T R O
U ■ N ■ L ■ C ■ ■ ■ ■
E X T O L ■ V E N U S
```

SOLUTIONS

541

```
.PRESCRIBE.
C.A.U.E.E.E
ALTER.CALYX
R.E.LEA.L.P
TALLY.PASTA
H.I...L.N
OFTEN.BLISS
R.R.AGE.N.I
SLANT.GECKO
E.D.A.I.A.N
.REPLENISH.
```

542
```
STALLS.N.J
C.N.AMUSED
RATE.V.R.W
E.H.REFEREE
ENEMY.Y.L
N.MEASLES.U
.A.N.AVIAN
INSTEAD.M.I
.N.I.L.BOSS
COYOTE.N.O
.Y.N.CANYON
```

543
```
COHERE.R.W
A.E.ANORAK
SHAVER.D.G
H.D.SLEEPER
FRANC.MOUSE
L.C.ORB.R.C
OTHER.LUCRE
WREATHE.H.N
.I.V.UMLAUT
TAPERS.S.L
.L.S.HUGELY
```

544

```
CLANG.PAUSE
A.F.L.P.A
S.F.ORDERLY
SWAPS.R.T
I.BESTRIDE
SILT.O.TIDE
.NEUROSIS.A
.K.L.AFOOT
SPEAKUP.B.S
.O.N.I.E.I
STATE.DOYEN
```

545
```
.ESCALATOR.
P.A.P.I.C.U
EQUIP.TIEIN
R.N.LAC.A.D
PEACE.HINGE
E.A.O.R
THANK.SNAIL
U.L.NIL.T.I
ABODE.ALLIN
L.U.E.K.A.E
.EDELWEISS.
```

546
```
FRANZ.NADIR
O.N.E.O.E
RENTAL.ROME
E.U.LEFT.F
SILD.TOAST.
T.A.ATE.T.D
.CRANE.DONE
I.DART.R.F
RIND.SALAMI
I.L.N.G.N
SLEEP.GEESE
```

547

```
SOFT.OSPREY
E.RAW.M
LOBE.LETTER
E.S.E.R
CONSPIRACY
T.E.C.H.I
.SWIVELLING
.A.R.E.U
CLIENT.VISA
.S.AXE.N
EARWIG.LAVA
```

548

```
.STATESMAN.
P.U.A.H.B.P
RELIC.AROMA
E.L.ILL.R.C
CHEAT.LATTE
I.I.I.V.M
SHARP.SEPIA
I.C.UZI.A.K
OSCAR.ROGUE
N.R.G.E.R
.MARESNEST.
```

549
```
BRAGG.ICONS
O.RAMROD.I
NAMES.ERECT
U.E.L.N.E
SPONTANEOUS
.P.M.R
LINENBASKET
E.P.S.T.E
WASPS.MOONS
I.REAGAN.T
SWIRL.READY
```

550

```
BEAM.UNLIKE
R.OAF.E
UNDO.OUTCRY
N.D.E.A
EASYSTREET
IRK.O.AIR
.MISFORTUNE
.H.O.E.N
POINTS.MINE
.L.PEP.G
BEAUTY.TYPE
```

551
```
BOP.SANDBAR
R.E.L.R.I
I.SCATTERED
NOT.V.S.N
GUSSET.SATE
.N.URINE.R
ACTS.TARGET
.E.P.T.EER
ASCENSION.A
W.C.V.I.C
LACTATE.EKE
```

552
```
THROBS.SALT
I.O.O.T.A
D.BARBARISM
ALE.N.I.T
LESSEE.PREY
.A.HORSE.R
ENVY.RUSSET
.T.N.P.NOW
BONECHINA.I
A.S.N.R.N
PASS.RECESS
```

SOLUTIONS

553

```
A . D C A T C H E R
F R I A R . A . U
F . W U N I C O R N
O K A Y S . H . E
R . L H U G E . K
D A I S . S . T S A R
. G . A J A R . H . A
. E . H . U N I O N
A N T A C I D . N K
. D . R . D W E L L
C A R A W A Y . R E
```

554

```
B U S S T O P . T . C
L . T . S . I C H O R
A D A G E . S A E . U
I . T E T E A T E T E
R E I N S . H . L
. C O E R C E D
C . C . A T O L L
A N T I P O D E S . E
C . E D O . D R A M A
T R E E S . I . G . S
I . M E V E R E S T
```

555

```
T R O O P . S A G G Y
U . T A C O . O . I
R A T T L E S N A K E
N . E . A . H . L
S M A R T S . N E E D
. M . E . A
S N A G . F O D D E R
H . T . I . I . A
E L E C T R I C I T Y
E . U . H E R E . O
P U R S E . A D O R N
```

556

```
P E N S . S O R R Y
I . C A S H . E . O
C A V A . O . S . K
K . E R S T W H I L E
S I N E W . G . D . L
. E D I F I C E
U . R . F . R A N C H
S M A R T A L E C . I
E . B . E . S E T T
R . L . S O D A . C
S L E P T . R A S H
```

557

```
F . J . S E T T I N G
I R A Q I . O . E
G . L . S C R A T C H
H O O H A . N . T
T . P O L A N D . A
S A Y S . F . F O R M
. N . P E T A R D . O
. C . I . M O I S T
C H A T E A U . O . H
. O . A . S A U C E
P R A L I N E . S . R
```

558

```
B A N A L . R . A R K
I . N A S S E R . E
S I T I N . V . T . E
E . U . C A P T I O N
C O R T E Z . C
T . N . R U G . H . S
. T . R A G O U T
S E A W E E D . K . A
H . B . A . G H E N T
O . L Y C H E E . U
W E E . H . T R U C E
```

559

```
A . M E A S U R I N G
S . U . G . S . D
S O F I A . A L I C E
I . T . P E G . O . A
S M I L E . E N T E R
T . E . . A . T
A D L I B . G N A S H
N . I . A I R . P . W
T O N E S . A L A M O
. E . T . D . C . R
P E R S E V E R E . M
```

560

```
A R E A S . O . B U S
D . P H O B I A . A
R E C T O . E . L . F
I . O . R . S H A K E
F I N A N C E . L
T . S . A . A . C
. T . S T A M I N A
B U R N T . L . K . R
A . U . E . B L A S E
L . C H E Q U E . S
D O T . L . M Y T H S
```

561

```
D O G M A . S C O W
I . U . M A K E R . E
S H Y . N . T U N A
C A S T E R . T . N
. C . S E A L E G S
. K . S I N G E . R
I S O L A T E . I
N . E . S L O W L Y
E D G E . E . A L A
P . E V A N S . D . W
T W E E . S E E D S
```

562

```
O C L O C K . D . L
V . U . I M P E D E
E L A T E S . F . V
R . L . S P L I C E
S T E A M . U . A . R
. S W A G M A N
A . C . C . A N T I C
R E A M E R . T . E
M . P . A L L I E D
E V E L Y N . E . A
D . E . T E R R O R
```

563

```
F L O R A . T O U C H
R . S . C . B . O
E V I C T S . S W A B
E . E . L I C I T
S C R I B E . U N I T
I . N . N . R . A
A C N E . D E E P E N
. H O R D E . L . N
C A R T . R E L A T E
. S . I . L . C . R
P E N A L . F I E R Y
```

564

```
K O W T O W . H . B
I . I . R E T I N A
R O A R . I . B . G
O . C E N T I P E D E
V E R D I . N . R . L
. O . G N U . N
S . B H . R E A C T
A P A R T M E N T . A
L . T . I . N E A R
A N I M U S . U . R
D . C . S H I F T Y
```

SOLUTIONS

565

```
H A Y D N ■ B I S O N
■ T ■ O A P ■ D ■ ■ O
A T T U N E ■ L E S S
■ A ■ B A R B E C U E
L I N T ■ C ■ R U B Y
■ N ■ ■ A ■ ■ ■ A ■ ■
A D E N ■ P ■ T O L L
N E G A T I V E ■ T ■
T R O T ■ T A M P E R
O ■ A ■ A M P ■ R ■ ■
N E W L Y ■ P O I N T
```

566

```
C L I M B ■ C ■ A U K
O ■ O O D L E S ■ E ■
M A C A W ■ E ■ T ■ E
I ■ A ■ S A F F R O N
C O B W E B ■ O ■ ■ ■
S ■ R ■ R U B ■ L ■ S
I ■ ■ S O L A C E ■ A
S H O R T E N ■ B ■ A
N ■ L ■ O ■ N E E D S
U ■ E S T H E R ■ O ■
G U T ■ E ■ T A L O N
```

567

```
H E S S ■ ■ C U R D S
U ■ ■ T O G A ■ O ■ L
M A R E ■ ■ R ■ Y ■ E
A ■ I M M E D I A T E
N A G ■ A ■ I ■ L ■ K
■ ■ M R R I G H T ■ ■
J A ■ I ■ A ■ I L K
A R R O G A N C E ■ A
C ■ O ■ O ■ A S A P
O ■ L ■ L A M P ■ U
B R E A D ■ S O R T
```

568

```
P R E D E C E S S O R
R A G ■ L ■ I ■ E
A U G U R ■ B O N D S
C L ■ E G O ■ C ■ P
T R E A T ■ W H E E L
I ■ B ■ ■ O ■ E
C A S E S ■ S W O R N
A ■ E ■ T O T ■ L D
B U R K A ■ A N I S E
L ■ G R ■ I V ■ N
E J E C T O R S E A T
```

569

```
C A N T ■ S A F E T Y
A ■ H O E ■ ■ R
L A C E ■ A C T U A L
C ■ M ■ ■ O ■ P
I N T E R S P E R S E
U O ■ K ■ O N
M A R C H I O N E S S
■ B O ■ O ■ L
C O R N E T ■ R I G A
V ■ A N T ■ V
B E H E A D ■ H I V E
```

570

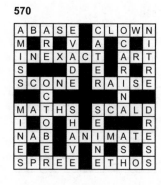

```
A B A S E ■ C L O W N
M R ■ V A ■ C ■ I
I N E X A C T ■ A R T
S ■ D ■ E ■ R R
S C O N E ■ R A I S E
■ C ■ ■ N
M A T H S ■ S C A L D
I O ■ H E ■ R
N A B ■ A N I M A T E
E E V ■ N S S
S P R E E ■ E T H O S
```

571

```
B A N A L ■ S U S H I
Y ■ V ■ L ■ H ■ N
L I D O ■ S O N A T A
A ■ A I M ■ V ■ N N
W I L D E ■ A N G L E
■ A ■ E L K ■ R
S H I R K ■ I C I N G
L L ■ N ■ A L L U
A M A Z E D ■ O A K S
N M ■ S ■ N H
G L A S S ■ B E E F Y
```

572

```
P L A I D ■ S W A R M
O C ■ I ■ T ■ N ■ I
S H E L T E R ■ Y E N
E ■ T ■ A ■ T T
R U M M Y ■ P A I N S
■ I ■ ■ M
M I L N E ■ C H E F S
I I X H H
M A T ■ C H A M B E R
E I E O A U
S N A R L ■ S P R I G
```

573

```
C R U D E ■ L I S T S
H ■ E ■ I ■ O ■ L
A B A C K ■ T O N G A
R ■ E ■ B ■ R ■ M
M E R I T O R I O U S
■ V ■ T ■ G ■ G R
S E L F R E L I A N T
P ■ U ■ Y ■ N ■ R
O D D L Y ■ R A D I O
T U A T V
S T O R M ■ H E D G E
```

574

```
R E C E N T ■ I ■ C
O ■ L ■ H E R N I A
L O R E ■ A ■ S M
L ■ V ■ I G N I T E
S O B E R ■ R D L
■ O N E T I M E ■
A L ■ I ■ M A R C H
P L I A N T ■ T U
A V A T A P S
R E A D E R ■ E S
T R ■ E E R I L Y
```

575

```
R ■ D ■ S ■ B A D G E
A N O T H E R ■ A A
B C ■ A ■ A L B R
B A T E D ■ E A S E L
I ■ O X E N ■ M Y
■ F R O S T B I T E ■
K C ■ H O N E A
O U S E L ■ M A N O R
P PTA B D I
E A ■ C H A M O I S
K A Y A K ■ Y N E
```

576

```
L H A S A ■ L A G O S
A R ■ G ■ S ■ O
R E T I R E ■ T U B A
I D ■ A N T E ■ P
A F E W ■ T O R S O
T C WRY T A
■ M O C H A ■ B A R S
B ■ L O N G ■ G P
A L T O ■ T H R I C E
C C E N C
K H A K I ■ E I G H T
```

SOLUTIONS

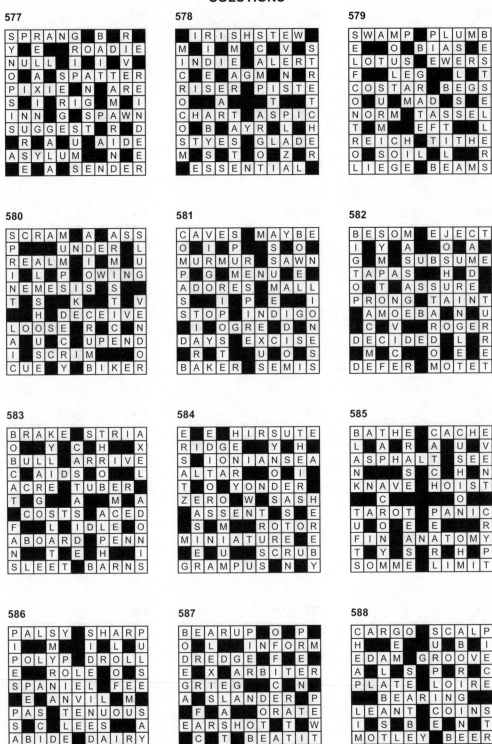

577

S	P	R	A	N	G		B		R	
Y		E			R	O	A	D	I	E
N	U	L	L		I		I		V	
O		A		S	P	A	T	T	E	R
P	I	X	I	E		N		A	R	E
S		I		R	I	G		M		I
I	N	N		G		S	P	A	W	N
S	U	G	G	E	S	T		R		D
	R		A		U		A	I	D	E
A	S	Y	L	U	M		N		E	
	E		A		S	E	N	D	E	R

578

	I	R	I	S	H	S	T	E	W	
M		I		M		C	V		S	
I	N	D	I	E		A	L	E	R	T
C		E		A	G	M		N		R
R	I	S	E	R			P	I	S	T	E
O			A				T		T	
C	H	A	R	T		A	S	P	I	C
O		B		A	Y	R		L		H
S	T	Y	E	S		G	L	A	D	E
M		S		T		O		Z		R
	E	S	S	E	N	T	I	A	L	

579

S	W	A	M	P		P	L	U	M	B
E			O		B	I	A	S		E
L	O	T	U	S		E	W	E	R	S
F		L	E	G			L		T	
C	O	S	T	A	R		B	E	G	S
O		U		M	A	D		S		E
N	O	R	M		T	A	S	S	E	L
T		M		E	F	T		L		
R	E	I	C	H		T	I	T	H	E
O		S	O	I	L		L		R	
L	I	E	G	E		B	E	A	M	S

580

S	C	R	A	M		A		A	S	S
P			U	N	D	E	R		L	
R	E	A	L	M		I		M		U
I		L		P		O	W	I	N	G
N	E	M	E	S	I	S		S		
T		S		K			T		V	
		H		D	E	C	E	I	V	E
L	O	O	S	E		R		C		N
A		U		C		U	P	E	N	D
I		S	C	R	I	M				O
C	U	E		Y		B	I	K	E	R

581

C	A	V	E	S		M	A	Y	B	E
O		I		P		S		O		
M	U	R	M	U	R		S	A	W	N
P		G		M	E	N	U		E	
A	D	O	R	E	S		M	A	L	L
S			I		P	E		I		
S	T	O	P		I	N	D	I	G	O
	I			O	G	R	E		D	N
D	A	Y	S		E	X	C	I	S	E
	R		T			U		O		S
B	A	K	E	R		S	E	M	I	S

582

B	E	S	O	M		E	J	E	C	T
I		Y		A		O		A		
G		M		S	U	B	S	U	M	E
T	A	P	A	S			H		D	
O		T		A	S	S	U	R	E	
P	R	O	N	G		T	A	I	N	T
	A	M	O	E	B	A		N		U
	C		V		R	O	G	E	R	
D	E	C	I	D	E	D		L		R
	M		C		O		E		E	
D	E	F	E	R		M	O	T	E	T

583

B	R	A	K	E		S	T	R	I	A
O		Y		C		H		X	
B	U	L	L		A	R	R	I	V	E
C		A	I	D	S		O		L	
A	C	R	E		T	U	B	E	R	
T		G		A		M		A		A
	C	O	S	T	S		A	C	E	D
F		L		I	D	L	E		O	
A	B	O	A	R	D		P	E	N	N
N			T		E	H			I	
S	L	E	E	T		B	A	R	N	S

584

E		E		H	I	R	S	U	T	E
R	I	D	G	E			Y		H	
S		I	O	N	I	A	N	S	E	A
A	L	T	A	R		O		I		
T		O		Y	O	N	D	E	R	
Z	E	R	O		W		S	A	S	H
	A	S	S	E	N	T		S		E
	S		M			R	O	T	O	R
M	I	N	I	A	T	U	R	E		E
	E		U			S	C	R	U	B
G	R	A	M	P	U	S		N		Y

585

B	A	T	H	E		C	A	C	H	E
L		A		R		A		U		V
A	S	P	H	A	L	T		S	E	E
N			S		C		H		N	
K	N	A	V	E		H	O	I	S	T
		C					O			
T	A	R	O	T		P	A	N	I	C
U		O		E		E			R	
F	I	N		A	N	A	T	O	M	Y
T		Y		S		R		H		P
S	O	M	M	E		L	I	M	I	T

586

P	A	L	S	Y		S	H	A	R	P
I		M		I		L		U		
P	O	L	Y	P		D	R	O	L	L
E		R	O	L	E		O		S	
S	P	A	N	I	E	L		F	E	E
	E		A	N	V	I	L		M	
P	A	S		T	E	N	U	O	U	S
S		C		L	E	E	S			A
A	B	I	D	E		D	A	I	R	Y
L		O		S		K		S		
M	I	N	D	S		P	A	T	I	O

587

B	E	A	R	U	P		O		P	
O		L			I	N	F	O	R	M
D	R	E	D	G	E		F		E	
E		X		A	R	B	I	T	E	R
G	R	I	E	G			C		N	
A		S	L	A	N	D	E	R		P
	F		A			O	R	A	T	E
E	A	R	S	H	O	T		T		W
	C		T		B	E	A	T	I	T
M	E	X	I	C	O			L		E
	T		C		E	N	D	E	A	R

588

C	A	R	G	O		S	C	A	L	P
H		E		U		B		I		
E	D	A	M		G	R	O	O	V	E
A		L		S		P		R		C
P	L	A	T	E		L	O	I	R	E
		B	E	A	R	I	N	G		
L	E	A	N	T		C	O	I	N	S
I		S		B		E	N		T	
M	O	T	L	E	Y		B	E	E	R
P		E		L		R			I	
S	T	R	U	T		P	A	Y	U	P

378

SOLUTIONS

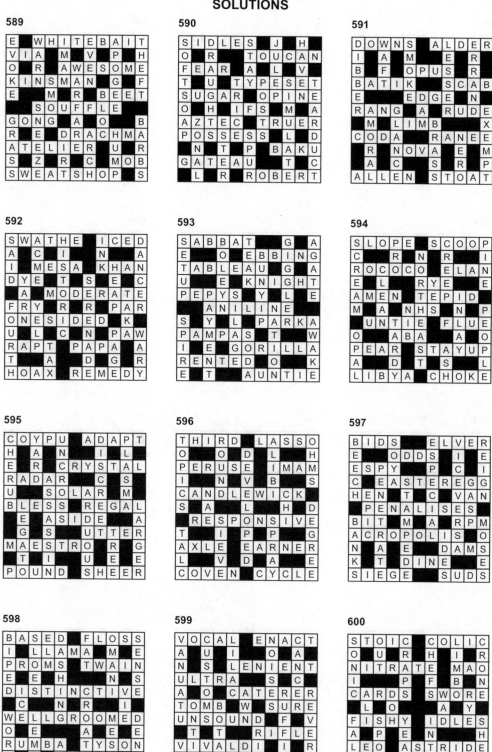

589

```
E W H I T E B A I T
V I A   M   V   P   H
O   R   A W E S O M E
K I N S M A N   G   F
E   M   R   B E E T
  S O U F F L E
G O N G   A   O   B
R   E   D R A C H M A
A T E L I E R   U   R
S   Z   R   C   M O B
S W E A T S H O P   S
```

590

```
S I D L E S   J   H
O   R   T O U C A N
F E A R   A   L   V
T   U   T Y P E S E T
S U G A R   O P I N E
O   H   I F S   M   A
A Z T E C   T R U E R
P O S S E S S   L   D
  N   T   P   B A K U
G A T E A U   T   C
  L   R   R O B E R T
```

591

```
D O W N S   A L D E R
I   A   M   E   R
B   F   O P U S   R
B A T I K   S C A B
E   E D G E   N
R A N G   A   R U D E
  M   L I M B   X
C O D A   R A N E E
  R   N O V A   E   M
  A   C   S   R   P
A L L E N   S T O A T
```

592

```
S W A T H E   I C E D
A   C   I   N   A
I   M E S A   K H A N
D Y E   T   S   E   C
  A   M O D E R A T E
F R Y   R   R   P A R
O N E S I D E D   K
U   L   C   N   P A W
R A P T   P A P A   A
T   A   D   G   R
H O A X   R E M E D Y
```

593

```
S A B B A T   G   A
E   O   E B B I N G
T A B L E A U   G   A
U   E   K N I G H T
P E P Y S   Y   L   E
  A N I L I N E
S   Y   L   P A R K A
P A M P A S   T   W
I   E   G O R I L L A
R E N T E D   O   K
E   T   A U N T I E
```

594

```
S L O P E   S C O O P
C   R   N   R   I
R O C O C O   E L A N
E   L   R Y E   E
A M E N   T E P I D
M   A   N H S   N   P
  U N T I E   F L U E
O   A B A   A   O
P E A R   S T A Y U P
A   D   T   S   L
L I B Y A   C H O K E
```

595

```
C O Y P U   A D A P T
H   A   N   I   L
E   R   C R Y S T A L
R A D A R   C   S
U   S O L A R   M
B L E S S   R E G A L
  E   A S I D E   A
  G   S   U T T E R
M A E S T R O   R   G
  T   I   U   E   E
P O U N D   S H E E R
```

596

```
T H I R D   L A S S O
O   O   D   L   H
P E R U S E   I M A M
I   N   V   B   S
C A N D L E W I C K
S   A   L   H   D
  R E S P O N S I V E
T   I   P   P   G
A X L E   E A R N E R
L   V   D   A   E
C O V E N   C Y C L E
```

597

```
B I D S   E L V E R
E   O D D S   I   E
E S P Y   P   C   I
C   E A S T E R E G G
H E N   T   C   V A N
  P E N A L I S E S
B I T   M   A   R P M
A C R O P O L I S   O
N   A   E   D A M S
K   T   D I N E   E
S I E G E   S U D S
```

598

```
B A S E D   F L O S S
I   L L A M A   M   E
P R O M S   T W A I N
E   E   H   N   S
D I S T I N C T I V E
  C   N   R   I
W E L L G R O O M E D
O   E   A   E   E
R U M B A   T Y S O N
K   U   T R I O S   I
S T R U M   A B Y S M
```

599

```
V O C A L   E N A C T
A   U   I   O   A
N   S   L E N I E N T
U L T R A   S   C
A   O   C A T E R E R
T O M B   W   S U R E
U N S O U N D   F   V
  T   T   R I F L E
V I V A L D I   I   R
  M   N   F   A   I
B E R Y L   T I N G E
```

600

```
S T O I C   C O L I C
O   U   R   H   I   R
N I T R A T E   M A O
I   P   F   B   N
C A R D S   S W O R E
  L   O   A   Y
F I S H Y   I D L E S
A   P   E   N   H
L E O   A S T R I D E
L   I   R   E   V   L
S A L O N   R O Y A L
```

379

601

```
S A F E S   C O P R A
W   I   P   H   R   P
A F G H A N I   O P T
M     D   P   R   L
P A S T E   S H A K Y
    H         T
G U A R D   B R A C E
A   T   U   R     E
L E T   C L A M O U R
E   E   H   Y   V   I
S T R A Y   S N A K E
```

602

```
A C I D I C     Q   W
C     Y   L A Z U L I
R O U N D U P   I   D
E     A   E P E E   E
S W I M S   L   T I N
    C O L L E G E
D U E   A   T O N G S
E   B A C H   S   H
A   E   K A M P A L A
T H R U S T   E   F
H   G   E N L I S T
```

603

```
H A N D Y   B L I N D
A   R   B   N   I
L I N O   E C L A I R
V   I N F E R   M   G
E A G E R   A D O B E
    H   A R T   R
S A T A N   E M A I L
A   F   C A R A T   U
L E A D E R   R A M S
E   L   K   S   T
S O L V E   S H Y L Y
```

604

```
C O R E S   S E D A N
H   A   T N T   I   U
A L G A E   O   S U M
I     S T I R   C   B
R A L P H   Y O U R S
  E   O U T   S
B R A G S   E N S U E
O   R   C O L E   L
G U N   O   L E A V E
U   E   P O E   S   G
S U R G E   R I S K Y
```

605

```
S C O O P   D R O O P
W   M   R U E   B   I
A R I S E   I D E A L
R   T   E F T   S   E
M A S O N   Y I E L D
  F   N     O   E
S T E E P   T U B E R
C   M   E R A   L   E
O N A I R   U N I O N
U   I   C A N   N   A
T I L T H   T R I A L
```

606

```
S   P   A L A R M E D
P L E A D   I   M
I   A   I C E C U B E
D E N S E   H   A
E   U   U T T E R L Y
R O T S   I   S U M O
S U S P E N D   N   U
  T   O   A G A I N
T S U N A M I   W   G
  E   G   S T A L E
S T E E P L Y   Y   R
```

607

```
E A R S   S C R I P T
X     P E A     R
P O L O   C R E D I T
R   R     T   M
E A G E R B E A V E R
S   E   E   I   E
S E L F R E S P E C T
  L   I   I   I
Z A G R E B   C H A R
  T     U F O   E
C E N S U S   T R O D
```

608

```
M E D A L   P I P E R
A   I   A   O   I   H
T E N D R I L   L E I
H     G   K   L   N
S A B R E   A L O N E
  O       R     I
B R A I D   M A Y B E
E   R   R   U     I
F A D   A R M B A N D
O   E   K   P   G   E
G O R G E   S M E A R
```

609

```
  C H A I R L I F T
M   U   N   E   A   W
A I M E D   V O U C H
K   U   E K E   N   E
E S S E X   E N A C T
H   M       I   S
A M O U R   A L L O T
S   N   O U T   A   O
T H I R D   E N D O N
E   O   E   A   E   E
  E N J O Y M E N T
```

610

```
F L A T S   R E A L M
I   P   A   L I E U
T   P   T I M E L A G
T A R R Y   V   N
E   O   R E V E R T
D I V A   V   N E O N
  N E T H E R   G   E
  S   H   O V A L S
P I M E N T O   L   T
O D I N     T   I   L
T E X A N   S H A R E
```

611

```
C R E P T   S L A P S
A     L   T   L   H
R E H A B   R A I T A
E   I O T A   A   D
S C O T T   T   S T Y
  I   S H E E P   I
W A S   E   G A V E L
I   A   R E I N   O
D E L H I   C A I R N
O   V   N   M   E
W R O N G   P A P E R
```

612

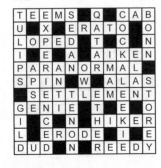

```
T E E M S   Q   C A B
U   X   E R A T O   O
L O P E D   T   C   N
I   E   A   A I K E N
P A R A N O R M A L
S P I N   W   A L A S
  S E T T L E M E N T
G E N I E   T   E   O
I   C   N   H I K E R
L   E R O D E   I   E
D U D   N   R E E D Y
```

SOLUTIONS

613

```
S E L L E R ■ A I M S
L ■ A ■ G ■ B ■ ■ E
O ■ S T O M A C H E R
T O T ■ M ■ C ■ A ■ E
■ ■ S T A N C H I O N
M ■ T ■ N ■ R ■ R ■ E
A I R L I N E R S ■ ■
N ■ A ■ A ■ T ■ P A L
T O W N C R I E R ■ U
I ■ E ■ O ■ A ■ G
S C U T ■ E N Z Y M E
```

614

```
C O M M O N ■ P A R A
Y ■ A ■ E ■ F ■ N
N E E D ■ S P O T O N
I ■ P A S T A ■ E ■ U
C R I M P ■ E N R O L
■ C ■ A W L ■ C ■ ■
S W E A R ■ L E A V E
U ■ N ■ S T A I R ■ V
G U T T E R ■ G E N E
A ■ R ■ I ■ H ■ R
R E E D ■ P A T C H Y
```

615

```
S P A S M ■ A N E L E
K ■ E A G L E T ■ I
I R O N Y ■ L U C I D
M ■ T ■ C ■ R ■ E
P A R I S H I O N E R
■ D ■ M ■ O ■ L ■ A
B O X E R S H O R T S
I ■ N ■ E ■ G ■ E
R E C T O ■ R I F L E
C ■ R A D I U S ■ D
H O Y L E ■ E T H O S
```

616

```
C H E W Y ■ C A K E S
U ■ H ■ E ■ T ■ ■ P
D U R I N G ■ T A P E
G R I N ■ G ■ A ■ W
E L D E R B E R R Y ■
L ■ G ■ E ■ U ■ A
■ V E R N A C U L A R
P ■ E ■ T ■ M E N D
A L G A ■ E M B R Y O
R ■ C ■ R ■ R ■ U
T R I T E ■ N A D I R
```

617

```
A C R O S S ■ G ■ N
R ■ A ■ C R A V A T
R U M P ■ U ■ L ■ V
E ■ R ■ A D M I R E R
S L O W S ■ L ■ L
T ■ D O S S I E R ■ A
■ E ■ O ■ M O U N D
B A I L I F F ■ N ■ H
V ■ L ■ I ■ D O V E
L E V E R S ■ U ■ R
■ S ■ N ■ H U R T L E
```

618

```
B I T M A P ■ F ■ A
U ■ A ■ E L D E S T
S O O N E R ■ N ■ O
E ■ B I L I N G U A L
S I N A I ■ U ■ G ■ L
■ O ■ C O T ■ R
T ■ X ■ I ■ R E E V E
W A I S T L I N E ■ N
I ■ O ■ Y A N K E D
N E U T E R ■ U ■ E
E ■ S ■ E D I T E D
```

619

```
C ■ P ■ B ■ A R A B S
R E E M E R G E D ■ A
E ■ R ■ A ■ A L A ■ L
E D I C T ■ R A M P S
P O O H ■ ■ X ■ ■ A
■ E D E L W E I S S ■
A ■ R ■ ■ N O U S
M U G U P ■ A G O N Y
O ■ A B A ■ L ■ T ■ L
N ■ L I G H T S H I P
G R A C E ■ O ■ E ■ H
```

620

```
S E T U P ■ S C O F F
U ■ A ■ I ■ U ■ L
S I N G E R ■ S O A P
T ■ G ■ C A R T ■ I
A V O C E T ■ O U R S
I ■ ■ O ■ T ■ M ■ E
N A A N ■ R U S S I A
■ R ■ C L A N ■ T ■ W
D O Z E ■ P I R A T E
■ M ■ D ■ T ■ K ■ E
B A K E R ■ Y I E L D
```

621

```
H A U N T ■ G R I N D
E ■ N ■ O ■ U ■ E
R E C T U M ■ P A P A
B ■ L ■ R O D E ■ L
A B E D ■ N I E C E
L ■ A ■ G I G ■ H ■ R
■ C R E E K ■ C O R E
B ■ M E E T ■ C ■ J
L O V E ■ R A V I N E
O ■ R ■ P ■ C ■ C
C A L Y X ■ S C E N T
```

622

```
C U R D S ■ A P P A L
I ■ A ■ I N S ■ A ■ O
R I N S E ■ H ■ N E W
C ■ O G L E ■ T ■ R
A P P L E ■ N A S T Y
■ O ■ V ■ G ■ A
A T S E A ■ B L A D E
B ■ L ■ B I R O ■ V
B O O ■ O ■ A W A K E
O ■ O ■ D I S ■ G ■ R
T E P E E ■ S C A N T
```

623

```
L A U G H ■ S W O O P
■ G ■ O ■ E ■ P ■ O
P O P S ■ C A M P U S
A ■ S P A T ■ R ■ I
N A Z I ■ L ■ M E L T
D ■ A P P L I E S ■ I
A L M S ■ O ■ A S B O
C ■ B ■ S U D S ■ N
A L E R T S ■ L A S S
R ■ Z ■ A ■ E ■ E
S L I N G ■ A S K E D
```

624

```
C A R O B ■ N A V A L
L ■ E ■ R ■ S ■ M
A ■ O ■ A P P L A U D
M A R T Y R ■ E ■ S
U ■ D ■ S E C E D E
P I E R ■ C ■ P O S H
■ G R A T I S ■ L ■ U
U ■ T ■ S T E E R S
F A R T H E R ■ F ■ T
N ■ L ■ A ■ U ■ L
L A B E L ■ W I L D E
```

SOLUTIONS

625

```
B A T H E . S T A N D
R . O . K E E N . I
A B O U T . T A I L S
H . R A F . S . I
M I A S M A . W E A N
A . D . P I N . E . T
P L O T . R O A D I E
U . R . Y A P . R
T H I G H . H A L V E
R . N O O K . R . S
A R G O T . S T A R T
```

626

```
P O R O U S . C . G
R . U . O R A T O R
O B S E S S . S . R
V . H . H O S T E S S
O C H R E . T E N E T
K . O . R . I . E . R
E Q U I P . G O R K I
S A R C A S M . G . C
. T . H . L A R I A T
J A C O B I . S . L
. R . R . M E R E L Y
```

627

```
B L E W . S E P A L
E . A N T E . E . E
L E S S . N . R . D
L . U P S E T T I N G
Y E N . C . I . P . E
. S C R E E C H
A . T . A . N . E L F
B A R O M E T E R . I
O . O . B . L Y N X
R . K . L I D S . E
T H E M E . E K E D
```

628

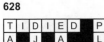

```
T I D I E D . P A S S
A . J . A . L . A
P . I R R I T A T E D
I A N . W . N . N
R U N W A Y . E D A M
. P . E X E R T . M
B A Y S . W A S H E R
. I . T . C . A L I
F R E E P R E S S . G
A . R . M . T . H
T O W N . R E G E N T
```

629

```
T H E B E S . D . S
U . A . U P S I D E
N E I T H E R . O . I
I . H . T A L C . N
C H A O S . Y . E V E
. U S E L E S S
C O S . N . R E E K S
R . T R A P . C . M
O . E . T O R T U R E
W A R M E R . O . L
N . E . T A R G E T
```

630

```
S . G I F T T O K E N
I . O . U . R . N
G L U E D . I C O N S
N . R A G D O L L . E
P A D R E . S O L I D
O . D . S . E
S T A R K . L U P I N
T . G U N F I R E . T
S W A M I . M E C C A
. P . F . B . K . R
E L E V E N S E S . Y
```

631

```
A . M . S T R A U S S
C R A W L . L . P
A . N E U R A L G I A
C A M E R A . U . D
I . A . P I E R C E
A I D S . M . E U R O
. N E A R E D . T . U
. T . L . N O B L E S
M I N I A T U R E . T
. M . N . B A R G E
R E C E I P T . Y . D
```

632

```
A R C H . I B E R I A
B . I N K Y . N
S P U N . E R E B U S
U . D . O . R
R E J U V E N A T E
D . A . A . A . W
. P R O P R I E T O R
. L . U . A . I
R A R E L Y . S P O T
. Z . S O M E . H
G A R D E N . L O N E
```

633

```
C R A S S . D W A R F
H . I . T . E . P . I
A I R M A I L . P I G
M . . K . F . O . H
P R O B E . T W I S T
. C . . N
C U T U P . M O T I F
O . O . E . A . I
C O B . C O N C A V E
O . E . A . G . N . R
A A R O N . O D D L Y
```

634

```
. E L U C I D A T E
E . E . H . E . I . U
S H A L E . B R A W N
T . R E E N T E R . A
I N N E R . S C A L D
M . T . R . V
A D L I B . S U S H I
B . I D I O T I C . S
L O B E S . A T O N E
E . E . O . S . R . D
. B L A N C H I N G
```

635

```
A S S A M . B O A S T
D . E . O . N . U
D . A . S O M E O N E
I M B U E . S . K
C . I N S C R I B E
T O R I . A . D E N T
. A D V A N C E D . H
. K . E . O D O U R
E L G R E C O . U . I
. E . S . L . I . V
B Y T E S . S I N C E
```

636

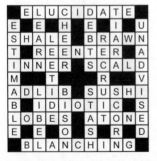

```
V I S T A . E L A N D
A . H . F B I . L . W
S H E L F . F L A K E
E Y E . I . F . R . L
S E T F R E E . M O T
. N . M . L . C
F A R . A R T I S T E
A . O . T . O . M E N
I R A Q I . W R O T E
N . S . V I E . K . M
T I T L E . R E E D Y
```

SOLUTIONS

637
```
J A P A N . C . G U Y
A . . O T H E R . A .
S H I R T . U . E . W
P . R . C E R T A I N
E A R T H E N . T . .
R . I . R . . B . L .
. T . S I N C E R E .
S T A N L E Y . A . G
A . B . O . M A R I A
G . L A P U P . . C .
A V E . E . H A I R Y
```

638
```
H E T U P . . M A S S
E . E . R E M U S . W
S H E . E . . S H O O
S Y S T E M . C . R .
. D . . M I S L E A D
. R . S P A C E . U .
M A H A T M A . . D .
O . D . I R O N I C .
T O L D . L . E T A .
H . A L G A E . S . I
S A G E . . T Y S O N
```

639
```
D U T C H . A T T I C
R . . A . I . R . O .
U S S R . B R E A K S
I . T A M . S . V . T
D R A M A . P R E S S
. . G E N T E E L . .
F I E L D . E C L A T
R . D . I . D Y E . A
A M O E B A . C R O P
N . O . L . L . . E .
C U R V E . W E I R D
```

640
```
R O W E R . S E L L S
A . N . O . E . U . .
B A T C H . T O T A L
I . H . E . P . L . .
D E L I N Q U E N C Y
. B . L . U . R . U .
A B R A C A D A B R A
S . D . L . T . B . .
K E B A B . K I T T Y
E . A . U . V . S . .
W A D E D . V E N U S
```

641
```
S H O R N . B A R N S
E . U . P . L . E . .
T A N N E R . L I M E
T . A . E F T . D . .
L O O M . M . O R C .
E . M I R A C L E . D
. T I N . T . D A R E
T . E M U . R . B . .
Y E A R . R E A M E R
P . A . E . P . I . .
E A G L E . S T U N S
```

642
```
H O T T U B . C . A .
A . W . . U N A B L E
R H E S U S . P . B .
D . N . S H O T G U N
L I T H E . . U . M .
Y . Y A R D A R M . C
. B . M . . B E A N O
C A P S U L E . N . W
. B . T . A T T U N E
V E N E E R . . R . R
. L . R . K N E E L S
```

643
```
C Y P R U S . . M . S
A . . U . A D R I F T
R I B B O N . . N . E
E . B . D R Y I C E .
R A V E N . A . C . L
. . A R A B I C A . .
L . M . P . D E B U T
A P P L E T . L . H .
T . I . H A L T E R .
E N R A G E . A . E .
R . E . Y A R R O W
```

644
```
C . V . P . T U R N S
O R I G A M I . A . M
V . R . R . D I N . A
E X A C T . E N T E R
N . G E E S . D . T .
. C O N D I T I O N .
O . . S . N I G H . A
C R U E T . S O D O M
E . F R O . S . E . B
A . O . E D U C A T E
N O S E S . E . R . R
```

645
```
A N T I C . U S A G E
R . H . H . I . E . .
A M E L I A . C A N E
L . T I M B U K T U .
S T A T E S . L E S T
E . . T . C . E . E .
A C M E . E R A S E D
. A B R A S I V E . I
C R A B . S T E R E O
. G . U . . E . G . U
D O U G H . S T E M S
```

646
```
B L A N C . H U R O N
A . R . L . N . . I .
R U M P U S . P E N N
R . I . B E T E L . E
O U S T . A R G O N .
W . T . P L Y . C . L
. D I T T O . A U R A
Z . C R A F T . T . B
I D E A . F A M I N E
N . . I . R . O . L .
C H I L E . T O N G S
```

647
```
C R O S S . S O A K S
U . U . O . C . T . P
F O R M U L A . O W L
F . . S . R . M . A .
S T O R E . F U S S Y
. O . U . . L . A . .
B O M B E . S T U M P
A . I . X . P . . U .
N A N . P A R T N E R
N . D . E . E . O . E
S I S A L . E Y R I E
```

648
```
I B S E N . T A B L E
. O . P . S . . O . L
B A L I . P A T O I S
I . T I E . . T . E .
R I C H . C . F L E W
T . R E S T O R E . H
H E A T . A . O G R E
M . Z . . C O G . . R
A N I M A L . M A D E
R . E . . E . A . U .
K E R R Y . A N D E S
```

SOLUTIONS

649

L	Y	R	I	C		T	R	I	P	E
I		I		O		E		A		
Z		V		V	E	N	T	U	R	E
A	B	I	D	E			A		S	
R		E		R	E	T	I	R	E	
D	I	R	G	E		E	L	E	C	T
	M	A	D	D	E	N		L		A
	P		A			S	H	A	W	L
C	A	R	N	A	G	E		P		M
	L		S		U		S		U	
T	A	C	K	Y		P	L	E	A	D

650

B	A	S	R	A		D	A	W	N	S
L		T		L		I		A		U
I		U		T	A	S	T	I	N	G
M	A	N	S	E		O		V		A
P	U	G		R	O	B		E	R	R
	N		I	N	D	E	X		I	
A	T	M		A	D	D		S	P	A
Z		A		T		I	M	P	E	L
T	E	N	S	I	L	E		O		I
E		N		V		N		K		A
C	H	A	F	E		T	I	E	R	S

651

D	I	S	C	U	S		A		A	
I		H			U	N	S	U	R	E
S	P	A	M		R		T		I	
A		V		O	F	F	I	C	E	R
B	L	I	T	Z		A	R	O	S	E
L		N		O	H	M		L		V
E	G	G	O	N		E	N	D	U	E
D	E	S	C	E	N	D		S		R
	L		C		U		B	O	S	S
M	I	N	U	E	T			R		A
	D		R		S	Q	U	E	A	L

652

J	A	I	L			T	A	I	N	T
A			E	A	C	H		N		W
D	E	B	T			O		S		E
E		A	S	S	E	R	T	I	V	E
D	O	D	G	Y		O		N		T
	M	O	L	L	U	S	C			
A		I		L		G	H	E	N	T
S	U	N	B	A	T	H	E	R		A
H		T		B			K	E	R	B
E		O		U	R	G	E			B
S	I	N	G	S			L	A	Z	Y

653

A	S	T	U	T	E		B	E	T	S
R		A		I		E		E		E
A		P	R	E	S	C	R	I	B	E
B	S	E		D		R		O		
S	T	R	A	Y	S		I	R	O	N
	O		P	E	A	C	E		T	
C	O	O	P		T	A	S	S	E	L
	G		A		V		K	E	A	
S	E	C	R	E	T	I	V	E		N
O		E		A		I		A		C
B	A	I	L		F	R	I	N	G	E

654

B	R	A	S	S		A	C	R	E	
U		N		I	R	O	N		O	
T		N		R		T	A	C	K	
T	H	E	M	E		E		K		
E		A	N	G	E	L		E		
R	A	S	H		I		O	A	T	H
	R		O	W	N	U	P			E
	T		G			S	E	P	I	A
V	I	S	A		U		A			T
	S		N	A	S	A		W		E
S	T	A	Y		L	I	N	E	D	